The Many Colored Coat

Macmillan Paperback 29

Morley Callaghan
The Many Colored Coat

MACMILLAN OF CANADA
A Division of Canada Publishing Corporation
Toronto, Ontario, Canada

Canadian Cataloguing in Publication Data

Callaghan, Morley, date.
   The many colored coat

(Macmillan paperbacks ; 29)
ISBN 0-7715-9277-9

I. Title.

PS8505.A41M36   1988   C813'.52   C87-095263-3
PR9199.3.C343M36   1988

Originally published in hardcover 1960 by
Macmillan of Canada
First Laurentian Library edition (LL12) 1972,
ISBN 0-7715-0787-5
Reprinted 1983, under ISBN 0-7715-9715-0
First Macmillan Paperbacks edition 1988

Macmillan of Canada
A Division of Canada Publishing Corporation
Toronto, Ontario, Canada

Printed and bound in Canada

To Loretto

The Many Colored Coat

Chapter 1

ONE evening last spring Scotty Bowman, the bank manager, was on Peel Street, standing at the lighted entrance of the Mount Royal Hotel. In front of the entrance the black rain-washed street gleamed in the light, but unmelted ice hung on at the curb. Spring had come late that year. The weather had only become mild after the heavy rain. There was music in the air, stringed music coming across the street from the wide-open upstairs windows of the Wishing Well. Voices sounded loud in the soft dark night.

Scotty Bowman was one of the best known and most respected bank managers in town. In front of the hotel he was really in his own neighborhood. His branch of the Crown Bank was only four blocks away. Most of his bank customers came from this metropolitan neighborhood of hotels, depots, trust companies, insurance offices, big and small businesses and night clubs and restaurants. The people, his customers, were executives, professional men, shopkeepers and entertainers, whores and bookies. No matter who they were they all trusted Scotty Bowman.

Wearing a blue overcoat and a black Homburg hat, and with a florid jolly face, gray hair and shrewd blue eyes, he looked every bit the solid substantial citizen. But not a stuffy one. That night he had been to the fights with his admiring friend Mike Kon, the tailor. Afterwards they had had a drink and Mike now had gone back into the hotel to get some cigars before going home. Standing with his hands in his pockets, Scotty hummed a little tune to himself and looked idly up the street at the mountain and the line of trees stark against the night sky. The mountain still looked bare and cold with patches of snow on the slope. It wasn't really spring, he thought. Spring came for him when he could stand idly at the bank window at noontime and watch the girls come along the street in light open coats and light high-heeled shoes. They always seemed to come toward him with a light gaiety, as if they had eagerly stepped out of heavy galoshes, bulky coats and thick scarves and were there in the strong sunlight smiling, fresh, and free. Each year it had been something to watch for; the one special day when he could smile to himself at the window, feel years younger and say, "Now it's spring."

His friend the tailor came sauntering out of the hotel, biting off the tip of a cigar. Always the best of cigars now and a hat that looked too new. Scotty smiled—he was very fond of Mike. Before speaking, Mike lit the cigar and in the light from the match the scar tissue over his brows showed up. He was an old middleweight fighter who had injured the optical nerve of his left eye, and had retired and opened a tailoring shop. Scotty knew that the bank superintendent, Slocombe, joked about his having a tailor and an old fighter as such a good friend, but Slocombe didn't know Mike. He didn't know what a great reader and talker Mike was and that he was called "Mike the Scholar" by the sports writers. Scotty often thought that in going bowling and to the fights so often with Mike, and in listening to him tell in his colorful language about the old ring days in other cities, his own life had been opened up in a way a bank superintendent could never understand.

"One thing, Scotty," Mike said.

"What's that?"

"Don't forget to apologize to your wife for me, eh?"

"Apologize! What for?"

"I didn't like the way we just ate and ran. I like those nights at your place, Scotty. I mean, just sitting around and talking to your wife and your boys. You tell her, will you? I like those nights."

"Don't worry. I'll tell her, Mike," and Scotty gave him an affectionate pat on the shoulder.

Mike's concern for him and his family always impressed Scotty. He was sure that no man had ever had a more devoted friend and he was touched. Mike seemed to think if it hadn't been for Scotty, he'd be just another old fighter working as a bouncer in some joint down in the East End instead of being an ambitious businessman, with a passion for respectability. But it was absurd, too. The only thing Scotty had done for Mike, as he had told him many times, was to recognize that a game old fighter would have a following if he opened a clothing store. It hadn't been hard to get him a loan and a silent partner. The rest of it Mike had done for himself. Anyway, he had got as much out of Mike's loyalty as anything Mike had got out of him. "You come out to the house next week, Mike," Scotty said. "I'll tell Paula you're coming."

Then, as he started to say good night, Scotty saw a man and a woman getting out of a black Jaguar that had parked a little way down the street. The couple came toward them, into the street light. The man was tall and about thirty and carried a black fleecy overcoat on his arm; the girl, tall and proud, wore a long beaver coat draped on her shoulders. They were holding hands as if they shared a distinguished secret.

"There's Harry Lane now," Scotty said softly. He couldn't hide his interest. Harry Lane was a big success as Public Relations Director for the Sweetman Distillery. He had a lot of money to spend and often had his picture in the papers talking to the mayor. That fine girl there was Judge Morris's daughter. But more than all this, one afternoon when Harry had come into the bank with a regular customer, Scotty had had a few words with him. Scotty had felt strangely drawn to him, and when Harry had given him the fight tickets it had seemed to verify his hunch that some of Harry's ease and luck and success would rub off on anyone who stayed close to him.

"I'd better thank him for those fight tickets," he said.

"Why bother?" Mike said. "It was just another little Sweetman handout. The guy hardly knows who you are. Why bother with him?"

"I think he's got a lot of natural charm, Mike. Who else do you know with his talent for making people feel all his success belongs to them too?"

"Sure, he can charm the birds off the trees if it'll sell his liquor. He's a phony, Scotty."

"I think you've got him wrong, Mike. I detect a little prejudice on your part."

"Those guys are all the same."

"Nobody does the job he does, Mike."

"Sure, he's big right now. So what? All he needs in his phony job is to be a little smoother, a little faster on his feet and a little more intelligent than most guys. I don't go for them, Scotty."

"Keep it down, Mike," Scotty said, for Harry and his girl were opposite them; they went by, then Scotty said quietly, "Hello, Harry."

Lane turned, then came back a few steps, leaving Miss Morris out of it, and he laughed. "Hello, Scotty," he said. "I should apologize for giving you those tickets. That was a lousy fight."

"Just a workout for Bruno," Scotty said. "I didn't expect anything more." Mike had said nothing. Turning, Harry said, "You're Mike Kon, aren't you? I used to watch you in the ring. How's that tailoring shop coming along?"

"Mike makes good suits, Harry," Scotty said.

"That's right," Mike said, feeling uncomfortable.

"Well, maybe I should come in and get a suit."

"I'll bet you don't," Mike said.

"Sure I will. You're over near Bleury, aren't you?"

"That's right," Mike said, looking at his watch. "Well, I've got to leave you, Scotty. So long. Nice seeing you, Mr. Lane."

"I'll be in for that suit, Mike."

"If you're really on the level," Mike said earnestly, "I'd take it as a privilege to make a suit for you." Then he left, and Scotty too would have gone on his way to the station to catch his train to the suburbs, but Harry suddenly put his hand on his arm.

"Just a minute," he said. Train bells were clanging in the station yard down the hill. Harry's eyes were on Scotty. His smile was half-baffled, half-curious, yet warm. Something about the solid, middle-aged banker, standing there alone with his hands in his pockets, seemed to stir in him some memory. It was as if he had known Scotty for a long time and they had once been close. Across the road three pretty show girls came noisily out of a night club on their way to the next-door restaurant. One was laughing loudly. Over the mountain at the end of the street, a patch of stars appeared in a break in the clouds.

"I think you know Mollie," Harry said, drawing her in. He was still engaged by some vague thought about Scotty that seemed to please him. "Mollie goes for you bankers, Scotty. The bond boys and bankers have no trouble getting along with her." Mollie didn't notice the broad friendly smile on Harry's face as he eyed Scotty.

"There you go again, Harry," she said, laughing. "Always trying to give someone the wrong impression of me." A strong gust of wind blew back her open coat, it blew her dress against her, and she grabbed at her pink silk hat which was like an inverted bowl on her black hair. "The fact is, Mr. Bowman, I don't know any bankers," she said.

Then Harry impulsively linked his arm in Scotty's. "We're going into Dorfman's for a bite," he said. "You're coming along with us. I'll buy you a drink."

"Not this time," Scotty protested. "I've got to catch my train. I've only got half an hour."

"There's always another train. Don't worry," Harry said. "Come on."

Scotty had no intention of going into Dorfman's, but Harry

had his arm, walking him up the street. When they got to the short flight of iron-railed steps and Scotty looked at the light over the door, the graceful words of excuse he had prepared wouldn't come. Dorfman's was an old conservative steak house and bar, and Scotty had always felt that the taste of the crowd that went in there was a little too rich for his blood. Thinking of his train, he did try good-humoredly to break loose; then he shrugged, gave up and went in with them.

In the hall he began to feel he was just tagging along and shouldn't be there. The night crowd was coming in, plump sleek-looking men and women with blued-gray hair, and young men with tall girls who acted as if they had been coming to Dorfman's all their lives. The men all bowed to Mollie as she went off to the ladies' room. Then they said easily, "Hello, Harry." It was all Harry: "Hello, Harry." "Good evening, Harry." "Nice seeing you, Harry." "How's Max, Harry?" "Soon be golfing again, eh Harry?" Even the little Negro hat-check girl called, "Hello, Harry." "How's your mother getting on, Mimie?" Harry asked, going over to her. The girl told him how her mother's abdomen had swollen with a tumor, and Scotty, listening, looked at Harry in wonder. Scotty felt ill at ease and out of place. Yet Harry, managing to keep an eye on him, seemed to confirm to Scotty that it was important they were there together.

Then a thing happened that gave Scotty real satisfaction; it made him feel sure Mike Kon was all wrong about Harry. "Why, Harry, old boy, there you are," someone called from the stairs. A balding, red-faced man was coming down the red-carpeted stairs from the plush Peacock Room. His name was Ogen Jones, a big man in the Sweetman Organization, the sales manager in New York. "I tried to get hold of you, Harry," Jones said, patting him on the shoulders with both hands. "No matter. I feel so good now I'd like to go back to the hotel and get laid. What about it, Harry? You guys always have lots of stuff for guys like me. Fix me up, boy.". . . "What you want, Jones, is a good pimp," Harry said with a little smile at Scotty. "Why don't you

14

speak to the doorman? He can get you anything," and he gave him a little push toward the door. Apologetic and humiliated, Jones went on his way and didn't look back. "To hell with him and his sales in New York," Harry said, shrugging, and Scotty liked him all the more.

Then Mollie joined them and they went into a small dining room. The tablecloths looked rich and white, the paneling rich and dark, and Alfred Dorfman, thin, balding and long-nosed, came toward them with his hand out. "Good evening, Miss Morris. I was wondering if you'd be in, Harry. I was saving a table for you." He then shook hands with Scotty. There had been other times around town when Alfred Dorfman had shaken hands with Scotty, but not with this warmth and respect, and Scotty beamed. Dorfman led them to a table. Ordering three steaks, Harry wouldn't accept a protest from Scotty. What goes on? Scotty wondered. Why is he being so good to me? I can't do anything for him. Yet it seemed to him that all the other patrons were also drawn to that sense of well-being he himself found so attractive in Harry. People coming in stood at the door looking at him hopefully. They would have come over if Mollie hadn't put them off. She showed no interest in them; not that she turned up her nose exactly; she knew how to look at people blankly. Scotty began to enjoy his thick steak.

A rich, fashionable doctor stood impatiently in the doorway with several people looking as if he had realized at last that he, a distinguished, witty man, had no real friends. Then he saw Harry and brightened. The doctor was with a tall pale red-haired young actress from a visiting musical, *Fifth Avenue Bus*, as well as Eddie Adams, the fight promoter, who was with an elegant pretty blonde in a pale green dress. The doctor led the way over. In all the shifting around of chairs and the standing up for the introductions Scotty lost his place at the table. Someone had deftly taken his chair. He knew he could have sneaked away right then and caught the last train; no one would have missed him. Now's the time, right now, he thought. Harry'll understand. I really must go. Paula won't be able to sleep.

Then he saw who had taken his chair. It was the big broad-shouldered flat-faced man, Eddie Adams, who often came into Scotty's bank. Scotty wasn't going to be pushed around by Eddie Adams; he got his back up. "All right, Eddie, I'll take my chair," he said, and he did, and so he stayed.

No one paid any attention to him now; that is, no one but Harry. From the other end of the table Harry would smile or wink at him. It was a funny thing, Scotty thought, that Harry was the only one he felt at home with.

So he sat back listening with his good-humored tolerant deprecating smile to brisk bright conversation, gossip about glamorous personalities. It gave him a chance to play a little game he often played in the bank. He tried eying them all one by one and sizing them up shrewdly. He was proud of his knowledge of human nature and his good judgment. Take the doctor there. He had a pretty girl with him but he had a malicious homosexual kind of wit. Obviously stage-struck too.

"There's lots of room, Annie. Move your chair a little," Eddie Adams said. Out of the corner of his eye Scotty appraised the blond girl. He couldn't figure her out. No one like her had ever come to him for a loan. Every expression on her face seemed to be genuine. Yet Mollie Morris had avoided speaking to her. Annie called herself a high-fashion model, and maybe she did a little modeling, but her whole appearance suggested a training to give pleasure to men. Her freshness touched Scotty. The whole place took on a glow. And there was Harry, simply making a little twisting motion with his finger toward an emptying glass as he caught the attention of the waiter, who understood that it had become Harry's party.

"Oh, excuse me," Annie Laurie said. In moving her chair, her shoulder had bumped against Scotty. "Oh no, excuse me," Scotty said, and she turned and looked at him thoughtfully. She had a lovely wise face. Her eyes, as shrewd as his own, took in everything he stood for; then she smiled gently.

"Hello," he said, self-consciously.

"What do you do?"

"I'm a bank manager."

"A bank manager. What are you doing here? Slumming?"

"What?" he said.

"Doesn't anybody ever kid a bank manager?" and her smile broadened. She made him feel more at ease and gradually his steady pale blue eyes lost their alertness. He smiled happily. He was charmed. The women were young and pretty. Everybody was opulent, everybody was successful, everybody bright and entertaining, drawing him into a world far away from the bank. And there was Harry Lane quietly beckoning to the waiter, making everything go smoothly with his distinguished air.

"My train," Scotty said, suddenly stricken. "My train has gone."

"There you are, Harry," Mollie said sympathetically. "Poor Scotty and his train. It's your fault, Harry. You said you'd see he got on the train." For the first time Scotty had their attention, but he could only shrug helplessly, thinking of his wife, who would wake up, look at the clock, then get up and watch at the window and worry. "Well, I'll phone," he said. "I'll stay in town."

"Ah, Scotty," Annie Laurie said, teasing him. "It's a pity I've such a small place, or you could come home with me and teach me how to open a bank."

"I'd like to," he said, trying not to sound worried.

"You know what I'm going to do? I'm going to drive old Scotty home," Harry said. "How far away is it, Scotty?"

"I wouldn't think of it. It's twenty-five miles. Stay with your friends, Harry."

"What's twenty-five miles?" he said. "We'll drop Mollie off and be there in no time."

The waiter had brought the tab and Dr. Malone reached for it; he had it in his hand. "No, you don't, Doctor," Harry said. He grabbed the check. He looked offended. The rich doctor also looked hurt, but Harry and Mollie and Scotty were on their way out. When Harry had signed, they went down the street to the Jaguar.

Scotty had to squeeze himself into the small rear seat, his forearms on the front seat, his head almost between Harry's and Mollie's.

"Harry, you know I don't like sitting with that woman," Mollie scolded.

"What woman?" Harry asked innocently.

"Cut it out, Harry. That Annie Laurie."

"Now, now, darling," Harry said, and he turned, laughing. "Don't get it wrong, Scotty. This isn't Mollie now. It's her Baptist grandmother."

"It's not my Baptist grandmother. It's me, and I'm not ashamed that it's me," and she tried to laugh, but a passing street light shone on her face and showed the defiant flash in her eyes. Scotty knew all about the Morrises. They were related to the Bensons, who used to be called the lumber kings, and the McHughs, and Mollie knew her ground. And Scotty wasn't surprised that her street, C—— St., had such big old houses, all in darkness now. It wasn't a street on which children played in the daytime, nor a good street for a bread man; most of the families went south for the winter and to their mountain cottages in the summer. Nor were the houseowners apt to come into Scotty's bank for a loan, unless it was a big loan. The slight accent he had noticed in her speech belonged to this neighborhood; a kind of English accent that had been gained twenty-five years ago when it had been the fashion to import English nannies for the nursery, although most of these nannies had cockney accents which the children had then picked up and smoothed out.

The Morris house, a big darkened mausoleum with one tall tree on each side, was the only house with a light on, the light over the front door. While Harry was taking Miss Morris to the door, Scotty got into the front seat. Harry, returning, touched the starter. The engine, turning over and over, wouldn't start. He whirled it and whirled it again, the grinding noise like a shriek on the sedate and quiet street. "It did it at an intersection this afternoon," Harry said, cursing. "If we don't get out of here, this place will light up like a Christmas tree. I know it all too well."

As the long grinding wail echoed down the street the lights began to come on one by one. In the Morris house the Judge, listening for Mollie to come in, lit his light. Across the road Dr. Henshaw's bedroom light came on; he was waiting for his delinquent fifteen-year-old daughter. "Look, what's that?" Scotty asked, startled. The front door opened in the Marston place and an elderly woman stood there peering anxiously at her front lawn. "She's looking for her old brother Joseph," Harry said, spinning the starter savagely. Mrs. Marston slept lightly because Joseph, aged sixty-two, had taken to going out to the front lawn and wetting in the moonlight. "And now there's Mollie out," Harry said.

She stood there watching as if afraid somebody would phone for the police car. Then the motor caught and they roared away, laughing.

"I'd hate to come home drunk and singing in this neighborhood," Scotty said.

"Mollie probably thinks we did it on purpose," he laughed. "By the way, Scotty, how old are you?"

"Fifty-two."

"Really?"

"That's right."

"I'd have said about forty-five."

"Oh, I wish I *was* forty-five, Harry."

"What's the difference, Scotty? What's there you can't have now that you could have had five or ten years ago? The world is still your oyster." And as Scotty laughed the world did seem to open up brightly to him.

Driving with his eyes on the road, Harry said suddenly, "That Mike Kon is quite a character, isn't he?"

"He's interesting. He has his own angle on things."

"I know what you mean. I like him."

"You like him?"

"A down-to-earth guy."

"He sure is," Scotty said, feeling uncomfortable.

Fields and trees and the dark and then light came at Scotty faster than they had ever done before, yet he felt exhilarated. The headlights of a passing car flashed on Harry's face. Why was he drawn to the man? Scotty wondered. Was it only his affability? No, Harry had to be affable, dealing with radio and television people, and speaking at banquets, and organizing golfing tournaments and spending Sweetman's money right and left to sell whisky. Why didn't all the phoniness rub off on him? What was that astonishing air of well-being which seemed to suggest that all the phonies in the world could come against Harry Lane and he would shame them because he knew that nothing evil could happen to a good man? Was that it? A naïve man? A man of simple good feeling under the glad-hand role?

Then they came to Scotty's town and his house in a row of similar neat houses. There was no light in the window. "Well, here it is," Scotty said, and he got out and put out his hand. "Many thanks, Harry." He raised his hand, ready to go in. That it should end in this way, that they should fall back on casual encounters such as they had had before tonight, seemed all wrong to Scotty. Standing with both hands on the car door he wanted very much now to hang on to the friendship he had been enjoying so much these past few hours.

"How about a drink again sometime, Harry?"

"That's an idea, Scotty. Any time. Drop into Mother Martin's around five, I'm there usually."

"I'll do it. It's right near the station where I catch my train."

"Glad to see you any time, Scotty."

"So long, Harry."

"So long, Scotty," and the car pulled away.

Scotty, standing there, watched it until it was out of sight. He went in, sat down, took off his shoes, then climbed the stairs. In the hall outside the boys' room he listened anxiously until he could distinguish their separate snores. Philip was there in the bed to the left and sound asleep, so he must have come home at a decent hour. That was good.

In the bedroom his wife lay curled up, well over on her own side of the bed, half asleep, and she didn't open her eyes. In that light he could see the little crisscross of wrinkles on the side of her neck. For a year now they had had no sexual relations. It had just dropped off. They didn't miss it, and didn't talk about it. Yet he always liked having her in the bed beside him. Sometimes, half asleep she would whisper, "Ready to turn on the other side, Scotty?" He could hear this whisper even when asleep and they would both turn. With her beside him, he liked reading himself to sleep, her gentle snoring never bothering him. He read only the articles in magazines, although when he had been a boy he had been fond of stories. The last time he had tried to read a story he had read slowly and painfully as if his imagination now worked too slowly, so he had given up. Every month he cut out the articles on business conditions or general affairs from *Fortune* magazine and put them in a file for future rereading.

Rubbing his hands through his thick gray hair, he yawned and smiled at his sleeping wife, wanting to wake her and talk to her about Harry Lane. No, he thought, Paula likes our life. The way it is, dreadfully dull and all as it is. He took his time undressing, then got into bed, turned out the light and lay with his hands linked behind his head, thinking how pleasant it would be to have other nights with Harry and his friends. Tomorrow he would certainly look into Mother Martin's as Harry had suggested. In a daydream he saw himself in close friendship with the sporting editors, old Haggerty and Frighten, whom he had often seen at the fights getting the real low-down cynically and wisely on the gangsters who controlled so many fighters. He could see himself going to Dorfman's, and to the Ritz bar, places where Harry met his friends and where now Scotty Bowman also called famous people by their first names. He became a confidant of the rich and celebrated, shared their chaotic and interesting lives just as Harry Lane did. As a matter of course, he might become the confidant of Annie Laurie, too. Everybody in that crowd had money to spend and didn't watch it. They were lively and gay, or alcoholic and sad, the whole of life suddenly loosened up charmingly and amusingly when you were with them, completely unlike his dull bridge-playing neighbors. Feeling that a little of that splendid sense of well-being he found so attractive in Harry had rubbed off on him, Scotty fell happily asleep.

Next day at five, a half hour before traintime, he went into Mother Martin's. Harry, there with two advertising men, looked surprised, but asked him to have a drink. From then on, Scotty showed up every afternoon—either there or at the Ritz. He joined the crowd hanging around Harry Lane. It was a big crowd, for at that time Harry was at the height of his popularity, and no other public relations man had his prestige or as big a following. In restaurants, bars and clubs there were always free-loaders and whiskey drinkers waiting for him to come in, not just the businessmen. Scholars and poets and painters also sought Harry out and flattered him because he had charge of the Sweetman Cultural Foundation, which awarded scholarships in the arts. Scotty used to see obsequious waiters toadying to Harry, hoping for a ten-dollar tip; he also saw Harry in the barbershop with the fawning manicurist and the shoeshine boy and the barber handling him lovingly.

For a while after the first meeting at Dorfman's, Scotty was still on the outside with Harry hardly noticing him. Scotty noted he still hadn't been invited to any of those social parties in Harry's lavish apartment up on Sherbrooke. He had heard a lot about that apartment though—he had heard there were always turkeys and cold cuts and hams in the refrigerator, and an endless supply of gins and wines, and Sweetman's fine old whiskeys, of course. Harry's friends could telephone him and get the key to his place and take special friends around and drink his liquor and eat his food. Scotty wasn't sure that he would ever be offered the key himself, but he didn't like hearing those who had, talking about Harry being so careless with his money. For some reason, too, he didn't like hearing Harry's friend Ted Ogilvie, the advertising man with the bright hard eyes and the fixed little smile, say that Harry was a lucky man to have the job he just naturally fitted.

Chapter 2

But it wasn't so at all. The simple truth was that Max Sweetman had got hold of Harry at just the right time. Harry was the son of John Lane, an investment banker who had lived in some style. The Lanes had had a happy home. They had liked and admired each other. Harry had been able to go to his father and talk to him about his problems. He had felt very close to him. His father had wanted Harry to be a doctor, and he had taken a year in medicine, but when the war came Harry had enlisted in the air force and had remained in Europe for five years. Six months after his return his father had gone bankrupt and had died of a stroke, leaving many debts. Within the year his mother died of cancer. He had felt at loose ends and too old to go back to medicine. Then Max Sweetman had come along, valuing the Lane family's social connections, and had offered Harry ten thousand a year to start and some quick raises.

At first Harry had felt a little ashamed of himself, cultivating good will for the distillery with all the Sweetman money behind him. Harry had always been honest in all his feelings about people. Now he felt he was developing a false relationship with the whole world. He started to drink heavily. Once, he disappeared for three days. Sweetman found him holed up in a bordello drunkenly happy, reading the plays of Shakespeare to the girls. Harry did these foolish things because it went against his grain to be consciously putting himself in a good light, always doing complimentary things for people. But he wasn't aware yet that the job, with all the money it gave him to spend, was gradually appealing to a quality in him that was inseparably honest and attractive. He had always had a talent for generosity. Even when he was a kid, if he had an all-day sucker and he saw some other kid looking at him enviously, he would give the kid the sucker just to see the surprise and pleasure in his face. This good natural talent was now flowering outlandishly in this job; he felt it all the time. People might think he was simply doing a cynical job. They would say to a fellow in trouble, looking for a handout, or wanting a good word to be put in for him somewhere, "Tell you what to do. Go and see Harry Lane. He won't mind. He'll look after you."

Perhaps it was that such increasing incidents made Harry know he needed a simple solid honest friendship of an older man like Scotty Bowman. Without noticing it Harry began to talk increasingly to Scotty about confidential things in his life, asking him questions he would otherwise have only asked himself. Men came into Harry's office every day, asking for help of one kind or another, *and* getting it, he told Scotty. Why didn't he ever hear from them again? And why had it never before bothered him? The other day though, a man named Dan Gorman, a college classmate, had come into Harry's office to see him. Dan looked down at the heels, sick and out of work, and had sat in the waiting room dying of shame. Suddenly he had fled. The fact was Harry had to chase after Dan down the street. It had been raining. There was Gorman ahead of him with his hands in his pockets. Harry had caught him at the corner and had dragged him back to the office and had spent the rest of the afternoon getting him a job in an aircraft company across the river. Well, afterwards he hadn't heard from Dan either. But why in this case did it make him feel lonely? He had never felt lonely before.

Scotty seemed to understand Harry's feeling; he would have felt the same way himself, he said. Harry thought he knew why Scotty seemed to understand his feeling for Dan Gorman. Scotty himself had never asked him for anything; he was the only one who sometimes tried to persuade him not to pay for something, the only one who seemed to be glad to sit with him, away from the others, and just talk. Harry began to think of Scotty as a real friend. He started giving him tickets for the theatre and the hockey games as well as the fights, and the other invitations and the key to the apartment came too.

"What's the attraction in old Scotty?" Ted Ogilvie, the advertising man, asked. "Why are you always looking after him?" It was Ogilvie, sitting at the bar wearing an expensive lightweight English felt hat Harry had given him just because he had admired it, yet asking him this question. "Oh, I don't know," Harry said, smiling. "Maybe he's the kind of a man I instinctively respect."

And it was true that there was now a lot that Harry saw in Scotty; the honest thinking behind the slow words and the thoughtful smile that made Harry want to be at his best with him. Scotty seemed to be very deprecating about himself. It seemed to be genuine modesty. He was not humble. It was just that he made you feel he didn't have to pretend about anything. If he gave an opinion about anybody, Harry seemed to feel the fairness in it. Sometimes Harry took him to the ball park. While they sat behind third base, with the floodlights on the diamond, the older man would begin to ask Harry questions about his life, and smile and nod as if it gave him real pleasure to know the little things about him. Scotty, in turn, would talk about his own life and his family. His older boy, Philip, was giving him a little trouble, hanging out with the wrong people.

One day Scotty asked Harry to have lunch with him and the boy. "Just so the boy can see something for himself," he said simply. That same night, coming into the Ritz bar where Harry was sitting with Mollie Morris, Scotty stopped to say warmly,

"Thanks, Harry, I knew you'd make things look a little different to Philip."

"Glad to be of some help, Scotty," Harry had said, looking pleased.

"So Mr. Bowman really approves of you," Mollie said as Scotty left.

"Do you think so?"

"I don't know why you get such a kick out of his approval," Mollie said, "particularly since I notice he always lets you pick up the check just like everybody else."

"Always scolding me," Harry said, laughing, yet loving her concern for him as something warmly familiar. His mother used to scold his father for picking up checks.

Earlier in the evening, he had come out of his apartment and was loafing along waiting for her. She had taken an apartment only two blocks away from him, after persuading her parents she needed a studio so her newspaper friends wouldn't be tramping through their house. In the afternoon he had played golf with Sweetman and his legs now felt a little stiff. It was a lovely night, the lights had come on, there were patches of light in the apartment buildings on the North Side; behind them the mountain was darkening, and along the wide avenue with its old stone mansions the street lights began to gleam through the leaves of the trees.

A new spring suit in a lighted dress shop window caught his eye and he was wondering how it would look on Mollie, when he saw her coming toward him, bright and fresh in a new lime-green dress and looking proud of being a Morris and her father's darling. Her slow elegant stride made him think of the peculiar faint honey fragrance of her body. She was still a virgin, but she had let him take certain liberties. He would laugh and brush down with his hand the straight short hair at her forehead and temples. Or he would brush back her hair so he could see her ears, small and flat against her head. On a picnic beach, both half asleep, his fingers had gone slowly back and forth, back and forth, rubbing the roots of her black hair till

27

she gave a small sensual snort of pleasure, as if she were being debauched. Drowsy, her brown eyes, when they opened, were vague and dimmed, not seeing him, some secret stirring still holding her; then as her eyes really turned to him, a faint slow wondering smile. And now here she was, coming to him.

"Hello there," she called. "Why the funny little smile?"

"I think there'll always be something about you, Mollie, to make me wonder."

"I certainly hope so, darling. Well, what's this about what's-his-name, your stockbroker friend?"

"Just that McCance asked me to meet him."

"But why see him now, Harry?"

"Remember I told you he gave me those five hundred shares of Western Oil and told me to keep them?"

"Ah, I see. Now the big money."

"Mind you, I don't know. It's just that he sounded so elated. Something's in the wind. Come on, we're meeting him in the Ritz bar."

Linking arms, feeling good and full of approval of each other, they turned into the Ritz and downstairs to the bar where they saw McCance sitting by himself.

He was a big florid man with closely cropped red hair, wearing a brown suit with a white shirt showing an inch and a half of cuff. He was expansive and happy and a little exhilarated from the drinks he had already had. But as soon as he had bowed to Mollie and kissed her hand, he was ready for another one and he slapped Harry on the knee. "Old Harry," he said warmly. "All I can say, Miss Morris, is that you don't know how this man has been on my mind for a long time. Not that I've seen so much of him, mind you, but he's been here," and he tapped his head. "You see, if it weren't for Harry I wouldn't be here. This guy saved my life."

"I saved my own," Harry said laughing. "You just happened to be along."

"Our plane," McCance went on, "made a forced landing and burst into flames. When Harry had dragged himself out he had realized I wasn't around and he went back and dragged me out just in time. It was nothing to Harry, but I valued that aid very highly."

"What's on your mind right now, McCance?" Harry asked.

"Money," he said solemnly, and he took some silver out of his pocket and let it drop into his other hand. "A long time ago I made up my mind that if ever I ran into anything big I'd let Harry Lane in on it."

"All right. Come on. What is it?"

"Like I asked, you've hung on to the Western Oil stock?"

"So what about it?"

"The news I expected to have for you isn't quite ready. That's all right, Harry. It's in the bag. Now just let's let it go at that. No more questions, man. I'm not saying a word more. You'll be hearing from me. Rejoice, my friend, rejoice."

They laughed. They had a drink on it. Harry couldn't doubt that a nice little piece of change was coming his way. A man like McCance wouldn't show so much pleasure thinking he was displaying his gratitude unless he had something in hand.

"Harry, why is it we hardly ever see each other?" McCance asked, draping his arm sentimentally on his shoulder. "How is it you never see any of the old crowd now?"

"Oh, I see them, here and there."

"Oh, come on, Harry. Who do you ever see?"

"You know the way it is," he said, defending himself. "I have to see so many people. Wait a minute—I saw Dan Gorman. Remember Dan?"

"Of course. He was in our class. Married, isn't he?"

"Yeah, three kids. There's always a guy in your year who's had it rough."

"Well, well, well. How's he doing now?"

"I haven't heard from him in six weeks," Harry said, looking troubled. "I think he's all right though. As I say," he said, shrugging, "I'm on the go all the time. Hotels, bars, golf courses." Suddenly McCance's flushed smiling friendly face made him feel lonely and his hand went out to Mollie's arm and he groped for her hand. The strange thing was that he hadn't bought McCance a drink in years. McCance had asked for nothing. Yet there he was, full of affection, someone actually seeking him out and wanting to do something for him. "McCance, old boy," he said fondly, raising his glass.

"To the old days, Harry."

"May they always be as good."

"Come on now," McCance said warmly. "I've set this night aside for a little celebration. Where'll it be? Now don't argue with me, Harry. I'm celebrating, and this is on me. No nonsense, now, Harry."

The three of them linked arms, laughing, and went out, all warmth and good feeling, Harry smiling a little at the strangeness that he and his girl were being taken out and treated. He felt shy, almost uncomfortable. Wherever McCance wanted to go was all right with him, he said, as they turned down Peel. Mollie said she didn't want to go to the Wishing Well, she hadn't been there since poor old Paul, the fat bald fairy manager, had been knifed by a male dancer in a roominghouse. Then they were on St. Catherine, crossing the road turning east and an elegant girl and a middle-aged man were also crossing, not in their path but from the other corner. "Good heavens, that's Scotty Bowman and Annie Laurie," Harry said, and he stopped and turned. Scotty and Annie had not seen them.

"Well, just imagine," Mollie said. "Mr. Bowman and that woman. Good heavens."

"Maybe he's only checking her account," McCance said, snickering.

"I think he saw me," Harry said. "I'd better speak to them."

"Now don't, Harry," Mollie scolded. "Don't embarrass the man. Come on," and she took his arm, hurrying him along. "Well, there you are, Harry," she said primly. "You never know what *any* man's up to, do you?"

"You hear her, McCance?" Harry asked, laughing. "Now that's a woman for you. Use your head, Mollie. Why would the lovely Annie be bothering with old Scotty? He's a great guy.

I don't know what it is about him . . . maybe it's the way he gets such a kick out of the little things. Maybe the way he makes me feel my own life is big and important. No, you don't need to worry about old Scotty. People like him are the salt of the earth."

"Just the same," Mollie said, "he's at a bad age to be going around with a girl like that one."

"Not old Scotty," Harry said, smiling and looking back at them.

Chapter 3

Scotty's own wife, Paula, had said to him only last night at bedtime, "What's the matter with you, Scotty? Why are you always complaining about Philip's manners? Whoever heard of a boy his age having polished manners?" One strand of graying hair fell untidily on her ear as she spoke.

"It's my job to complain," he said sternly, and then the sight of her in her plain brown dress irritated him a little. "For heaven's sake, Paula, why don't you get some new clothes? Fix yourself up," he said.

"What with?" she asked. "My goodness, you certainly aren't yourself these days." She started to laugh, so he felt foolish.

He stood at the bedroom window, looking at the apple tree in the moonlight that flooded the back yard, and Philip's bicycle there by the garage. He thought it was quite remarkable how the boy's manners had indeed been improving. That luncheon with Harry had helped Philip. The boy had been impressed by Harry's ease and grace, and had been charmed when Harry had asked him to come to the big splashy party Sweetman was giving for some visiting Texan golfers. And as for himself, Scotty had never felt such a sense of well-being. Even at the bank they noticed it. His secretary, Miss Wilson, had wondered why he seemed more amiable, his laugh a little softer, and Slocombe, the superintendent, had said he had even more of a proprietary air as he came out of his office to survey his customers. Yet there were many times when he had the thought, frowning to himself, that many rich men came here to rely on his judgment, that he watched over hundreds of thousands of dollars and yet—how unfair it was that the price of a few drinks and an evening's entertainment worried him.

That same night he had worked late with Slocombe and the bank inspector, and before catching his train he had come into Mother Martin's for a drink. He was sitting with Ogilvie, an adman named Nelson, and Annie Laurie. The two men were trying to persuade her to go to the Press Club. Newspapermen and their interminable drinking and yacking didn't interest her, she said; she was going home. She had one elbow on the table, her head on one side, and as Scotty stared at her, bright little laughs flowed from her lovely red mouth. For years many handsome women had been coming into the bank and not one of them, no matter what she offered, would have been able to get Scotty to cash a check without looking at her account. Yet recently, in the presence of pretty women, those friends of Harry's, he would notice himself feeling younger. Now he wanted to reach out, press the tip of his finger against Annie's cheek and see the little spot he would make slowly redden. Scotty wondered what it was that was happening to him. Then the others left and he was sitting there alone with Annie Laurie. A dreamy smile came on his face. Having her there delighted him and she was looking back at him, frank curiosity in her eyes. Desire for her suddenly stirred in him. How long since I felt like this, he thought exultantly. Oh Lord it's not too late!

"Well, I'm going, Scotty."

"Where are you going?"

"Just walking home."

"I can't see a girl like you taking a very long walk," he said, and as she smiled slowly he fumbled around for words of great gallantry.

"That's where you're wrong," she said. "At least once a week

I take a long walk by myself for the sake of my figure. You can walk me up as far as St. Catherine if you like."

"I might as well, since I have time."

"Come on then, Scotty."

In the fine spring night the lights were shining gaily on the mountain, and they began to loaf up the hill, with Scotty keeping a step away from her.

"It's a grand night," he said.

"Isn't it though."

"Most of my walking is done in the bank. I guess I'm past the age of walking for pleasure."

"Why, you're not old, Scotty," and she said it so naturally he felt close to brightness and warmth. She was as tall as he was and she kept turning and smiling at him. The shyness of so shrewd and practical a man seemed to amuse her. "Tell me something about yourself," she said.

"What's there to tell?"

"Aren't you happy at home?"

"Of course I am."

"Really satisfied?"

"Certainly. Why?"

"I think of you as one of those men's men."

"Well . . ."

"They sit around and tell their stories. Life is a big happy stag party, and they'd rather chase a bottle of booze than a woman because the bottle can't scare them."

"That's not me. Thank the Lord."

"You're not telling me anything about yourself."

"Oh, I don't talk much about myself."

"No, you never do. But what goes on in you?"

"In me?"

"I'm curious."

"Why nothing at all that you can't see."

"Well, what do you want?"

"Just a minute," he said, and he started to laugh. "What about you?"

"Oh, you've probably got my credit rating. You've probably read a book about me, Scotty. You don't fool me. Anyway, it's a fine night."

"How far do you walk?"

"About ten blocks."

"I'll go to the corner," he said and his sense of prudence told him to leave her before they got to the corner; no one in the business community should see him and get the impression that he spent his time with a pleasure-loving expensive woman of dubious reputation. Still, he was interested in the fact that the price of her company for these idle moments was merely the satisfaction of her curiosity. "I didn't see Harry Lane around today," he said.

"I don't know what you think of Harry," she said. "But for my money he's the best man in this town."

"He's a prince, all right," Scotty said. "But you know—I think he's got a bad flaw. He's a kind of innocent guy."

"Innocent?"

"Why, yes," Scotty said, knowing he had caught her interest. They had half stopped again in front of a lighted shoe-store window and she turned to him, earnestly concerned, "Harry's a very intelligent man," she said, "but sometimes I think he does too much thinking with his heart."

"Yes. Yes. That's accurate enough. He's rather imprudent, that's true," he agreed smiling. "Maybe that's why he's so likable though, and it seems to me he does all right."

"Other men at the top are usually pretty ruthless, aren't they?"

"Well, the old rat race, you know."

"Then Harry must have something else."

"Yeah, a lot of money to spend," he said cynically. Immediately he felt half ashamed. He didn't know why he had made such a cynical remark about Harry. "Don't get me wrong," he added quickly. "I know he has his own quality. I have to have business judgment. I have to be able to size a man up pretty shrewdly. With Harry it's different. You get the impression he's completely disarmed and somehow it makes a shrewder man want to lay down his arms too. Quite a quality, eh?"

"My goodness, Scotty, he *has* come under your gimlet eye."

"In my business I have to study people carefully," Scotty said.

As they started to walk on he watched her out of the corner of his eye, fascinated by her luxurious freshness. With each step she took there was a movement of her breasts and all his senses quickened. He knew he should stop and say good night and hurry down the hill and catch his train; he seemed to see himself running through the station. Then Annie Laurie, turning her head with a pretty gesture, seemed to be waiting, hanging on his words, and he couldn't drag himself away. If he could only hold her interest, all her delightful expressive freshness would be held within his reach, he thought. For the first time he was touched with envy of Harry. The envy flared up so swiftly it almost got out of hand. How unfair it was that Harry could have this woman any time he wanted, he thought. For Harry she was simply one of the pleasures that went with the rich world he had never had to work for. She was just part of the luck that went with Harry's business personality. How different it had been with him, Scotty thought. It had taken years to develop his judgment and get where he was in the bank. Any way you looked at it he had ten times Harry's experience, ten times his judgment. He could buy and sell Harry. Yet to hold the interest of Annie Laurie he had to talk about Harry.

Then suddenly he saw shrewdly how he could take advantage of this situation, and he became himself again. If all he had to do to keep this lovely woman beside him was to go on talking about Harry, he would talk all the way to her place. She would have to invite him in, and in her place, once he felt sure of himself, he would be at his best. If he handled her right, he would have a lovely part of Harry's world for himself. It might be just a crumb from Harry's table, but who knew when something bigger might come along? As he took her arm firmly he felt himself tremble.

Chapter 4

IT WAS unseasonably warm for late spring with the mountain looking very green against the blue sky, and they had put out the chairs at the sidewalk café on Sherbrooke. Men had begun to put on light summer suits and students sat or stretched out on the campus lawns. During the week, Scotty saw a lot of Harry. Harry was very busy with his public entertaining and Scotty began to stay in town for dinner. The people were so interesting that Scotty managed to be along with Harry. He found excuses for not going home. They enjoyed each other's company in different ways. Scotty would marvel that Harry could be so much at ease in the company of Rocky Marciano, the retired heavyweight champion of the world, who had come to town to speak at a dinner for crippled children, or with some television star; and Harry would look at Scotty, see him beaming happily, and feel touched.

Each night there was someone Scotty would never have met in his own world. Sitting around in Harry's world of easy money Scotty enjoyed himself hugely. Not that he didn't offer to pay his own way. He always did. But naturally he was included when Harry footed the bill. One night Scotty would find himself sitting in Dorfman's with Mona Maxwell from Hollywood, with her great smooth breasts. Next night he would drop into the Wishing Well at ten, knowing he would miss his train, and there would be Harry sitting with that gray-haired Senator from a New England state whose girl, Joy Martin, was an exotic dancer in the show. After Joy did her number she would join them and when she caught Scotty staring at the strange bags under her eyes, she said solemnly, "Don't worry, honey, it's not a hard life. It's a liver condition." The embarrassment on old Scotty's face had been so comical, Harry had laughed out loud and put his arm around him. They had all laughed, looking at him indulgently. On those fine nights the windows were always wide open. In that neighborhood there was always music in the spring air.

At the end of the week the late spring showers came, brief showers ending suddenly with the clouds breaking up, the sun shining, then going behind the clouds again. There was a splash of sunlight on the Peel corner as Scotty, blinking his eyes, pulled the rim of his soft gray hat down lower and crossed the road to get an evening's supply of cigars from the tobacco shop. His wife had said, "Try and remember that John Olsen and Stanley Tibbs liked those cigars you had last time." Then he saw Harry waiting to cross the road on his way up to Sweetman's. Stopping to pass the time of day, Harry said he had been to a funeral parlor; an old professor had died, and Harry had represented ten of his friends. One word led to another. It seemed to Scotty that Harry was restless and he asked him what was on his mind. Harry told him about McCanse having given him the five hundred shares of Western Oil.

"I guess the guy wasn't kidding about the stock paying off. I had lunch with him and, well, he got the wire he had been waiting for from the drilling superintendent. So you see, Scotty, I've been in a kind of a dither all afternoon. In three days they bring the well in. The thing is, according to McCanse, if the well merely repeats the pattern of the other western wells that stock will open at five dollars a share. How's that, Scotty?"

"And you have five hundred shares," Scotty said. "Congratulations, Harry. That's nice, *very* nice."

"It could be a hell of a lot nicer. I'm the one guy he'll let have shares at a dollar, so he says. It's his pay-off. Tears in his eyes and all that. Why he goes on thinking he owes my anything is out of this world."

"What are you going to do, Harry?"

"Me? Nothing at all. I've got my five hundred shares. It'll be a windfall. That's fine. I'll quit while I'm ahead."

"Things certainly come your way, Harry," Scotty said enviously, for there was Harry, so much younger than he was, with that unbelievable luck which was like a magical adjustment between himself and the world. He had a hunch about this luck of Harry's, and a hunch about Harry, too. It began to rain. As Scotty slowly raised the collar of his coat, his eyes turned inward.

"Don't you realize, Harry," he said, "that if you had fifteen thousand shares you could make at least seventy thousand, maybe more?" Scotty's eyes were alight like a shrewd businessman's; yet he seemed to be concerned as a banker might be concerned for a client.

"Hold on there, Scotty," Harry said, laughing. "I haven't got fifteen thousand."

"Maybe so. *But that's what banks are for,* Harry."

"I know about banks, Scotty. There's always the question of security."

"It's too bad. Really too bad," Scotty said, and as he pondered over this question he continued to look like the banker trying to be helpful. But he could hardly conceal his exasperation at Harry's lack of appreciation of his opportunity. If Harry had left suddenly he would have grabbed him by the arm.

"What about McCanse?" he asked.

"What about him?"

"I was just thinking—would he let you have fifteen thousand dollars' worth of stock and trust you for a few days?"

39

"Would he? Well, I don't know. I just don't know. Why?"

"If McCanse would do it, well, maybe the bank might take the stock as security at the present market price—a dollar a share—for a very short-term loan. I don't know, of course. It might though. It just might," Scotty said, not fully meaning it at the moment, but in the desperate necessity of holding Harry there till he got adjusted to what was going on in the back of his own mind. He had no clear plan yet, just a shrewd urgent awareness. Harry, he knew, standing there with his hands in his pockets and the drizzle darkening the shoulders of his light top coat, would trust him completely. "Of course, I can't say off-hand," Scotty repeated.

"Why, you'd have to get the approval of God almighty for such a loan, Scotty."

"Oh, that's right," Scotty said, smiling. "Which is a good thing, you know." Standing there in the rain, his hunch about Harry seemed to keep prodding away at him, and making his heart beat unevenly. "Of course bank loans are made as much on reputation as on security, you know, Harry. You have a good reputation. I don't know. I'd have to think it over. Anyway it would be up to the head office, so don't let me build you up."

"My God, you mean there's actually a chance, Scotty?"

"Now don't count on it, Harry."

"No, no, I won't but . . ."

"Why don't you see if you can get that stock?"

"Oh, McCance'll give me the stock all right." Harry laughed. "Wait a minute, Scotty," he said. "What about you?" It was just like Harry. Scotty smiled. He could have predicted that Harry would say it. "For heaven's sake, Scotty, why don't you go to a broker and try and get some of the stock yourself?"

"Me?" Scotty said innocently, and he held up both hands, smiling broadly. He had absolute faith now in his knowledge of Harry. "Don't talk about me, Harry. Very much against the rules. Anyway I'm broke. But the loan—I'll think about it." Rubbing his face, he nodded, then conceded like a cautious.

businessman, "Yes, no harm in that . . . I'll see if it's worth while sounding out the head office. If it is, I'll call you."

"Gosh, thanks, Scotty."

"Just bank business, Harry."

"Just the same, Scotty—"

"I'll be missing my train. I'll keep it in mind, Harry. Call you tomorrow. So long."

"So long, Scotty," and Harry crossed the road.

Going into the cigar store Scotty stood for a moment in a trance. "Yeah?" the clerk said, but Scotty, looking up vaguely, couldn't remember the name of the cigars. The salesclerk had a crew cut and glasses and both of his hands were on the glass case. "I want some . . ." Scotty said, then the name came back to him and he smiled apologetically. He got the cigars, went out and began to go slowly down the hill to the station, trying to remember every word he had said to Harry. Not one word had committed him to anything; that was just like him. Yet he wasn't himself. Going down the hill slowly, then turning into the station, Scotty had a sudden shocking apprehension that he was tired being himself, and that Harry Lane from the beginning had been heaven-sent to draw him out of himself and into a big new wonderful world.

Then Scotty started to run through the station toward his train, puffing heavily, his heart beating alarmingly. But what really worried him was that now, almost mournfully, he seemed to be watching someone else he hardly knew, puffing and stumbling toward a suburban train.

On the train it took him a long time to get his breath. I'm too old to run like that, he thought, and he lay back and closed his eyes. Sweating and puffing, he tried to forget his conversation with Harry by thinking of his son Philip. Suddenly he was pretending pleasantly that he had *at last* found the money to send Philip away to colleg—Philip at college, his ways all changed. And there he was himself, visiting Philip's residence. "This is the Dean, Dad." "So you're Mr. Bowman. Philip has

41

often mentioned you." "And you too, Dean. Let me say you're doing a wonderful job with him. Nothing like a good school," he would say with an air of well-being. "Oh, no, don't you bother, Philip'll show me around." Scotty stayed in this happy dream the whole journey. When he got home it again seemed to be someone else using his key to open the door, someone he didn't know, going in quietly.

Chapter 5

MORE as a daydream than anything else, Harry had asked McCance if, supposing something turned up, he could buy him fifteen thousand shares at the market price, one dollar, and wait for a few days for payment? Just supposing? And McCance had said of course he could. Harry still really didn't believe he would hear from Scotty. But just before noon, Scotty called him. "If you can get that stock from McCance, bring it around," Scotty said. "I think it's okay." He sounded like a completely unemotional businessman doing something he did every day.

At one o'clock Harry came to the bank. Customers were lined up at the tellers' cages. Scotty's office door was open; he was talking to a Chinese and his lawyer. "Come on in, Harry," he called, so the others, turning, had to go. Standing up, Scotty put out his hand. "Got the stock with you, Harry?"

"Here it is."

"Fine. No trouble with McCance at all, eh? Sit down, Harry." Scotty talked at once about a short-term note of two months, and when Harry mentioned that he knew the stock wasn't the best security, Scotty repeated his earlier phrase that a banker's real risk was in the man himself, his character. Then too there was Harry's excellent job. Everything Scotty said seemed to be sensible to Harry, but what really moved and impressed him was the faith Scotty showed in his eyes. Scotty made him feel he couldn't miss. They seemed to be there in the bank office because they had their own secret faith and knowledge of each other.

When Harry had signed the papers, he asked Scotty to join him for lunch, and they went to Drury's. They didn't talk much about the oil well or of Harry's getting rich, yet it was a kind of celebration. They were relaxed and good-humored and very considerate of each other. After lunch they walked across the square in the bright spring sunlight. Old men were sitting on the benches sunning themselves comfortably. Some pigeons came waddling along the path. Taking the last cigarette from a pack, Harry rolled up the pack into a little ball and threw it at the pigeons and they all took wing in a short hop of ten paces.

"As for me, Harry," Scotty said suddenly with his shy friendly smile, "I may really have been of some service to you, eh?"

"You certainly were, Scotty. That's a fact."

"Well, it was a real pleasure, Harry."

"I just wish you were in it with me."

"Oh, you couldn't have done anything for me before the loan went through."

"No, I'm aware of that," Harry said, showing his surprise.

Scotty took a little time, a long deliberate pause before he spoke again. "But now that the loan has gone through, Harry, and of course it has, there's no reason why you couldn't do something. I could take over, oh, say five thousand of those shares."

"Five thousand shares!" Harry was stunned and he couldn't hide it, either. The nerve of the cool bald proposition shocked him, and for the first time he wondered if Scotty all along had been waiting for a pay-off. Harry felt something was terribly wrong. He felt a genuine twinge of apprehension. What did he really know of this middle-aged man whose eyes lit up when they met? "What the hell, Scotty," he said uneasily after a long worried pause. "You're reaching a little, aren't you?"

"I guess I am, Harry," Scotty said awkwardly. "I guess I was just dreaming." Trudging along with his slow heavy stride he looked hurt. He even fumbled for an apology. "It was like thinking that what was happening to you, I mean the luck, might be happening to me too. I'm not you though, am I?"

They had always spoken with such respect to each other. In a strange way Harry still felt close to this man. It was painfully embarrassing to see Scotty so hurt and apologetic, telling how close he felt, too. In all fairness Harry knew that if it hadn't been for Scotty there wouldn't have been any loan. Laughing awkwardly he slapped Scotty on the shoulder. "Take it easy," he said generously. "Come to think of it, maybe it's not too many shares. I really think you should have them. You hear me, Scotty? In fact, I insist. I'd have seen it myself. You know I would, don't you?"

"Thanks, Harry. I shouldn't have mentioned it, I see. I'd feel a lot better now if I just left the whole thing up to you."

They went on through the square to St. Catherine, talking about opening day at the ball park. The street at this hour was crowded, and the day was so mild that some of the girls were out on their lunch hour without their coats. It was good to see the bright-colored dresses out on the street at last in the sun. People passing Harry and Scotty on the street called out to them and they kept bowing and waving. Some knew Scotty. Some knew Harry. They were two well-known men in that neighborhood, and they walked as far as the bank together and stood at the entrance talking amiably.

"Hi, Mike," Scotty called out. Mike Kon was hurrying by. He raised his right arm in a formal salute. "I'm coming in for that suit, Mike," Harry called and Mike half turned, then he was lost to them, in the noonday crowd.

"Old Mike. Always in a hurry," Scotty said, and he laughed. "You shouldn't have forgotten about that suit."

"Who says I forgot?" Harry said. "I'm only waiting for the warmer weather."

Chapter 6

MIKE hated seeing Scotty standing there at the bank entrance with Harry. In the evenings now Mike hardly ever saw Scotty. They had gone bowling only once in the last two weeks, and it had been a full three weeks since Scotty had asked him to come out to the house for dinner. Until now Mike hadn't realized how much he would miss the cosy, easy, domestic security of the Bowman home where he had always been treated as a family friend, an interesting colorful man, so interesting that the Bowman boys had made sure they were there for dinner so they could listen to his stories. And Paula Bowman, smiling, showed in many ways that she admired him. Was she missing him now? Mike wondered. And Scotty had always prodded him and questioned him with insatiable curiosity about his old exciting life, asking his opinion as if he had the highest respect for him as an intelligent man. Mike wasn't merely grateful to Scotty for helping establish him in his business. Now that he was missing his company, he realized that he loved the man.

Usually on this noontime walk along the street he exchanged greetings with friendly shopkeepers at their doors and clerks at the windows. If he was in a good mood, and warmed by these signs of approval, he liked imagining he had become president of the local businessman's association, or that a deputation of merchants had come to him asking him to run for alderman. Now he didn't say hello to anyone all the way to his store.

Just to the right of the entrance of his shop was the door to the stairs that led to the upstairs apartment, and after lunch, before going into the store, Mike always climbed these stairs to see his father and spend a few minutes with him and Mrs. McManus, the nurse. The remodeling of the old apartment, which he had paid for himself, had been costly; he had wall-to-wall broadloom on the floors; there was a smart modern living room and three bedrooms, one for himself, and one for his father, and one for the nurse. He could not be sure that his father, since his stroke, appreciated how different this place was from the old one, and the doubt always saddened Mike.

His father was in the living room in his wheel chair, the light glistening on his bald head, his big nose shining too. On the right arm of the chair they had rigged up a board about a foot wide, and on this board there was a pad and a pencil on a string. Old Mr. Kon had been paralyzed on the left side; he couldn't speak, but sometimes, two fingers on his right hand seemed to have a little life in them. Every morning Mrs. McManus would stick the pencil between these two fingers and urge him to scratch away. A week ago there had been marks on the pad.

"How are you today, Poppa?" he asked. The one good eye, the right one, glittered at him fiercely till he pressed the hand gently. It was always hard for him to do this. He couldn't bear the touch of the inert, watery and swollen hand. "Mrs. McManus," he called.

"Is that you, Mr. Kon?" she called, coming from the kitchen in her white smock. She was a gray-haired jolly Scotswoman who seemed to have some affection for the helpless old man. "He seems to be pretty much himself today," she said, looking at the old man reflectively. "Don't you think so?"

"Look at those scratches on the pad," Mike said. "I think they're getting firmer all the time." He sat down beside him.

Years ago he couldn't have sat beside his father as he did now, feeling at ease with him. In those early days he had had no understanding of him at all. He had been ashamed that the old man had sold newspapers, had a bad accent, wore ill-fitting clothes and was called Old Chris, the Christian. At his corner newsstand in the winter, Old Kon's red nose had been always running. He used to wear a cap and ear muffs and call out hoarsely the names of his papers while he danced around to keep his feet warm. Chris the Christian used to come home and waste his time trying to read high school poems aloud in a heavy accent. In those days just being near his father had offended him.

"Michael," his father would say, looking up, his finger on a sentence on the page. "This I don't get. Make it clear, please."

"Why don't you call me Mike like everybody else does?"

"Because with you and me it is not like it is with everybody else," he said mildly.

"Aw, hell, why don't you lay off those kids' books? Just be what you are. Everybody knows what we are anyway."

"What is it you say we are, Michael?" he asked gravely as he closed the book, his finger between the pages, and looked down over his glasses.

"We don't rate. Why does a newsboy want to use big words? Who the hell cares?"

Closing the book, his father let it rest on his knee and stared at the cover, and then he stood up and turned on the gas to heat the kettle and make himself a cup of tea. It was his only dissipation, the only one he could afford, the drinking of too many cups of tea. Mike had waited, hating the silence, his own uneasiness, and his father's familiar movements as he bent over the stove. "To insult your father, Michael, isn't good," he said finally. "I'm a poor man, okay. . . . The way it is with me there are no big jobs for me. But you are wrong. Nobody knows what we are in this place, but you and me. Maybe nobody but you knows what I would want to be . . . what we should be. The books—yes. Money—no. . . . A poor man can have some dignity. If I'm rich, can I buy it? No, it has to be here," and he tapped his head, "and here," and he tapped his heart. "Someday, when you see this . . . then you are my son."

"And then I go peddle the papers too," he said contemptuously, for he hated the religious streak in his father. But his father sat down again and picked up the book. The kettle began to boil. Waiting stiffly, Mike hoped his father would get up and pour the water in the teapot. The expression in the steady gray eyes began to bother him; he tried to outstare him, feeling big and belligerent. Then the very calm, innocent, steady eyes began to insult him, and he trembled. "Have a cup of tea with me, Michael," his father said mildly.

"I don't drink tea. To hell with it," he said, and he swaggered into the bedroom and got undressed quickly. Yet the sounds of his father making the tea, the cup going down on the table, then the silence, then the knowledge that he was sitting out there, patient and untroubled, reading the grammar, the high school poems, became an even deeper insult. At the end of the week he had left home, left that little room and his father and the few books and the silly, lofty, Biblical talk.

Years later, after he had hurt the optic nerve in his right eye and had wondered what would become of him, he found that he often thought of his father. On train trips and in cheap hotel rooms he began to read as if his father were beside him encouraging him to become an educated man. The more he read the more he was impressed by all the things his father had wanted. When he had saved a little money, he came home and met his father; that is, he seemed to know him for the first time. His father's terrible stroke had cheated him out of the beautiful conversations he had planned, but he refused to believe the old man couldn't hear every word he said to him, so he went on revealing himself to him. After lunch each day he gave the old man all the gossip.

Now he stood by the window, wrinkling his brow and squinting in the window sunlight that fell on the bald head of his father, so still in the chair beside him. "I saw Scotty with that Harry Lane again," he said contemptuously. "They must have had lunch together. I don't get it at all, Poppa, I really don't. Lane's all wrong for Scotty. They're not in the same league, but that crazy Scotty seems to think Lane lifts him way up. The thing is," he said, turning, worried and trying to hold the old man's wandering good eye, "why is this glossy smooth-talking public relations man throwing this stardust in Scotty's eyes? I mean, Lane's got to be buttering up somebody, that's the guy's business. Do you think he gives a damn for old Scotty? The thing I can't figure out is why Scotty falls for it. Scotty's a shrewd man, Poppa. Nobody fools him, and looking at the two of them you'd think they were related, and Scotty ought to know he has no place in the company Harry Lane keeps. You see, Lane is the kind of a guy who's always quick to say the thing he thinks you want to hear. What is it Scotty wants to hear? I mean, Lane sees me and he lets me have it right in the eye. 'I'm coming in for a suit, Mike.' That's the guy. That's what he thinks I want to hear, see, Poppa?"

A buzzer in the room connected with the store now buzzed three times. Mike hurried down to the shop and there was Harry talking to Willie, the fitter.

"Well, well, Harry," Mike said, feeling uncomfortable. "Look, I thought you were kidding."

"I said I was coming in, didn't I?"

"You mean you really want a suit?"

"That's the idea, Mike."

"All right. By God, it'll be a suit I'll be proud to have you wear, Harry. What did you have in mind?"

"Oh, some kind of lightweight summer suit."

"Not one of those tropicals?"

"Exactly."

"No. No, Harry. They're a mistake. You don't want one of those. I don't care how good they are, they don't hold a press at all. Why don't you get a summer worsted? That's what I wear myself."

"I've got a worsted, Mike. Anyway, what suit in the summer doesn't need a lot of pressing?"

"Well, I guess you're the boss, Harry."

"Look, Mike, I need a lightweight tropical and I don't need a worsted. Let's see what you've got. Anything new?"

"Nobody's got anything better than I've got. Come on, I'll show you," and he spent the next twenty minutes unrolling bolts of cloth and spreading them out on his long oaken table. It was a pleasure showing a suiting to Harry. He was a man who knew materials. He fingered each piece of cloth carefully, and when he liked one he took it to the window to see it in the sunlight. Finally he selected a very light gray with a fine blue check, a pattern with some real distinction. "Now let's have a look at the fashion book," Mike said. The model Harry selected was conservative, single-breasted, with natural shoulders, and of course there were to be real buttonholes on the sleeves and hand stitching on the lapels. "I'll tell you what I'm going to do, Harry," Mike said profoundly. "I'm going to let Willie measure you. He's better than I am," and he stepped into the office. "Willie," he whispered to the middle-aged English fitter, who had a tape measure around his neck and was wearing the vest he always wore even in the hottest weather. "This guy thinks he's slumming. He's a showboat. Butter him up. Make it look like something you'd see going into the Ritz. And maybe he'll send you a case of Sweetman's. Come on."

While Willie was thrusting the tape measure into Harry's groin for the leg length, then around his chest, Mike stood back thinking, These charm boys can pick the suits off the rack and they fit them. Everything's there to be used. Just the same, he's a perfect forty, and then he said, "You get to know a lot about people measuring them for suits, Harry. I could write a book on my customers. You build them up their shoulders and pad them here and there and you send them out looking like very normal guys. A tailor's kind of like a priest. The customers confess to him, see? A man's best friend is his tailor, I say."

"My father used to have the same idea," Harry said. "By

the way," he said, stretching out his right arm so Willie could put the tape in his armpit. "What about old Scotty, have you made him a suit?"

"Not yet."

"Not yet! Why not? What's the matter with him?" and he started to laugh.

"Don't get Scotty wrong, Harry," Mike said earnestly. "He'll be in all right. But you see Scotty has about four good suits. He doesn't have the money for extra suits. See what I mean? You know, I love that man. I could tell you little things . . . Well, look what he did for me?"

"That's all, Mr. Lane," Willie said. "Thank you," and he left them, and Harry began to put on his coat.

"What did Scotty do for you, Mike?"

"Why he went to the textile people. He arranged the whole thing, and he set me up with a loan."

"He did, eh? Hmm," Harry said thoughtfully. "Arranged the whole thing, eh?" and he looked troubled, then he smiled. "Well, looks as if he's done the same thing for me."

"You don't need anyone to set you up, Harry."

"I do if I need a lot of money in a hurry."

"You could borrow money anywhere."

"I could? What on?" and he laughed. "You don't know me, Mike." He was buttoning up his coat and not watching what he was saying.

"The thing is you've got a spell on Scotty," Mike said slowly. "If you really needed money, well, just being you, you could persuade Scotty."

"Well, he certainly came through."

"Nothing like having such a friend, Harry."

"It's a fact, Mike. Well, when will the suit be ready?"

"Come in in three days for a fitting, then you can have it in a week. How's that?"

"Just right. Many thanks, Mike."

"So long." He went out and Mike at the window watched

him going along the street and frowned. So he did come in for a suit after all. Mike wondered about it. It didn't take him long to use Scotty, did it? Mike thought. Those guys will always use somebody.

Chapter 7

THE day the stock collapsed—it had opened at one dollar and twenty-five and closed at ten cents—Harry had been in McCance's office three times. The third time McCance, sitting at his desk, his face a peculiar color, pale and yet bluish, admitted that word had spread around that they had got bad news from the engineer. The well was in the tar sand field, not beyond it. In twelve or thirty years a process might be developed to get the millions of tons of oil out of that field, but at present, a well in the area meant nothing at all; soon they would have to begin explorations in another area. And when he had made this explanation, a blank, startled look came in his eyes and he toppled forward on his desk, bleeding a little at the nose. His secretary began to cry. There was no doctor in the building so they got an ambulance.

McCance was a dead man, Harry knew, as he watched the white-coated orderlies close the ambulance door.

It was a cloudy afternoon. People who had come out of the office building were standing on the gray sidewalk and the gray limestone wall of the building rose behind them to the gray sky. McCance had come out of nowhere to do something for him, Harry thought, and it came to this. In war, men like McCance would give their lives for each other, and now a chance meeting was as tragic. Then the ambulance began to move away, slowly at first, then faster. The little group of office workers turned back into the building but Harry stood there alone, his hands in his pockets, thinking of McCance's wife, until the ambulance had turned the corner.

He went into a cigar store and telephoned Mollie at the paper and told her what had happened to McCance and to the stock, and asked her to meet him. When she did, she couldn't understand why he hadn't told her about the loan. It was to have been a big surprise, Harry said, but Mollie started to cry.

Neither that night nor the next day did he get in touch with Scotty. He figured that he would hear from the bank soon enough, and on the third day, at four in the afternoon, a thin gray man in a gray suit came to the office and said his name was Slocombe. He was a bank superintendent, he said, and he had a crisp businesslike manner and a tight smile and there was hostility in his eyes.

"I'm sorry, Mr. Lane. I'm usually pretty good at concealing my own feelings, but in this case. . . ."

"In this case?"

"Well, Scotty Bowman is an old friend."

"Look, Mr. Slocombe, I got a loan from the bank, not from Scotty Bowman."

"Now Mr. Lane, you're an intelligent man. Surely you know you'd have to put up more than twice the amount of that kind of stock to get such a loan."

"That's up to the bank, isn't it?"

"That loan never had the bank's approval, Mr. Lane."

"What's that?" Filled with dread, Harry could only stare at Slocombe. Then he recovered himself. "You must be mad. Why, Scotty called me and told me he had it approved."

"Didn't he tell you he misrepresented the amount of the security?"

"Misrepresented? Why, the man is incapable . . ." He felt so incredulous he couldn't go on. "My God, not Scotty," he whispered. Then he remembered Scotty asking for the shares, and he understood. "Oh, no," he said, half to himself in wonder that such a good strong man should get in this shameful position. Oh, poor Scotty, he thought, and he seemed to be someone so close to him he wanted desperately to protect him. "There must be some mistake," he said. "The way the thing happened may not look right. But surely it can be put right."

"Just what did happen, Mr. Lane?"

"As far as I'm concerned, I wasn't even dealing with Scotty, Mr. Slocombe. I went into the bank. I was dealing with the bank." He stood up slowly, flushing.

"It just doesn't look right, Mr. Lane."

"What doesn't look right?"

"It looks as if you and Mr. Bowman got together."

"What the hell, I'm not going to bother getting angry with you, Mr. Slocombe. I got a regular bank loan and Scotty will tell you I got it innocently. Haven't you asked him? What does he say?"

"Yes, you're right relying on Scotty," Slocombe said bitterly. " 'Whatever you do,' he said, 'don't say anything to hurt Harry Lane.' " Then he hesitated, wet his lips, looked down at his hands folded on the desk; on the back of his left hand were three brown spots. "No, you don't have to worry about anything Scotty might say, Mr. Lane. But just tell me this," he blurted out, looking up suddenly. "I've known Scotty Bowman for years. He's a fine honest man, the soul of integrity, and I'd trust him with my life. A man of good judgment and common sense, a family man, and the bank meant everything to him in the world. I don't just know him as a bank manager, I know him as a friend." His voice dropped, the words coming with a slow bitterness. "Surely you see it would take a lot of persuasion to make such a man disgrace himself."

"I owe the bank money and I'm aware of it, Mr. Slocombe," he said with quiet dignity. "What Scotty did is as incredible to me as it is to you. I don't understand it."

"I don't either. I'm sorry, Mr. Lane," Slocombe said, sighing.

"What else can I say?"

"Nothing, Mr. Lane," and he got up and went to the door, then hesitated awkwardly. "I'm sorry I let my personal feelings get involved. When you've known a man a long time it's hard to understand why he does a thing so far out of character. Well, that's all for now. Thank you. Good day, Mr. Lane."

"Good day," Harry said stiffly, and he went right into Sweetman's office. Sweetman was wearing a brown checked English jacket, sitting at his desk, the sunlight from the window touching his shiny thick black hair and one side of his rosy-cheeked, contented face. Other businessmen around town resented Sweetman's English mannerisms, his heavy mustache and his Oxonian accent, and his literacy too. But Harry liked him. He thought of him as a good friend.

Smiling amiably, Sweetman asked, "What's on your mind, old boy?"

Scotty Bowman could never mean anything to Sweetman, Harry knew at once. He told him about the loan and what Slocombe had said, waiting while Sweetman, looking out the window, reflected gravely and shrewdly, weighing all the factors. Finally he sighed. "My God, Harry, the people you get mixed up with. How do you do it?" Well, there was bound to be some unpleasantness, Sweetman continued. Just the same, it couldn't put Harry in a bad light if the silly bank manager had had the decency, as this fellow Slocombe said, not to involve him in any way. There was no point in looking so hurt and upset. What did Harry say if they both knocked off for the afternoon and went out to the golf course?

No, Harry said awkwardly, he had an appointment, and he went back to his own office and called Mollie at the paper and told her about Slocombe. She seemed to know then how much he needed her company and she said she would meet him on the Peel corner in half an hour. She was going over to Birks' jewelry to leave a silver necklace that had belonged to her grandmother, to have the clasp repaired.

He was on the corner waiting when she got out of the taxi

across the road and came hurrying toward him in her smart blue suit, the traffic cop trying to wave her back, then grinning when she smiled at him. They walked east in the sunlight. Rain had been predicted, but as yet there was no sign of it.

Mollie was as baffled and hurt as he was. Scotty was a man whose honesty in living had seemed to be apparent in his simplest gesture and in his straightforward warm smile. It didn't make sense, they agreed. Scotty was a man whose warm friendly interest in him, Harry said, had touched some good memory of his youth. He kept going over it. "What can you say about such a man?" he kept repeating angrily. His anger moved her because he was behaving as she would have expected him to. Everything he said now seemed to touch her love and respect for him. She couldn't imagine Harry behaving badly no matter what happened to him.

"You know what we should do? We should go and see Daddy," she said suddenly. "The fact that this man Slocombe comes to see you is important, Harry. Tell the whole thing to Daddy and see where you stand." She sounded like a young girl, and he smiled. Judge Morris was a fine man, and it was true he would have a clearheaded legal view of Scotty's position, but he was Daddy; she was always running to Daddy. He could see the Judge leaning back, tapping his forehead nervously, those shrewd pale blue eyes full of respectable disapproval of the whole business. No. He didn't need to see her father, and he wouldn't, he said stubbornly.

They were arguing as they went into Birks', but he had to wait while she went to one counter, then another, with her silver necklace. Whenever she moved away she would turn quickly to see if he was following, and that quick turn of her head, then the sudden bright anxious smile, almost took his mind off Scotty.

Chapter 8

THE sky clouded over at six and at nine it was still raining hard with gusts of wind sweeping rain into the doorways. Harry, caught on the street waiting for a taxi, started to run toward his apartment building. Splashing through pools of water, he got his feet wet, and as soon as he got in he dried his face, changed his suit and was putting on his slippers when someone knocked on the door. He went to the door. There was Scotty with a dripping umbrella making a little pool on the hall carpet.

"Hello, Harry," he said uneasily.

"Oh. Hello, Scotty. Well, come on in."

Scotty came in, but he didn't sit down. He stood awkwardly in the middle of the room as they faced each other. Then Harry noticed his wet and shining rubbers. They were old-fashioned rubbers completely covering his shoes. Harry hadn't seen such a pair of rubbers on any of his friends since he had been a boy, and the sight of them made him angry.

"Scotty, I know there's a little bit of larceny in everybody—" He stopped suddenly, for Scotty, standing there mutely, looked like a beaten old man. "Scotty, what happened?"

"They're going to arrest me, Harry."

"Arrest you?"

"Fraud and misrepresentation, Harry."

"Oh, Lord."

"Can I sit down, Harry?"

"Why ask me if you can sit down? For heaven's sake, sit down, man." So Scotty sat down in the big chair by the window.

"All right, Scotty," he said grimly, standing in front of him. "This is all yours."

"I know it is, Harry. Please listen . . . just for a minute. Now don't worry. I've told them you're not involved at all. Harry, I was waiting out there on the street."

"I wasn't even going to come home, Scotty."

"I'd have waited, Harry."

"Scotty, why did you do it?" he asked, flopping down in a chair and staring at him bitterly. "I'd have bet my life on you, Scotty."

"I don't know, Harry," he said, looking bewildered. "I've been thinking it over and—I guess I lost my head. I don't understand what happens to a man so he's suddenly not himself. He even thinks nobody notices it. But my wife noticed it, Harry. You know what she said? She said, 'You're not yourself, Scotty.' Just last week she said it—or was it two weeks ago? I don't know. Money in chunks never seemed to come my way, Harry. I never had much. I never had an extra cent. I never had any of the extras that make a man's life comfortable and easy. I got excited, hanging around with you; money suddenly all around me. Real money: I got dazzled. You don't know what it means never to have a roll and to be suddenly with people who throw it around. It makes your life seem small and cheap; I got dazzled, Harry." Their eyes met and for the first time Harry realized that the stock had corrupted Scotty from the very beginning. "This seemed to be such a *sure* thing, Harry," Scotty pleaded. "The kind of thing that is always happening to a guy like you but never to me." Scotty slumped in the chair, his bitter smile reproaching Harry for having been too lucky all his life.

Touch wood, Harry thought, and he touched the wood of the arm of the chair, and nodded at Scotty sympathetically.

"It's my wife and children, Harry," Scotty said. "I know I should have thought of them, yet I did think of them. It's crazy to say so, but when you're not yourself and something has given you a little push the wrong way, you do think of your wife and children, only they too seem to be pushing you the wrong way. You don't have a wife and family, Harry, and you don't get pushed the wrong way. I'll lose my job and my pension. All right. It's my own fault." Then he faltered and tried to smile. "There's just one thing, Harry."

"What?" The smile worried Harry a little.

"About those shares I asked for after the loan," he said desperately. "It was after the loan, you know, Harry, wasn't it?"

"Yes, it was. Why?"

"Listen, Harry . . . all they want to know about is the loan. If you mention those shares it'll look like a cooked-up deal." He patted the top of his gray head nervously. "Anyway, it might look to people—"

"Look like what?"

"Harry, for *my* sake, don't mention it. If you do it may hurt you too. People may say you were cutting me in."

"Not if you tell the truth."

"I don't want it to be misunderstood. I know it wouldn't stop you, but it may be hard for you to explain, Harry. I'm only saying—"

"Go on, Scotty."

"If you mention those shares it'll go hard on me, Harry," he pleaded. "If you won't think of yourself, for the sake of my wife and children don't mention those shares, Harry."

"What am I supposed to do, Scotty? I've got to tell the truth."

"I know you'll tell the truth. I'm not asking you *not* to tell the truth. Sometimes the truth gives a completely wrong impression—" His voice broke, then he went on: "Harry, Harry boy, you don't have to add it all up for them. You're absolutely blameless. Haven't I said so? Well, why give everybody a chance to think the worst of both of us?"

"Both of us? Oh, hell, Scotty," Harry said, growing more upset. Scotty suddenly did look old—frightened and not smart at all. What was this old man doing here in his life asking him to protect him? he thought. Why had he taken such a fancy to him and seem to know him so well? Then their eyes met and again those frank blue eyes of Scotty's seemed to draw him close and make him ashamed that he had had any accidental hand in the downfall of a fine man. "You know I'll do all I can to help you, Scotty," he said, deeply moved. "There's the truth about the loan, just the loan, I'll tell about. . . . That's all."

"Oh, thank you Harry," and the old Scotty smile returned briefly.

"I'll tell about getting the loan and where I stood. And no more." And then so like the Harry Scotty knew, he added generously, "After all, it's not for me to say what was in your mind or what went on in it *after* the loan."

"Thanks again, Harry," Scotty said, and he took a deep breath. "I'll owe you a lot for that."

"Do you want a drink?"

"No, thanks, Harry. I want to get home. My God, it's awful the way I want to get home." He stood up. "I left my umbrella in the hall."

"Are you going to walk down to the station?"

"I might as well."

"Not in that rain. Don't do it, Scotty."

"All right, just as you say, Harry." He went out, and from the window Harry watched him standing on the sidewalk with his umbrella up, looking for a taxi, but no taxi stopped so he moved slowly along toward the Ritz and out of sight.

Next day Harry didn't see him, or the next day either, and then he thought he had better not see him any more for a while because two detectives came to the apartment one night and questioned him sharply about the loan. He told the truth. He said that Scotty had telephoned him and that he had gone into the bank and arranged for the loan with Scotty.

Scotty was arrested and charged with fraud and misrepresentation. There was a brief preliminary hearing before a magistrate, then the case was sent on for trial. For days no one in the metropolitan section of the city talked about anything else.

Chapter 9

IN THE corridor outside the courtroom where Scotty Bowman was to be tried for embezzlement there was a gathering of people who wouldn't have come together at any other time. They had come from shops, brokerage offices and saloons, their own private homes, and even Chinese laundries. The corridor was wet and dirty with little pools of water from their wet shoes. All night long and during the morning it had rained, and there were puddles in the gutter and on the roads and everybody had got wet from the spray from passing taxis.

The troubled and wondering shopkeepers and small businessmen stood in little groups, all wearing their good suits out of respect to Scotty whose integrity they had always admired. Near the courtroom door, two tall neat bond salesmen, friends of Harry Lane's, looked around at the others with some amusement. "Look at those two Chinamen. Notice anything funny about them?" the taller one said. . . . "You mean they look alike?" . . . "No, not that. Neither one is wearing a hat that seems to fit him properly. Look." The two Chinese had done business with Scotty's bank and had often invited him to Chinese banquets. Two years ago now, Scotty had received a decoration from Chiang Kai-shek.

Two matrons from Westmount, walking up and down, gossiped in English accents that did not come from England. "Of course you know Harry's mother died without leaving him a cent." . . . "Well he certainly seems to have left this bank manager flat on his back without a cent." . . . "I must say I was astonished when he took that job with Sweetmans." . . . "That pushing Mrs. Sweetman. She'll do a little squirming over this kind of publicity. Say, isn't that Julie Stokes over there? Didn't she used to be stuck on Harry?"

Miss Stokes, in an open black coat, standing self-consciously by herself, had just come back from the Laurentians. She was staring at two blondes, two young women who had small savings accounts in Scotty's bank. One was a hat-check girl and the other danced in a night club. Frowning, Miss Stokes furtively tucked her yellow scarf under the fold of her coat; it was the same kind of yellow scarf the girl with the big red mouth was wearing.

The corridor began to smell of wet cloth and rubbers and there was a lot of coughing. The weather had been bad all week. A mild flu epidemic, an influenza that started with a head cold and coughing, was prevalent. Coming along the corridor was the newspaperman they called the Young Lion—because he was determined to outwrite, outdrink and outsmart all his older colleagues—and his grin widened as he recognized older men he respected. A few paces behind him was Lonesome George, the saloonkeeper, and when he caught up he said, "I wasn't sure whether any of the boys would bother coming. Jeeze, there's Eddie." Neither his expensive suit nor his new hat seemed to belong to him. He made his way toward big Eddie Adams, the rich fight promoter who was talking to Haggerty of the *Sun*, and Ted Ogilvie.

The hum of conversation was broken by a loud burst of laughter. "Less noise there, less noise," the gray-haired policeman at the door shouted belligerently. The laughter came from members of the sporting fraternity. No laughter came from the sedate little businessmen, who were surprised that they were there at all. Those who were laughing because it was their style, secretly marveled that Scotty Bowman and Harry Lane should end their friendship in a courtroom.

"Here's old Mike," Haggerty said, "looking like a funeral, too."

Mike Kon, coming toward them, looked so unhappy they all wanted to kid him.

"Don't be a brooder, Mike," Eddie Adams said.

"I'm no brooder, Eddie."

"Tell me something, Haggerty," Eddie Adams said, solemnly. "Here's Mike the Scholar, and he reads all those books and we look up to him, don't we? But tell me why guys who go for the books turn into brooders."

"It gets them thinking about things," Haggerty said. "It gets old Mike thinking about Scotty, doesn't it, Mike?"

"For me this is no joke," Mike said bitterly. "Scotty was my friend. Am I to stand out here clowning when my friend is on trial?"

"You say Scotty was your friend. Was? What's the matter, are they hanging the guy?"

"I don't mean was. I mean is."

"We're all friends. These things only happen among friends. What's the point of having friends if you can't get them into trouble?"

"But Scotty loses his job anyway," Mike said earnestly. "He loses his pension and he has a wife and children. I know what that means."

"The case hasn't been tried yet," Ted Ogilvie said hopefully. "Harry may be able to put Scotty in a very good light."

"By God, he'd better," Mike said. "This thing is all wrong, you know. Something is very wrong. Never in his life did Scotty get out of line and Harry Lane is—well—I'm sorry, I can't talk about it any more."

"You can't. Why not?"

"I'm a witness."

"You're a witness?"

"That's right," Mike said.

"A character witness for Scotty?"

"No. Just a witness for him," Mike said importantly. "So leave me alone," and he walked away.

The policeman suddenly opened the door and they all began to file into the big high-ceilinged, paneled courtroom. Two spectators had been let in ahead of the others: Mrs. Bowman and a gray-haired man, a family friend, had been allowed to enter with the lawyers from the side door. Paula Bowman wore a brown hat and a brown cloth coat with a little fur on the collar. As the benches began to fill around her, her neck and back grew rigid. The Chinese sat in one row and the shopkeepers who knew each other kept together in another. They all seemed to know where they belonged. Bright sunlight unexpectedly came through the high western window.

At the crowded press table Entwhistle, the dignified bald little court reporter for the *Sun*, couldn't find a suitable seat. "How can I work with someone sitting in my lap?" he snarled. Then Mollie Morris came in and everybody turned. No one had thought she would sit at the press table, since she only had the little job on the women's page. She was wearing a black suit and a little white straw hat and her face was flushed from hurrying.

"Remove that coat from the back of that seat," a policeman shouted, and everybody turned to see whose coat it was. Lonesome George had tried to avoid folding and sitting on his good camel's-hair coat. Grabbing at it he pulled it down to his knees with a big uneasy smile and he was glad when Scotty Bowman was led to the dock.

In the last two months Scotty had grown older. He still looked the family man he was, with a plump wife and two children. His hair had been quite gray anyway, but he had been plump and jolly and had now lost weight. He was stooped a little as he approached the dock. In one quick furtive glance he took in all the spectators, till he found his wife. Before, in the bank, or at the ball game or the fights, or sitting in Dorfman's, feeling so pleased to be there with more celebrated personalities who led expensive and glamorous lives, his glance had always been direct. Now he fumbled at his collar, shifted his eyes, and turned to the window and blinked at the shaft of sunlight that just reached the dock; then he lowered his head and his face became so pale his lawyer, Roger Ouimet, stood up and went over to speak to him. Scotty lifted his head as if the lawyer's consoling smile had given him some strength, and then he smiled, too.

When Judge Montpetit came in everybody stood up, although some of them couldn't see him at first, for he was only five foot four. His hair like a white plume rose above the heads of the lawyers and the clerks as he mounted the steps to his chair. He had a big head and heavy features and with his white plume he looked a little like Santa Claus without a beard as he glanced anxiously at the open window. He was afraid he was catching a cold and he had taken a mixture of lemon juice and baking soda before leaving the house. His hearing was not good and the courtroom acoustics were bad, and as always, he looked up resentfully at the high ceiling. While the jury was being selected he fumbled with papers, read them, wrote on many papers, leaning well over to the left, then folded his hands and waited.

The jury was selected quickly because there were no challenges from Roger Ouimet. They were salesmen, electricians, managers and an insurance man. One by one, they walked to their chairs, and when they were all together, their faces in two rows against the sunlit window, they did look like men of common sense. Then Scotty stood up and the charge was read. "Not guilty," he said firmly.

They didn't need a special prosecutor to handle Scotty's case. It was too simple. The case was being handled, as such routine cases were, by George Henderson. His tired eyes, his gray mustache touched up a little, and the network of red veins in his cheeks told everybody why he had missed having a distinguished career. "John Slocombe," he called, linking both hands behind him under his gown and swinging around to look for the bank superintendent.

The thin gray man in a gray suit, grimly doing a job he hated, clutched the witness box rail and never let go, as Henderson, in his ponderous style, brought out that he had been with the bank for fifteen years and a superintendent for five. Then Slocombe told how he had discovered that Bowman had misrepresented the security he had got from Lane; Bowman had represented to the bank that he had taken thirty thousand shares of Western Oil as security for fifteen thousand dollars he had loaned Harry Lane; the market value of these thirty thousand shares at the time he made the loan would have been equal to twice the amount of the loan. The fact was he had taken only fifteen thousand shares as security. Of course, by the time the deception was discovered the shares were worth about a thousand dollars.

"Did you ask Mr. Bowman why he misrepresented the amount of security he had got from Lane?"

"I did."

"What did he say?"

"He said he had wanted to be sure the loan cleared."

"And why the general misrepresentation of what he had done?"

"I asked him why, of course, and he said that after he had committed himself to making the loan he felt he owed it to Harry Lane to go through with it; he believed in it. There seemed to be no risk at all. The head office couldn't have the confidence in Harry Lane that he had and he said it was all a matter of confidence."

"He admitted he misrepresented the conditions of the loan?"

"Well, there it was, and he admitted it."

"Will the witness please speak up," the judge said testily. "Speak out. You have nothing to be ashamed of. It's hard to hear anything in this court. Now what was it you said? Turn this way a little."

Clearing his throat, Slocombe said, "It was the day the stock crashed—before noon, and I came in. Scotty—Mr. Bowman— had been busy and hadn't heard about it, or I suppose he could have rushed out and bought shares to cover him for next to nothing, but there I was confronting him, and he said he was afraid he would be prosecuted." Slocombe's voice faded as he looked at Scotty.

"I know this is an unpleasant task for you," the judge said gently. "But it is an honorable one."

"You said that Mr. Bowman admitted that his misrepresentation of the security he had taken for this loan would leave him charged with embezzlement."

"Or possibly conspiracy."

"There's no charge of conspiracy with anyone. Just this admitted embezzlement."

"Oh, but I object," Ouimet said, rising slowly. "My friend goes too fast. Mr. Bowman has pleaded not guilty. All that the witness has said is that Mr. Bowman told of his faith in his judgment of Harry Lane, and then in conversation with the witness, after he sees how bad his judgment has been, he says he can see now that it can be said he misrepresented things."

"That might be very well put in the defense counsel's argument to the jury," the judge said, smiling.

"Well, those are the facts," Henderson said simply. He didn't want to make a big thing of it. It wasn't necessary. Linking his hands behind him under his gown he shrugged. "Your witness."

"Mr. Slocombe," Ouimet said, with a courteous little bow and a friendly smile as if he only wanted to be helpful. "How long have you known Mr. Bowman? I mean, in your banking business."

"About fifteen years, sir."

"And what was your opinion of his character?"

"I had the highest opinion of him."

"Not a blemish on his reputation?"

"No, sir."

"In fact, would you not say that in your own bank he had always been considered a man of the highest integrity?"

"That's true." For the first time he was at ease with himself.

"Mr. Slocombe," Ouimet said, walking slowly toward the jury, yet apparently unaware that he was making himself one with the twelve men of common sense. "Supposing Mr. Bowman had made this loan to Harry Lane, just as he did—irregular and all as it was—and it had been repaid within a week with interest, as Mr. Bowman believed it would, what would have been the procedure?"

"Well, we might never have discovered that there had been a misrepresentation, I suppose."

"And he might not be here in the dock at all?"

"Well, I don't know. I can't tell about ifs and buts."

"Oh, I know bankers are cautious, but if Bowman's confidence in Harry Lane had been justified—"

"That wouldn't justify the misrepresentation."

"Now look here," Ouimet said amiably, and he smiled at the jury. "If Lane had repaid the loan, as he promised to do, in a few days, and picked up his security, where would we be?"

"But the thing was discovered."

"All right. Now has Mr. Bowman always shown good banking judgment?"

"The very best."

"Till he came to his friend Lane?"

"Well, yes, until this affair."

"By the way, when you questioned him about misrepresenting the security he had got from Lane, did you ask what in the world happened to his judgment?"

"I did."

"And what did he say?"

"He was upset. Seemed to feel he had committed himself, and he had confidence in Lane."

"He seemed to feel under an obligation, a personal obligation?"

"As far as I could see," the superintendent said, with a helpless gesture. "It was just because it was Harry Lane."

"Just because it was Harry Lane," Ouimet repeated softly,

71

and as he sauntered away and pondered, everyone, waiting and watching, was sure he was repeating the words over and over to himself. "Thank you, that's all," he said finally.

When Slocombe had left the dock, Henderson said, "Call Harry Lane." They called "Harry Lane." The policeman at the door repeated "Harry Lane," and it echoed along the corridor.

They all turned as Harry came in, but the jurors had the best view of him as he approached the box, his head up, his shoulders back like a man with some military training. Pale as he was, he still had his distinguished air. He wore a navy blue suit and a white shirt and a blue tie with a thin red stripe in it. Scotty, too, had on a good blue suit, but it didn't look like Harry's.

Yet Harry made a bad impression as soon as he got into the box. He began to yawn, then tried to suppress it quickly as his friends, watching him, smiled. But the yawn wasn't a gesture. He was very tired and troubled. He had been up nearly all night. He had gone home early enough, but before he could get undressed and into bed there had been a knock at the door. It was the young blond wife of the rich old painter who lived upstairs. "Harry, I think his nerves are really going to pieces tonight," she'd said. "Please come up. We mustn't be alone with each other tonight. He keeps saying he has no friends and is going to kill himself. I know it's silly," she had pleaded, "because he hasn't a worry in the world. He likes you, Harry. Won't you come up? You're good for him."

Harry had sighed and grumbled a little, then he had gone upstairs to drink with the old painter and cheer him up with amusing stories which he acted out for him. It had been comical really. The old painter didn't feel so insecure with his wife when someone else was there entertaining the both of them. "Things look different when you're around, Harry," he kept saying and wouldn't let him go till four in the morning; and afterwards, back in his own place, he couldn't sleep.

Chapter 10

FACING them all in the witness box, Harry wanted to tell the truth and nothing but the truth as he had just sworn he would do. He turned to look at Scotty, who was watching him with a friendly trusting expression in his eyes, and then he looked to the right of Scotty, under the clock, where Paula Bowman was sitting, and he watched her fumbling in her purse for her glasses which she put on and, as she eyed him steadily, the fear in her face disturbed him.

Then Henderson asked him who he was and so on. "I want to start right at the beginning with you—" And he had Harry tell about the meeting with Scotty that afternoon on Peel. Harry told the whole story as it had happened up until the time he got the loan.

"Now Mr. Lane, I put this to you," Henderson said, hitching at the shoulder of his gown. "When the subject of the loan came up, you were sure you were going to make a lot of money, weren't you?"

"Yes, I thought it was a sure thing."

"I put it to you that you and Bowman got together to work out a way of getting this money."

"I don't follow you," he said uneasily.

"Tell us how you got together on it."

"After hearing of my chance, it seemed to Mr. Bowman that I would be silly if I didn't go after a loan and make some real money."

"Did you hold out any inducement to him to make the loan?"

"I did not."

"And he was only trying to be helpful with business advice in his field?"

"Like any other businessman, I suppose, he saw that I ought to be able to make a lot of money."

"You mean like a banker looking for business?"

"No, it was just a businessman's observation, I thought."

"Then he suggested a loan?"

"Well, he smiled and said banks made loans."

"Did you offer him any inducement at all to make such a loan?"

"None at all. He just offered to look into it."

"When did he tell you his head office wanted twice the security that you could get?"

"Well, the truth is," Harry said reluctantly, "he never told me."

"You mean you thought you were meeting all the requirements?"

"Well, he had said that reputation was as important as security to a bank. They both added up to the loan."

"Hmm," Henderson said, with his dry smile. "He didn't bother to tell you that at least twice your amount would actually be required? A most helpful friend." He turned then to Ouimet. "Your witness."

Smiling politely, Ouimet came close to Harry, and he had cold sharp eyes. In one hand he was twisting a little gold knife on a gold chain, and the hand was thin and pale. His hair was clipped tight at the temples to conceal the grayness. They had known each other casually for two years but Harry had never felt any real friendliness in him, and they had shied away from each other. Ouimet was a strict Catholic, a French-Canadian puritan Catholic, and in his private life he had a spinsterish aloofness from any kind of self-indulgence. Harry had always felt he disapproved of him.

"What is your occupation, Mr. Lane?" he asked gently.

"I'm the public relations director for the Sweetman Distillery."

"And your job, I take it, is to promote good will," and he smiled, making a joke. "Should I say to soften people up?"

"No, you shouldn't say it."

"Then I apologize. But a man to be successful at your job would have to be affable, know everybody, have a winning personality, be persuasive."

"A man with those qualities would do well even in the legal profession," Harry said, smiling.

"But they are the necessary qualities for your job, I take it. Now how long have you known Mr. Bowman?"

"About three years, I think."

"How did you come to meet him?"

"One day I was in the bank with a friend and I was introduced to him and after that would sometimes see him at the ball games or at the hockey games and sometimes at the fights."

"He was very fond of sport and you were too. Was that the basis of your friendship?"

"No, I liked him the first time I met him. He had a kind of dignity, a simple integrity, a wonderfully kind open simple friendliness," he said slowly.

"Qualities rarely found in your world, I take it?" Ouimet said dryly.

"Very rare in any world," Harry said simply.

"And you knew that this honest bank manager, making six thousand a year, admired you?"

"I knew he liked me, as I liked him."

"And because he was fond of sport, you knew that he had a naïve admiration for champions, sporting figures and great entertainers, the kind of people you ran into every day. Did you ask him why he didn't drop into Dorfman's?"

"I knew he would like sitting around listening to the gossip."

"In this world of easy money, I suppose this bank manager was impressed by these celebrated figures, and Dorfman's is a famous old expensive restaurant catering to the elite, isn't it?" And among the spectators Eddie Adams, Haggerty and Ted Ogilvie in their row looked at each other with a new and grave respect.

"He only came there about once a week."

"Of course," Ouimet agreed sympathetically. "It was a little out of his reach, but he felt at home with you and your friends. It was a big thing for him, wasn't it? In truth, between us, wasn't he a little stage-struck?"

"Well, maybe he had a naïve admiration for some famous visiting firemen who weren't good enough to lace his shoes."

"The methodical banker, twenty years older than you, with a wife and two children, living in the suburbs, was secretly stage-struck, wouldn't you say?"

"Any time I was ever around," Harry said, wondering at how Ouimet had got so close to the truth, "I could see that he was liked and respected for what he was in himself."

"I see," Ouimet said, leaning amiably on the rail of the jury box so he could join with the jurors in watching Harry. "To come back to this rainy day—"

"It wasn't raining, it was drizzling a little."

"Oh, that's it. You want to be accurate. Good. You had just come from a funeral parlor. No?"

"That's true. Old Professor McLean had died."

"And when you ran into Mr. Bowman, what did you say you had been doing in the funeral parlor."

"You want me to remember the jokes?" Harry asked impatiently, and Henderson rose and said he didn't see the relevancy of the question, and Ouimet protested sharply that it had to do with the character of the witness.

"I'm not sure myself where this is leading," the judge said, and he started to cough. His left nostril began to run and he wondered why he had wasted his time trying a preventative like lemon juice and baking soda. "Continue, continue," he said irritably. "And speak up, please."

"I joked with Mr. Bowman. I said I was a public relations man for half the city. About thirty-six old classmates had phoned me, knowing I'd be going to the funeral parlor, and they asked me to sign their names on the book." Everybody snickered.

"I hope I wasn't one of those who phoned you," the judge said brightly.

"Not that I recall," he said gravely; then he laughed.

"Your friends are all a bit cynical," Ouimet said.

"No, they knew I'd be at the funeral parlor."

"And they knew you'd go through the cynical performance of making it look to the dead man's family as if they had come to pay their respects."

"Well, I was there, so I wasn't cynical," he said uneasily. Ouimet's little smile and the glitter in his pale blue eyes made him stiffen.

"Well, now you and Mr. Bowman, standing on the street have joked and you've told your cynical little story. Now how did the subject of the loan come up?"

"Well, I was feeling good. I knew I was going to make some money on the stock. I trusted Mr. Bowman. I told him about it."

"By the way, have you anyone else to support but yourself on your fifteen thousand a year?"

"No, sir."

"A free spender, easy come, easy go, I suppose," Ouimet said indulgently. "You go to New York to see the big fights, and to the world series, and see all the new plays, eh?"

"Now—now—now," the judge warned Ouimet.

"Surely it's important to establish the nature of Bowman's relationship with the witness—the fact that Mr. Lane saw the places and did the things Bowman only dreamed about," Ouimet protested.

"Well, only as to his credibility," the judge said. "Never mind these beautiful pictures of the witness."

"Only as to his credibility," Ouimet said, turning to Harry. "You've told your good, admiring and stage-struck friend, who happens to be a banker, that you need money, eh?"

"Quite the opposite. I told him I was going to make some money, and he saw how I could make a lot more."

"And finally he mentioned the loan, eh? That is to say, you let him mention it first. That's good salesmanship, isn't it?"

"What was I supposed to be selling?"

"Isn't that the art of letting the customer come to you?" Ouimet asked blandly.

"I wouldn't know. It isn't my style. Naturally the question of security came up."

"With you raising the obstacles, of course."

"I saw the objections. Yes."

"You put up the obstacles, and he came leaping over them—should I say 'eagerly'?"

"No, you should be accurate. Let's say there seemed to be no objections by him."

"Let's get the picture straight," Ouimet said, with an amused smile. "This banker influenced you to take a loan from him."

"He didn't influence me. I said it was his suggestion."

"And I suppose it was also his suggestion you go to McCance, and McCance would let you have the stock, trusting you."

"Well, yes, he did," Harry said reluctantly.

"And you would have been shocked if he had told you he hadn't got the loan approved?"

"There wouldn't have been any loan."

"He was afraid to tell you the money was tainted—afraid you'd let him down by not taking it."

"If that's the way you want to put it."

"Really," Ouimet said softly and then he turned to the jury, and some of them tried not to smile.

Harry looked around and saw that they all believed that in trying to protect himself he had gone too far and was willing to blame Scotty for everything. In the last row of spectators his own friend Ted Ogilvie, astonished and disappointed, had leaned close to Eddie Adams to whisper, and Scotty's wife, her mouth trembling, had turned to the elderly man, who held her arm restrainingly. Nobody believed him. Bewildered, he turned, half pleading, as he looked at Mollie Morris at the press table. Leaning back in her chair, she tapped her teeth with her pencil, and as their eyes met she slumped in her chair and let her chin fall on her chest, dejected.

"Mr. Bowman will stand here and tell exactly the same thing," he said angrily.

"Are all your friends anxious to do you favors?"

"I don't go around with my hat in my hand," he said, straightening up with his distinguished air. But someone had snickered. There was a little titter and the titter spread and there was a scraping of feet and everybody was smiling. Banging his gavel, the judge threatened to have the courtroom cleared. Turning suddenly, Harry stared at Scotty, the whole swing of his body angry and challenging.

Ouimet took advantage of this deftly. "Oh, let me reassure you," he said sarcastically, "Mr. Bowman may still believe that all the suggestions came from him, even if he's somewhat bewildered at how it could happen that he found himself doing— shall we call it—this favor?"

"At no time did I ask him to do me a favor."

"Oh, come now, surely by this time you'll have to admit that Bowman was trying to help you out, just a little—be generous."

"As I understood it," Harry said doggedly, "it was a loan to be acceptable to the bank in every way. Who gets loans from a bank by way of a favor? Is that the only way you yourself can get a loan?"

"Ah, now, let me ask the questions."

"Well, stop distorting everything I say."

"The witness shouldn't lose his temper," the judge said mildly.

"Let's go on," Ouimet said softly. "You admit you didn't use money as a bait?"

"I certainly didn't. It wasn't at all necessary." Taking out his handkerchief, he wiped his mouth. It felt dry, and he moistened his lips and said truthfully, "I asked if it was to be a regular loan, an approved loan, and it was, as far as I was concerned."

"You didn't use money as a bait—but you did use friendship, knowing this stage-struck manager believed completely in his distinguished friend."

"If I'm supposed to be the distinguished friend, that's absurd." And then he added slowly, "Mr. Bowman is a shrewd man—a banker—a much shrewder businessman than I am."

He couldn't take his eyes off Ouimet's feet. The black and very shiny shoes were very narrow and sharply pointed and Harry despised such shoes.

"A shrewd man," Ouimet said, and his tone changed. Dropping the soft insinuations he came closer, coldly aggressive, and Harry hated him. "If you were a clever man, a little cynical and reckless with money—" Ouimet began.

"Now, now," the judge complained. "Counsel should make his speeches to the jury and not to the witness."

"I'm sorry," Ouimet said, bowing deferentially, and then he whirled on Harry. "I put it to you that you were looking for money, that you knew that no bank in town would give you a loan on such security."

"It's not true."

"I suggest to you that you went to work on Bowman and he told you he doubted the head office would approve the loan."

"It's not true."

"And knowing he trusted you completely, didn't you insist that only three or four days were involved and you weren't asking him to take much risk, and you wouldn't let him down?"

"It's absolutely untrue," Harry said.

"And didn't you appeal to his friendship and faith in you

when he spoke of getting the loan approved by the head office?"

"I did not."

"Don't you see even now that you simply took advantage of his strong sense of friendship—that he was a dupe?"

"That he was a dupe—*really*. Nothing of the kind. There's not a word of truth in it. I tell you I was completely in the dark."

"But now, isn't there enough light for you to see that if it could be shown that you collaborated on getting this loan, you'd be here charged with conspiracy?"

"You know why I'm not charged with conspiracy? He'll stand here in his turn and tell you."

"Have you still got that much confidence in your influence over Bowman?" Ouimet asked, smiling as if Harry had said what he wanted him to say. "Well, that's all. Thank you."

But Harry remained in the box, troubled and yet grim. Then, half turning to the judge, he hesitated.

"Is there something the witness wishes to say?" the judge asked.

"There is," Harry said, with dignity. "There's one fact that may have been lost sight of, and rather deliberately, I'm afraid. The root of the whole matter. And it is this: I was not told that his loan did not meet the requirements of the head office and that it had been misrepresented"—and as Ouimet got to his feet, protesting, he raised his voice—"and Mr. Bowman will stand here and tell you I was kept absolutely in the dark. . . ."

"A speech, this is a speech," Ouimet cried, and in the hubbub the judge cried angrily, "Order—please."

When Harry stepped down, Ouimet, recovering himself, smiled. "I can sympathize with the witness wanting to make a speech to the jury. He seems to think that he and not Mr. Bowman is on trial. Oh, I won't ask that he be recalled," he said, and Harry, after turning belligerently, went to the seat near the door and stared at Scotty, waiting confidently for him to take the stand.

"Well, that's the case," Henderson said. "I have nothing more to add."

"Let's go on then with the defense," the judge said. "Are you ready, Mr. Ouimet?"

"Quite ready," Ouimet said, and he swung around in the direction of Scotty Bowman. Everybody looked at Scotty. Everybody was sure Ouimet was ready to ask him to take the stand. But Ouimet's eyes shifted away from Scotty, though he was still looking in the general direction, but over to the side; then he nodded. "Call Mike Kon," he said.

"Mike Kon. Mike Kon."

Mike came from his seat toward the stand, in his rolling stride, and he swore to tell the truth the whole truth and nothing but the truth. Straightening up he gripped the rail, looking better than he had ever done in his life because he wasn't thinking of himself at all, or how he was going to sound, or what impression he might make. He found dignity and a pride in his knowledge that whatever he might say, serving the cause of justice, would also serve Scotty Bowman, his friend, to whom he owed everything. He faced Ouimet calmly.

"What is your profession, Mr. Kon?"

"I'm a tailor."

"You have a place of business?"

"A shop on St. Catherine Street."

"On that day in April, when you were going back to your shop after lunch, did you pass the bank where Mr. Bowman was manager?"

"I did."

"Anything attract your eye?"

"I saw Mr. Bowman and Mr. Lane standing at the entrance, laughing, and I called out to them, and Mr. Lane said he was coming for a suit."

"They looked very friendly—very intimate?"

"They were real close friends."

"I don't see the relevance of this. Really I don't," Henderson complained as he stood up looking bored.

"It has relevance," Ouimet said. "This was the day Lane got the loan."

"Let him go on a little," the judge said. "What are you aiming at, Mr. Ouimet?"

"I assure the court I'll throw some light on why Harry Lane went to Bowman for the loan," Ouimet said, and then he turned to Mike. "What happened when you got back to your store?"

"Harry Lane came in and said he wanted to get that suit and so he selected a material and we got to talking very friendly about Scotty Bowman, and I said that Mr. Bowman had got me a loan that set me up in the store, and Harry Lane said that Scotty had just done the same thing for him. You see, we both had Mr. Bowman for a good friend."

"This is just gossip," Henderson objected.

"Not at all," Ouimet protested. "It is Lane talking about the loan."

"It's Mike Kon gossiping about the loan."

"If my friend will just wait a minute."

"I'm getting impatient," the judge said.

"Go on, Mr. Kon," Ouimet said.

"I said to Mr. Lane he didn't need anyone to set him up like I had been set up by Scotty Bowman."

"Go on."

"He said he did if he needed money in a hurry."

"And then?"

"I said he could borrow money anywhere and he laughed and said he couldn't. What could he borrow money on, he said."

"No security?"

"That's right, his words though were 'borrow money on what?' I didn't know him, he said."

"I see," Ouimet said, and he walked toward the jury, not looking at them but musing to himself. "On what could he borrow money? On what, eh, and where?" Then he turned to Mike. "He didn't say anything about having no security at all?"

"No, just what could he borrow money on. On what?"

"Go on."

"So I said, Well, Scotty knows you, Harry. . . . You've got a real friend there. If you say you went to him you certainly went to the right guy."

"And then?"

"He laughed and said, 'I certainly did.'"

"So Mr. Lane, who asked what he could borrow money on . . . on what . . . laughed and said he certainly went to the right guy, his admiring friend."

"That's right."

"Now just a minute," Henderson said.

"I'm finished," Ouimet said. "Your witness."

But Henderson, taking his time, looked troubled. His eyes shifted around looking for Harry, for he knew that everyone in the courtroom now felt that Mike Kon had told them definitely that Harry Lane had taken advantage of Scotty Bowman's friendship. And he was particularly bothered by the flat and simple finality of the impression Mike Kon had given the jury. He was sure it wasn't fair to Harry, yet he was afraid that if he questioned Mike he would only arouse more sympathy for Scotty Bowman. "Just one question, Mr. Kon."

"Yes, sir."

"Don't you feel under a debt of gratitude to Mr. Bowman?"

"I do, sir," Mike said openly and with dignity.

"And you'd help him if you could?"

"If I'm helping him now it's the truth that's helping him. I'm just telling exactly what was said. I had great respect for Mr. Bowman, sir, but I was proud to have Harry Lane in my shop."

"Why so?"

"Until all this, I looked up to him."

"That's all," Henderson said shortly, and Mike stepped down, and Ouimet smiled to himself.

On his way to his seat Mike passed within a few feet of Harry, passing slowly with his firm stride, and Harry, waiting, looked him right in the eye with contempt. You witless fool, he thought, I was only kidding and you know it. If you didn't have such a dull ponderous mind you couldn't repeat that senseless conversation. You're a clown, a stupid clown. Why would I talk to you seriously in your store? But Mike met his eyes without flinching. His head held high, he passed by, his moral outrage, his conviction that Scotty Bowman shouldn't be there at all, so strong in his face that Harry lost his scornful smile. He saw that Mike had told the truth, word for word; only it isn't the truth, he thought desperately. It was only the truth as those imprudent thoughtless kidding words had revealed it to him. My God, how could I have been so careless? he thought. He felt bewildered. He looked around furtively. Oh, no, he thought, Scotty won't stand for this. It's his turn now and when he's finished, God help me if I don't poke Mike Kon right on the nose. Come on, Scotty, he thought grimly, now it's your turn. You better make it good.

But Ouimet, having made exactly the impression he wanted to make on the jury, turned blandly to the judge and said almost idly he wasn't putting Bowman on the stand; he didn't think it was necessary.

"What?" Harry said, and he half rose, his mouth open in astonishment, his face white. But Henderson had begun his address to the jury. Slumping back on the bench, Harry turned and stared at Scotty, trying to get his eye, and very slowly Scotty did turn and their eyes met. "Scotty," he wanted to whisper, "you can't just sit there and watch this assassination of my character. You can't do it. You'll die of shame. You've always been a good man. How can a guy like you be such a coward?" Outraged as he was he still believed in Scotty's old integrity and thought he could reach into his heart with his eyes and shame him. And Scotty couldn't turn away. He blinked and stared, then took out his handkerchief and mopped his brow. But he gave no sign of recognition.

Then Harry seemed to give up on him. Sitting back, he folded his arms with a proud and scornful expression on his face as if he felt he was putting himself far above him. It hurt Scotty. He had to turn away to hide his anguish, yet he was consoled, too, by Harry's angry proud look. It seemed to assure him that Harry knew the whole thing was beneath him, he was massively untouched. Anyway, Scotty told himself desperately, everything Slocombe had said about him was true, and the picture Ouimet had drawn of him as a generous admiring friend was also true, and Harry knew it. Everybody knew it was true, so why shouldn't it be said? And his wife, sitting there broken-hearted, had a right to have him pictured as he was, as he wanted his sons to know him. His two sons, the night he came home on bail, had looked at him in such white-faced, scared silence. It wasn't his fault, Scotty thought, that Harry was being put in such a false and shameful light. I said I would take all the blame. I told them I didn't want Harry to be drawn into it at all. Whatever you do, please leave him out of it, I said. What more could I do? What more could I ask? But he didn't ask himself if it hadn't been to his advantage to appear to be protecting his friend—generously taking all the blame. Having been trapped there was no other way of winning more sympathy for himself. He didn't want to ask these questions; he didn't want to feel shrewd about anything. All that was left for him was the consolation of being seen in the light thrown on him by Ouimet; he needed it for the sake of his faithful wife, who was there watching.

But he had to turn again slowly, or feel more tormented. Whatever dignity there had been in his life seemed to be mirrored in Harry's eyes. Then suddenly he had the thought he needed. Why did you come into the bank that day and give me the tickets to the fight, Harry? he thought bitterly. Answer me that, Harry? Why didn't you leave me alone? If you hadn't given me those tickets I wouldn't be here and you know it. With this bitter cry in his heart he could resist Harry's proud contempt and think, Sure, that's the way to look, you're above this. It'll bounce right off you, you're such a well-liked man, and very soon everybody'll see it's all beneath you. Look at me here, you can afford to forgive me and you'll want to do it, Harry. Just to be big.

Even in his bitterness with his own thoughts twisting and squirming, Scotty still counted hopefully on Harry's generosity.

"I'm not asking that this man be punished with the full severity of the law," Henderson said, and both Scotty and Harry turned away from each other. "But punished he must be," and he sat down.

Ouimet rose slowly. He had a conversational, intimate style. He hardly raised his voice; he took the jurors into his confidence. He talked movingly about Scotty's family life and how he was respected by everyone who knew him. "Now we come to Harry Lane." Every time he used the name all the spectators turned and looked at Harry thoughtfully. Harry's hands clenched the seat ahead of him.

"You saw Harry Lane," Ouimet said. "Of course, he's not the kind of businessman Bowman dealt with every day, a man of charm and grace. Bowman was very fond of this man. If Bowman committed a crime, why did he do it? Out of avarice? Oh, no. What was there in it for him? He was very vulnerable to his dashing friend. Now you are men of common sense. At some time in your lives you may have been running around wanting to borrow money. Well, can you really imagine that the idea of a loan came from Bowman, that all the suggestion came from him, that he actually pressed Lane to take the loan, when he knew on the face of it he was risking his job and his freedom? Does this offend your intelligence? Can't you see him yielding reluctantly to the corrupting pressure of friendship—saying to himself, 'It is only for a few days. He won't let me down.' And why isn't the man who took the advantage here in the dock with Bowman, charged with conspiracy? Because Bowman still retains his pathetic loyalty to him. . . . He takes all the blame."

"No," Harry shouted, and he jumped to his feet, his head, caught suddenly in the last rays of the sunlight, sweating and shining, and crazy anger in his eyes as he glared at Scotty, and he thought Scotty was also going to stand up and protest for he looked ashamed and miserable, but he didn't; he shook his head helplessly. Then Harry turned, his hand up, facing the judge, who had been momentarily startled. And Ouimet, too, had turned indignantly, caught off balance. The words Harry wanted to use were on the tip of his tongue: *I want to be sworn in again. This is a disgrace. I have something more to say. Bowman came to me pleading. He knew he could get shares from me. He asked for them. Let me be sworn in again.* But in the moment, the little moment while they were all startled and facing him, his instinct made him aware, with a swift frightening clarity, of the consequence of such a statement now; it would look as if he had held back through fear of being charged with conspiracy. Ouimet would cry out that Harry Lane should be in the dock too—he had bribed Bowman with the promise of shares; and Bowman could still remain silent, for from the beginning he had known if he could get as far as the trial in this way, without being denounced by his friend, free of any resentment or hostility from his friend, his silence could protect him from the sentence he deserved.

While the light suddenly changed in the courtroom as if it were clouding up outside, and the judge cleared his throat angrily and raised his gavel, his face stern, Harry lowered his arm, looking stricken. Swiftly and intelligently he saw his real mistake. His mistake was in the beginning when the police were questioning Scotty, and him too. Why didn't I protect myself by denouncing Scotty? I should have been Scotty's accuser. I, as well as the bank, was the victim of his deceit; the police should have had my story. Long before the trial they would have had him face Scotty; as an accuser. Even Ouimet, who was an honorable man, mightn't have tried to pillory him, and Henderson would have been speaking for him as well as for the bank and for justice.

"Order, order," the judge shouted. "I won't have this in my court. You'll be ejected." But Harry, his mouth trembling, hurried toward the door, and the policeman opening it for him watched him go along the corridor where the wet blotches and muddy footprints had all dried, and he saw him stop and wipe his forehead, his hand trembling.

As the policeman closed the door Harry turned and looked back at the courtroom. The whole thing suddenly seemed incredible. "Nobody in there believed me," he whispered. "My God, nobody believed a word I said," and he turned and hurried out to the street. He didn't know where he was going. He started to curse Scotty. Finally he stopped and looked around; he was in the financial district. He went into a little bar and there he sat in a trance thinking of the way they had all come against him, led by Scotty. He lost all track of time. Suddenly he thought of Mollie and he got up and hurried back to the courthouse so he could meet her coming out.

Standing at the end of the long corridor he watched the courtroom door. No one came out. While he was standing there by the pillar he glanced along the other corridor, and there was Judge Montpetit walking slowly in step with Judge Morris, Mollie's father, pale and big-shouldered with a fringe of graying hair. Stepping behind the pillar so he couldn't be seen, Harry watched them. Judge Morris was lending an attentive ear to the little judge who had tried Scotty. The sight of the two judges, and his own gesture in ducking behind the pillar, humiliated Harry. His amiable relationship with Judge Morris now did not seem to be nearly as important as their alien temperaments. Then he remembered it was Mollie's day to go home and have dinner with her family, and he couldn't bear to think of her at home with her father, that sober conservative rigid man, who would put the worst possible construction on everything before he himself could have a chance to see her.

Chapter 11

WHEN Judge Morris came in and took off his coat and hat, all his movements slow and deliberate, he listened hopefully for some familiar sound to reveal that Mollie had come home. "Shouldn't Mollie be home for dinner now, Helena?" he called to his wife who was in the kitchen.

"She should be. What'll we do, John?"

"We'll give her a little more time," he said, getting his whiskey and soda from the drawing room cabinet—his arteries were hardening and his doctor had recommended a highball before dinner—otherwise he wouldn't have touched the stuff. He sat down and opened his newspaper. But Alyse, the maid, came right in. "Dinner is ready, if you're ready, sir." . . . "I'll take my time with this drink, Alyse," he said. "Give me another fifteen minutes, please." The clock in the hall began to strike, the mahogany clock which had belonged to his father, and he listened intently, telling himself he would hear Mollie's step at the door before the final stroke. And he was terribly worried.

When Mollie had taken the studio he had been convinced she was merely showing signs of traditional healthy revolt against her home. In his college days he had heard theological students, who understood the Methodist tradition, talking profoundly about the revolt against the tradition and of young people throwing themselves headlong in another direction; it was always followed by the return, they said. Now the apartment seemed to him to be a little hideout, where Harry would persuade her to stay tonight so he could try and draw her into his disgrace.

His wife called him to dinner. A place had been set for Mollie. "They gave that bank manager four months," he said quietly as he sat down, and he told his wife all he had heard about the trial. "The poor manager has the sympathy of everybody, Helena. I talked to Montpetit. That bank manager seems to have been putty in Harry's hands. It's a terrible thing."

"Oh dear, John. I'm thinking about Mollie."

"The question is, will it open her eyes to Harry? Why isn't she home?" he asked fretfully. "I want to put that girl straight about the situation before it's too late."

When he had eaten he wandered around the house with its dark paneling and Persian rugs, and all its shiny brassware. The furniture had belonged to his grandfather, and the English paintings too. In spite of his own wisdom about life, he had liked Harry and he felt cheated. "The way he'd come in here and look around as if he were the only one in the world who had any taste. It was a taste for ruining people," he snorted. Then he wandered out to the garden, where Green, who had been twenty years with the family and whose job it was to drive the old Cadillac and trail after Mrs. Morris in the chain stores, carrying her basket, was tending some rosebushes. He gave him some sound advice, although in the back of his mind he was aware that Green, nodding respectfully, had no respect whatever for his opinion on the proper care of rosebushes. So he went back to the living room and his deep comfortable chair. The late sunlight streaming through the long west windows bothered his eyes and he got up, moved the draperies, sat down again, and sighed. It was no good. He couldn't stop thinking of Mollie in an emotional state alone in her apartment with Harry.

His wife came in wearing a dark blue dress with a long,

flimsy white scarf. It was an odd thing; he never saw her in a
state of undress, or with her hair untidy or even without some
make-up on. Even in the bedroom in the mornings she had the
same perfect grooming; it was as if she had made up her mind
that he would never see her in an unattractive light, and whatever she had to do to her hair or her skin or her body she did
while he was away from the house.

"Helena, I'm dreadfully worried about Mollie. This is a very
serious matter," he said. "She must not feel committed to
Harry, you understand?"

"Mollie is twenty-four, John, and we might as well get used
to it, and if Harry has shown that he's unscrupulous she'll see
it for herself."

"He's let us down. I feel so let down because I know I should
have been hardheaded about him. Mollie'll be in an emotional
state, and he'll try and—oh, I don't know. . . . Why hasn't she
even phoned?"

"Mollie's a very levelheaded girl, John."

"Of course she is. But I know how persuasive that man can
sound. You may be sure, too, he knows how important it is to
get her sympathy. I won't have the world think we're standing
by him. Helena, I'm afraid that if Mollie thinks she's in love
with that scamp—"

"Is she in love, John? I wonder! She's our daughter and she
doesn't let herself go easily. Unless she's terribly in love, it'll
be pretty hard now for Mollie to see herself as Mrs. Harry Lane."

"Just the same, he's been able to do things with that girl
that no one else can. Does she ever see her Junior League
friends now? Oh no—they're not restless enough for her now.
What is it about Harry Lane?"

"With Mollie? I've watched it. Sometimes I think she feels she
comes to life with him. That's an upsetting feeling, John."

"I've always said he has no ethics, no philosophy."

"I suppose he's just not our style. I don't know. Yet, he's got
such a good face. I mean if you saw him in a crowd you'd say

to yourself that man has a good face, and he has lovely manners. I couldn't have foretold this thing, John."

"Well, I could. I've said all along a man should be some one thing," he said firmly. "What is Harry Lane?"

"Well, I suppose he's a Catholic."

"You mean his mother was. Naturally though, being Harry Lane, he doesn't go to church. Not him. He doesn't have to. That's this whole case, Helena," he said angrily. "He's a natural born anarchist. And his father was too. Do you remember how his father used to strut along Sherbrooke of a Sunday morning in the summer in a light gray suit, wearing a red tie and with all that gray hair of his? And wearing no hat, mind you! At his age why wouldn't he wear a hat? And those investment companies!"

"Still, he was well liked, John."

"That's the whole corrupting essence of this thing," he said emphatically. Then, putting his head back on the chair, he looked at the ceiling and tapped the tips of his fingers together nervously. "Make up your mind to it. Mollie isn't coming home tonight and you know what it means? She's ashamed."

"Yes, if she's ashamed—John, there's a defiant streak in her."

"He's on the way down now, you know. Those Sweetmans will drop him like a hotcake."

"And if she thinks he's down?"

"He's finished around here, Helena. Keep your eye on the Sweetmans."

"Don't you think she'll see it, John?"

"Even if she does, tonight she'll be his haven. From the courtroom to a woman. It's the way they go."

"Such a strange way to speak of Mollie. A haven. Well, I know how she'll be feeling as a woman and—"

"How can you know if you've never liked him?" he asked irritably.

"He's so sympathetic, John," she said, looking troubled. "Yet to have that job of his he must be a completely cynical man and I've known it and resented the way he smiles and makes me feel he sees things he shouldn't see. Well, it's like an invasion of one's privacy, isn't it?" she asked, growing flustered. "There are some things a well-bred man shouldn't see, or at least shouldn't let on he sees, and what I don't understand, I really don't, is it's all part of his attractiveness."

"What are you talking about, Helena. He's paid to be attractive, as that bank manager should know," he said resentfully. "This disgusting bedroom sense of intimacy"—then their eyes met, as they hadn't done for years, in a swift glimpse of each other with many layers of living together swept aside, and it hurt him and hurt her too. Her thin fingers were toying with the little green watch hanging from her neck and he patted the top of his head uncomfortably as she turned away, moving slowly over to the piano where she sat down, tapping idly with one finger at the keys.

He stole a glance at her. "Helena, we've had a good life," he wanted to plead with her. "Affection, companionship, sympathy, all the things that really hold a man and a woman together. Tell me it's so, Helena, please—" and tears came into his eyes. With a pang he saw how much she still looked like Mollie. She had had Mollie's full-breasted figure at the time she was married; when he had been so shy and nervous and awkward with her. Before his marriage he had been too serious and industrious to bother much with women. He had never had a girl on a bed or under a bush or on a beach. Helena was as innocent as he was, coming as she did from such respectable people, and on their marriage night she had been shy, wanting the room all dark. How she had stiffened up when he touched her! Yet she held him so tight in her arms it had shocked him, and then he had been embarrassed by his own frantic clumsiness. Growing angry and desperate, he had hurt her. That night no happiness at all touched them. They lay there far apart like strangers who had done something that was mutually embarrassing and beneath them. Humiliated, he got dressed; he had to get out of the house. He went out for a walk. It was in the winter. There had been a heavy fall of snow. Walking in the snow, he felt depressed. When he came home he found her in her dressing gown crouched on the floor in front of the grate fire in the living room, crying. "If that's all there is to it," she whispered, staring at the flames, "why do people tell such awful lies?"

From that night on their bed separated them, for he was always afraid he wouldn't give her any pleasure and the fear made him enormously self-conscious. Whenever he went to touch her he tried humming tunes and making his mind blank or seeing erotic pictures in fancy to take his thoughts off himself; he only achieved an awful embarrassment. She couldn't help him and her beautiful body brought neither of them the sensual delight she had dreamed of. Gradually she accepted their relationship by making their failure a virtue, a rare fastidiousness that showed they weren't of common clay.

Never had she looked so much like Mollie to him as she did right now; then he thought with a pang, Harry Lane would never walk out as I did and return later and find Mollie crouched on the floor crying. Two little spots of red appeared on his cheeks and he struggled to retain his self-esteem. No, Harry knew how to use a situation as he used people and with his terrible criminal attractiveness—his occupational weapon, as poor Bowman could attest—tonight, if he was alone with Mollie in her apartment, his haven, and if they were both excited, and if she was full of reproaches and emotional over what had happened to him, he'd break her down, make her prove she belonged to him.

"Well, I think I'll take my constitutional," he said, standing up nervously. "Clear my mind for court tomorrow."

"Which way are you walking?"

"Depends on how I feel," he said evasively. "If I keep on going, I don't know, I might drop in on Mollie and have a cup of coffee," and he went and got his hat and coat and she heard him go out the door.

Getting up from the piano bench, she stood for a moment staring at the pattern in the Persian rug. A little flush came on her face. She felt some vague unhappiness that frightened her. She wondered why Harry had made it hard for her to be herself with him. He had noticed that she laughed at the end of every sentence. No matter how plain or dull the sentence, she laughed, and he had looked at her sympathetically one night as if he was keeping track of what she said, just hearing the actual words as he would read a line in a play, and the words were neither bright nor funny, detached from the laugh, and at first she had felt almost indecently exposed; then, feeling drawn to him, she wanted to take him aside and talk to him intimately about Mollie and herself, but he had never known.

Going over to the window she watched her husband on the path, his heavy body erect, swinging his cane. Mollie had been his whole life. He's a good man, a gentleman, she thought sadly. But oh, Mollie darling, what does he know of a woman in love? And her mouth trembled.

Chapter 12

THE street lights had come on and children were play-
ing under the light in front of Mollie's studio, their cries clear in
the summer night. Fifty feet away from the house Harry
stopped and watched a figure crossing the road, a massive-
shouldered man with a cane who looked up at Mollie's lighted
second-floor window as he moved into the street light. It was
Judge Morris, wearing a double-breasted blue coat, a black
Homburg, and looking like a concerned father. Mollie couldn't
have gone home. Oh, good, good, Harry thought, watching the
Judge go in.

The three children who had been playing under the light
had gone across the road and were sitting in a row on the
stoop of the roominghouse, watching him. On the stoop was a
patch of moonlight, touching the faces of the children and their
hands. A voice called, "All right, kids, time for bed, come on
in," but the children didn't move. They kept on watching him
as he looked down the street, turned and loafed back to the
house, and stood looking up at the window.

If I see her shadow against the shade I'll know she wants me
to come right in, he thought, and he watched and waited, and
no shadowy outline of her form came against the shade. Then
he tried to draw her there, concentrating on her face, and when

he couldn't, he thought, If I see her shadow at all I'll take it as a good sign, and he waited, whispering, "Mollie, I love you. You're not listening to your old man. Show me you're not."

A black and white cat crossed the street slowly; its white spots shone in the pale light from the moon as it broke through clouds and touched the branches of the trees. The cat turned and looked at him.

"Come on, Mollie. Here I am," he whispered. "Come out to me. Come out." He began fingering a medal he wore under his shirt. During the war he had relied on many superstitions from his boyhood and this medal was one of them. It had grieved his mother, a Catholic, that he had stopped going to church, and when he had become a flier he had promised her he would wear this medal, and was sure it had brought him luck. Suddenly he saw Mollie's shadow, the shade moved, she was there, and he waved, but he had to wait ten minutes before she came out.

She was wearing a long black silk coat and she came toward him, then stopped, brushing back her hair with her right hand. "Harry," she said softly. "Oh, Harry." And the softness of her eyes and her trembling mouth made him put out his hand to her. But she rushed at him and threw her arms around him, and the loving concern he felt in her filled him with relief. It was like coming home.

"It was an awful mess, wasn't it, Mollie?"

"I looked all over for you. Where did you go?"

"Just wandered around."

"I know. I know." She sounded so worried he knew her father must have been pounding away at her. . . .

"All right," he said gently. "What does your father say?"

"With him it's the law. How it looks to the law."

"Sure. Well, I knew what he'd say."

"All he would say was that you must have been afraid to go to the police and tell about those shares, because you knew you ought to have investigated that loan. He made me so mad. But come in. You talk to him. Only now walk me down to the corner. I'm supposed to be getting some cigarettes."

Her fingers tightened on his arm as if she felt she had been close to losing him, and as they walked down the street and into the drugstore he was letting himself go, saying all the things he had wanted to say in the court; he called Scotty a Judas, a Scotch bastard, and she just listened, holding his arm tight.

But when they sat down at the counter for a quick cup of coffee, and he kept muttering bitter insults at Ouimet, he noticed that her fingers were toying with the gold clasp of her handbag which she had placed on the counter. He had given her this bag for her birthday. And he looked at her and knew she was alone in her thoughts.

"What are you thinking? Come on, say it," he said.

"Why didn't you go on with medicine?" she whispered.

"What?"

"By this time you could have been a doctor if you hadn't listened to Sweetman."

"What the hell is this, Mollie?"

"You had two years of medicine, Harry and—"

"I didn't want to be a doctor," he said angrily. "What is this?"

"The counterman is listening."

"It's time someone listened to me."

"Come on, let's go," she said and he followed her. On the street her hand came out apologetically. "Harry, Harry," she said wretchedly. "I just can't get used to the way they made you look. I hated it, don't you see? It cut me to pieces."

Coming toward them was a little girl with a big red balloon which she kept bumping into the air, and as they watched her, they smiled at each other wanly. His big mistake, he said more calmly, sounding to her like an ancient Greek hero, was in violating his nature in not telling the whole truth. And then, as if something else gnawed away at him, he blurted out, "The awful thing is that nobody in that court believed me. Why, Mollie? Why?"

"It's frightening, Harry."

"It was that crazy stupid tailor's doing."

"Putting you in that light! Who is that man?"

"A stupid fool with a pants presser's view of everybody."

"The thing is, they believed him, Harry."

"God Almighty, how stupid can people get? As if I'd tell a tailor the details of a loan from Scotty. It's mad."

"Maybe it wasn't just that tailor, Harry," she said hesitantly. "Maybe no one has a right to take it for granted people are going to believe in him no matter what the situation is."

"Situation be damned. Have I no reputation at all?" and he stopped under the street light.

Her head lifted in the pale light, her cheekbones looking higher, she said wretchedly, "I'm a little puritan, Harry, it's ground into me, and I can't forget it. That's what you've told me, anyway. I sat in that court, my eyes closed, hating all those drinks you buy, hating the faith you have in the things you're expected to do for people, hating the times I've seen you foot the bill for cynical people. I was wondering if even Sweetman would really believe anything you said. It was awful, Harry."

"My God," he said slowly, "what are you trying to do to me?"

"Harry," she pleaded, taken aback, "you said yourself nobody believed you."

"I was cheapened in that court, goddamn it. What are you trying to do now? Cheapen my whole life?"

"You say that to me?" she asked, astonished. "You put me with all those people!" Her eyes in the street light were glittering fiercely. "Oh, I could pound you." Jerking away, she raised her small fists helplessly, then fled up the street, her high heels clicking on the pavement.

He wanted to cry out to her, "Mollie! Mollie!" Trembling a little, he tried to hold on to the last shred of his dignity, of his faith in his friendships and his actions. "God Almighty," he whispered, and turned away.

Chapter 13

As soon as he entered his apartment, even before he turned on a lamp, he saw the chair by the window, just touched faintly by the street light, and he seemed to see Scotty sitting there as he sat that night with the water on the toes of his old-fashioned rubbers. "You bastard," he said aloud. "You can't put me in this position," and he hurled his hat and coat at the chair. "Well, I know something about you too. Your Calvinistic soul will be tormented. I'll get to you, Scotty. You can't face me and you know it."

From the street came the sound of car wheels licking over the pavement, then a young woman's voice talking baby talk to a little dog. The front door opened. The old painter and his wife came in and went upstairs.

I've got to get to Scotty, he thought, jerking open his collar. The fact was nobody could know the truth but him and Scotty, and as the walls of the room seemed to come against him he thought he would call Ouimet, then he thought he would call the newspapers. "I'm not letting that little Judas cheapen me," he said aloud. Then his mahogany desk in the far corner of the room caught his eye. Opened letters and unpaid bills were scattered on the desk top, all mixed up and pushed aside. Some of them had been there for weeks. He always paid his bills promptly and sooner or later he answered all the letters. But now the careless disorder of it worried him. Frowning, he walked over to the desk and almost furtively he began to straighten out the papers. When he had finished he threw himself on the bed without even taking off his coat, and he was so exhausted he fell sound asleep.

The telephone ringing on the table beside him woke him up, and he grabbed it. "Hello, Harry," the voice said. Suddenly he was wide awake and worried. It was Sweetman. "Have you seen the morning paper, Harry?"

"No. What time is it?"

"Around midnight. You won't like the story, Harry. What in hell happened?"

"What happened?" and then he started to curse Scotty.

"I'd like to talk to you, Harry. Why don't you run up to the house? My wife and I just came in. Come on, old boy. I'd certainly like to hear your story."

"I'd certainly like to tell it," he said grimly. "I'll be there in twenty-five minutes," and he hurried into the bathroom. When he looked at himself in the full-length mirror on the door, he saw that his coat and his trousers were wrinkled from sleeping in them. Without attention to what he was doing, he took from the closet the tropical suit he had got from Mike Kon, and started to put it on, then he scowled, remembering. To hell with him, he thought, and he hurried out.

He had the greatest faith in his affectionate knowledge of Max Sweetman. Some people were amused or scornful of Max's affectations, the Oxford accent, the walrus mustache, the handkerchief in the sleeve of the English suits, but Harry thought he understood the Sweetman story; he had a kind of admiration for Max.

In the old days of prohibition Max's father, Moe, had been a bootlegger in Detroit. In those days many bad things had happened to Moe's friends but nothing bad had happened to Moe, a family man whose wife rarely met his business friends. After prohibition Moe Sweetman had come to town and bought the old Carney distillery which was close to bankruptcy. Moe introduced a brand of rye he called Sweetman's, aged in the wood for eight years and bonded; after three years he changed the name of the distillery to Sweetman's. But nobody in town had met Moe. They thought he was dead. Even Max hardly ever saw his father, though he had got letters from him when he was at school, and he used to say to Harry, with a lonely light in his eyes, that ever since his mother's death he seemed to have been at one school after another, and always in a foreign country, but mainly in Switzerland, then France and finally at Oxford, where he had read history and won his blue for rowing. And as for his walrus moustache, well, fighting with the British army in Africa, he had learned to wear it with distinction. But honestly he wasn't a pretentious man, Harry would say, defending him. He would have been happier in the history department of some university, and he didn't want that big old Frohman place on Pine that cost him ninety thousand. He only got it for Esther after he met her in New York on Central Park West and married her and understood she wanted to cut a social figure, and as a matter of fact, as he had said himself, his happiest hours in the house were those he spent in the billiard room, leaning on his cue remembering the days when he had played billiards in the Café Des Lilas on the left bank in Paris.

The night was cooler now. The sky was a rash of stars on the rim of the mountain. At the end of the street where the slope was steep there was a flight of steps and Harry climbed them so quickly he had to stop and get his breath, and there below him was the pattern of city lights, Mollie's city and his; what good times they had had here! How often they had agreed it was one of the exciting cities of the world, and he was so moved he had a lump in his throat. A puff of air rustled the leaves of the trees alongside the steps, a nighthawk swooped overhead, and as he leaned on the rail it was Mollie's city rising around him. Well, we'll see, Harry thought and he hurried along to the big French colonial house, and the moonlight was silvering its steep sloping roof.

But the house made him think of Esther Sweetman and as he rang the bell he wished uneasily that he had shown a little more affection for her, he wished that Max sometimes hadn't looked at her with his off smile as if he wasn't quite sure why he was living with her.

The door was opened by Sweetman himself, wearing a black tie, his face a little flushed from too many brandies after dinner. The rosy flush and the black mustache gave him a friendly warm opulent look, and his hand came out quickly. "We were out for dinner, Harry. The Silversteins. What an evening! That Percy Silverstein still talks like the dress salesman he was. Come on in," and he led him across the big black and white tiled hall. "Esther," he called. "Harry's here."

"All right, so am I," she called, coming down the spiral stairs. She was wearing a black sheath dress tight at the waist and tight across the breasts. Her skin was golden, her black hair parted in the middle was drawn back, and her hand was on the wrought-iron banister as it had been in the fashion picture the newspaper photographers had taken of her when she had worn a flowing white dress, and Ted Ogilvie had said she looked like a Modess advertisement. She had that same bland smile too, but Harry knew by her eyes that she had talked it all over with Max, raising the whole question of the damage to his prestige as a public relations man for Sweetman. "What's it all about, Harry?" she asked innocently. "Let's sit in the library. Look a little more cheerful, please. Come on," and she took his arm and led him into the bleached-oak-paneled library and sat down and patted the chair beside her. "Get the poor man a drink, Max," she said.

"How much of the story does this tell, Harry?" Max said, taking a morning newspaper from the end table and handing it to him.

"I'll soon tell you," he said.

On the first page were pictures of himself, Scotty and Mike Kon, and a factual report of the trial with a quotation from Ouimet's speech to the jury. There was another quote from the judge expressing great sympathy for Scotty, a man whose friend took advantage of him. The name Harry Lane was mentioned six times. He counted them. Rolling up the paper into a club, he clenched it and looked up, very pale.

"Well, that's their story," he said quietly. "What do you think, Max?"

"What do I think?"

"Yes."

"Harry, you ask such a question?"

"Well, you know what it sounds like, Max."

"Yes, it sounds as if you led a little bank manager right down the garden path. It isn't the story you told me, Harry. And it doesn't sound like you at all. What in the world did happen at that trial?"

So he told them exactly what had happened, and how Scotty had betrayed him with his silence and run out on him. He wasn't put off at all by the look in Esther's shrewd appraising eyes. Max was his friend and he wanted to be utterly candid. "That's the true story," he said.

"Hmm. Quite a story," Sweetman said, reflecting as he took out his briar pipe, his pouch, and filled the bowl. "Put a little pressure on some of those nice fellows, and well, there's such a thing as a gentleman, you know." He smiled sympathetically. "I'd say, Harry, it all sounds like you. Doesn't it, Esther? Always going around with your chin stuck out. *L'homme de bonne volonté*. Take it easy, old man," he said affectionately. "It may not be such a big thing at all," and he reached over and patted Harry's shoulder reassuringly.

"I'm not worried, Max, but just the same . . ." He took a deep breath, and all his liking for Max was in his eyes.

"There's just one thing, Harry."

"What's that, Max?"

"This tailor."

"Oh, he'd give his right arm for Scotty. You see, he owes his business to Scotty. Owes everything to him, Max. Scotty's his bible."

"Odd, I never heard of him as a tailor. What in the world is a man like you doing getting a suit from that kind of a fellow? You usually take such pains about a suit and a tailor," he said, looking disappointed. "That's a nice-looking suit you've got on. Allow me," and he stood up. "There's a smudge on your elbow." He tried to dust it off for him. The smudge was from the step rail where he had leaned on it. It was like a grease mark. He would have to get it cleaned, Harry said, too embarrassed to mention it was the suit made by Kon.

"You know, we should have foreseen all this," Max said, deeply troubled as he sat down again. "I remember you told me how sorry you were for poor Bowman. Poor Bowman! Knew you too well, that's the shame of it. Well, to hell with him, Harry."

"Take it like that? What about my honor?"

"Never mind the sense of honor," Esther said cynically. "Honor won't put money in the bank, sell whiskey, or buy one of your twenty-five-dollar shirts."

"He's taken my shirt—my whole reputation."

"Oh, I think your credit is still pretty good around here, Harry," and she shrugged.

"Well, thanks. Thanks," he said reaching for his drink. Gulping it down, he tried to relax and instead, couldn't stop talking. "I liked the man, that's what hurts so much," he said apologetically. "I feel like a fool. I mean the man seemed to command my immediate respect. I mean, well, look here," he said as Max poured him another drink, and he told them that the night he had seen Scotty standing at the hotel entrance he had been reminded of his own father, the same build, something solid, unshakable and good-humored about him. It had touched him, you understand. It must have been why he had invited him into Dorfman's.

"So right to the end you pitied the guy," Max said. "All I

can say is that pity is a luxury, and it's damn corrupting too."

"Oh, balls," Esther said suddenly.

"Balls, Esther?"

"Yes, balls," she said impatiently. "The thing is, what does Harry do now? Do we just wait and see?"

"Certainly we just wait and see."

"Wait and see what?" Harry asked, flushing.

"Why, how the public takes it."

"Not on your life," he said angrily. "I'm not letting Scotty put me in this humiliating position. Don't worry, I'll get to him."

"What for?"

"It's the only way to get at the truth, isn't it?"

"But he's in jail."

"If he's run out on you," Esther said, "you're not catching up with him that quickly."

"Now look, Harry," Max said philosophically. "You want the truth about him to be known. Well sure, so would I. But the truth about any man is pretty hard to tell, because someone else always has another angle on him, do you see?"

"I see, sure. But listen, Max," he pleaded, "I only need to face Scotty to get the truth out of him. What about our lawyers? Isn't there someone in town who can fix it so I can visit that jail?"

"Take it easy," Max said, looking worried. "Certainly I'll speak to our lawyers. But the trial is over. I'm trying to tell you I can't believe anything said against you in that courtroom is going to count with people who really know you. I think you'll get a lot of sympathy. In a few months, when that bank manager comes out, he'll come crawling to you, Harry."

"Max, I've got to get to him."

"And you really think he'll see you?"

"I think he will."

"Well, okay," Max said. "Now forget it. Let's go into the kitchen and rustle up something to eat."

In the kitchen Harry did try to forget. The Sweetmans were

wonderful. They joked and tried to be jolly so he wouldn't start brooding, and he made a few jokes about Ouimet's pointed shoes, and Esther laughed. She really laughed heartily and he felt better.

They both came to the door with him. Max said not to worry; in the morning he would speak to his lawyers. On the way along the street, realizing he was still carrying the rolled-up newspaper, Harry smiled and tossed it contemptuously in the gutter.

The first thing he did when he got home was to call Mollie. "Are you still my girl?" he asked. . . . "Of course, I am." . . . She sounded lonely and forlorn so he knew she had quarreled with her father. Laughing indulgently he told her Sweetman was with him all the way.

"Oh, Harry, I feel awful," she said in a small ashamed voice. "It was the atmosphere of that courtroom. Everything's different outside, I know. It's so good to hear you sounding like yourself. I've been lying here in bed thinking of you." She waited, letting the picture get into his mind; it was like a yielding after a worried flight from him.

"I'll get into bed myself," he whispered. "Good night, darling."

In bed, as soon as he closed his eyes, he could hear Esther Sweetman saying, "We'll just have to wait and see." As he lay in the dark, kicking the sheets off him restlessly, there came to him out of his deepest knowledge of Scotty's life and spirit, and out of the wisdom of his own heart, a hunch that there was nothing in the world Scotty really wanted now as much as to see him. It became such a profound conviction he couldn't lie still. He had to get up. He walked up and down waiting for daylight to come.

Chapter 14

NEXT day in the office at four in the afternoon Sweet-man told him the lawyers advised him that only Ouimet could insist on an interview with Scotty. Sweetman said that if he were Harry he would forget the whole thing, as everybody else would, he was sure. When Sweetman left the office Harry got up and went to the window, wondering if Scotty really believed he was now screened off from him. Suddenly he thought that Ouimet, too, could actually have been taken in by Scotty. After all, Ouimet had the reputation of being a scrupulously honest man, a Catholic puritan who had headed a committee to investigate a charge of corruption against certain police officers accused of taking bribes from brothel keepers. Unlike some Catholic lawyers, who personally disapproved of divorce and yet did divorce court work, he wouldn't touch a divorce case. He had three black-stockinged daughters in a convent. No humor in him. But, after all, a man of principle. It seemed to him that if Ouimet, having been Scotty's lawyer, learned now that he had been a character assassin to save his client from a stiff sentence, his fierce puritan conscience would compel him to go around telling his friends that he had wronged Harry Lane. Harry stood in a trance, then suddenly walked out of the office, out of the building and across the road to the hotel, where he got a taxi and drove to Ouimet's office on St. James Street. It was a beautiful day, not too hot, with the sun shining, and a little puff of wind, and the sky very blue and cloudless.

Ouimet's old-fashioned office done in quarter-cut oak was like a lawyer's office of forty years ago, and the secretary said, "Harry Lane, oh!" She was a plain-faced serious woman of thirty in a sleeveless pale blue print dress. "Well, just a minute," she said doubtfully. But when she got up to go into Ouimet's office he saw that she had a slender waist and lovely big high breasts, and he felt more hopeful; he was glad Ouimet had her in the office looking at her every day. "Mr. Ouimet will see you," she said. "Would you go in?" and he went in and there was Ouimet sitting behind his desk, in his gray suit, looking so well manicured, fastidious and untroubled. "Hello there," Ouimet said and didn't get up.

"I know this is a surprise," Harry said awkwardly.

"What's on your mind?"

"Look, Ouimet. I took a beating in that court. All right, I'd be a fool to blame you for what happened."

"Go ahead."

"Did Scotty tell you anything about having asked me for five thousand of those shares—as soon as he put through the loan?"

"What's this? He asked you for shares, you say?"

"That's right. Didn't he mention it to you at all?"

"Hmm. No, he didn't," Ouimet said thoughtfully.

"Well, there you are. Now I understand your attitude," Harry said, drawing his chair closer to the desk, full of relief. He told him about Scotty coming to his apartment and pleading with him not to mention asking for the shares. "That certainly puts a little different light on it, doesn't it?" he asked, smiling hopefully.

"You know, Lane," Ouimet said softly, "I think you believe it."

"Believe what?"

"That you were making a sympathetic generous gesture."

"It's the truth," Harry said, flushing.

"And I wasn't able to drag it out of you in court."

"That's right."

"I must be slipping," Ouimet said looking amused. "And I thought I was making a fool out of you. Not that big a fool, eh?"

"What do you mean?"

"Don't look so angry. I'm interested, Lane. There's a nice problem here in human behavior. Quite fascinating." Leaning back in his chair he meditated, his eyes brightening with intellectual interest in the problem. "I've known men with your temperament, Lane. An interesting temperament. An impulsive man full of generous gestures." Then he leaned forward, his elbows on the desk, his left hand caressing his right, lovingly. "Now let's consider the nature of your gesture. I believe you can tell yourself you were helping Scotty. It's in keeping with your character. No? But what went on in the back of your mind is something else. You had your own interest at heart, masking it from yourself, of course, to satisfy your egotism."

"My egotism?" he said indignantly.

"It's beneath a man like you to feel like a conspirator, isn't it? So you make a gesture. In the name of compassion and charity. To the point of being harmful to yourself. A little reckless. Oh, but charitable. A touch of compassion. Ah, but in the back of your mind, weren't you protecting yourself?"

"Protecting myself. My God, it's the one thing I didn't think of," Harry whispered, and the fine late afternoon sunlight coming over Ouimet's shoulder shone on his stricken face. Why did I come here seeking this humiliation? he asked himself desperately. What drove me here? With all the anger he had felt for Ouimet in the courtroom he laughed. "You're a fool, Ouimet," he said. "The funny thing is Scotty is shrewder than you are about me. He knew I'd make that gesture."

"Of course he did. Come on, man," and he leaned forward

111

placatingly as if he now had a gentle understanding sympathy for him, "tell the truth. I'll bet Bowman told you it was in your interest, didn't he?"

"You know, Ouimet, I ought to poke you right in the nose."

"But you don't and I know why. It's beneath you. But you know what I wish you would do?"

"No, tell me," Harry said, very pale.

"I wish you'd examine your own conscience."

"My conscience? What a fraud you are, Father Ouimet."

"Don't get sore, Lane. Just look into your heart, why don't you? Ask yourself by what means you conveyed to Bowman that there would be something in it for him if he got you the loan." He sounded so gently persuasive and helpful Harry was bewildered.

"It's incredible," he whispered.

"Oh, come on now."

"It's like listening to a priest in a confessional, a priest with a bad understanding," Harry said softly. "A cynical priest in love with guilt, twisting all motives till there's nothing but the impurity of purpose that's really in his own mind. Ouimet, you're a fool about people. Oh, you can smile, yes." Hating him, he took out his handkerchief and wiped his mouth. "I've been a poor innocent fool," he said.

"Innocence is a very fragile thing," Ouimet replied, smiling.

"I had that Calvinist Catholic conscience of yours all wrong. To save your own client you know damn well you put me on trial."

"Oh, you and your damnable innocence," Ouimet said angrily. "Just answer me this then. If it weren't for you, would Bowman be where he is? Think about it, man." He got up to walk toward the door, but Harry grabbed his arm, so they were face to face, Ouimet startled and white and Harry trembling.

"Take me to see Bowman," Harry pleaded. "For the sake of your own wise and tricky conscience, you be there. It's all I ask. Will you do it?"

"Let you go on bothering Bowman? I'm not such a fool," Ouimet said. "Let go my arm."

"It's Bowman's arm I'm twisting," Harry said, knowing he should go with dignity; and he did. But at the door he turned, hating himself for having pleaded with Ouimet. "You see, Ouimet, smart and all as you are, you missed something in that courtroom."

"Did I? Oh, I don't think so," Ouimet said, but he was trying to remember. "What did I miss?"

"Me on the witness stand and Scotty in the dock. Why shouldn't you miss it though? It wasn't a legal twist. It wasn't something for a smart lawyer to distort. What you missed, Ouimet, was that Scotty is a human being."

"A human being? Well, well, well——"

"And now he's ashamed."

"You don't say."

"He's sitting there in jail knowing he can have no life at all around here with me on his back. . . ." Then he laughed angrily. "All right, Ouimet. Don't tell him to talk and clear me. You're too stupid. He's only your client. Why should you give him a break?" And he walked out past the plain big-breasted secretary who half rose, putting her hand out as if she would stop him. He hurried home and sat down to write a letter to Scotty.

Harry wrote bluntly that he understood Scotty had been cowardly because he had felt old, and had been thinking of his family; his cowardice had got him a short sentence, but he had to come out of jail, and he couldn't hide. By that time the whole town would be waiting to tell him what a son of a bitch he was. . . .

There at his desk, his eyes angry, Harry wrote rapidly. Suddenly he seemed to run out of words. Leaning back, troubled, he put down the pen. He kept thinking of the way Scotty's eyes used to light up when they met, of the way Scotty, with such respect, had asked him to talk to his boy. He kept thinking of these things as if he couldn't get rid of his own faith in the honesty of their friendship; again he had a curious conviction that Scotty, ashamed now and wondering if he could ever have any future, would see that he needed Harry. Just as much as Harry needed him. He couldn't send the abusive threatening letter. He just couldn't. After all, he was not alone, he had Mollie with him and Sweetman behind him.

From the open window came a street voice: "This is really a crazy country. Here it is hot again. Maybe it stays hot till we wake up some morning and find snow on the ground." It did look like an unseasonable hot spell. Getting up he went to the closet and got out his tropical suit and looked at it. The smudge on the sleeve needed to be cleaned. On the way out he wondered if Sweetman would suggest they go down to New York together for the world series.

Chapter 15

LATE in the afternoon Max Sweetman had come out of Morgan's department store where he had made a purchase for his wife and was walking east with the hot sun shining warmly on the back of his neck. He wore his hair a little long; he hated the clipped tight look. He was wearing a checked jacket and gray flannels, a jacket similar to one Harry had worn which he had liked very much. His cheeks were rosy. He walked with a light springy elegant stride. Just ahead of him was a figure he recognized, gray-haired old Muldoon, the economic advisor with the military bearing, an old scamp, a ruthless gossip, but genial and influential too. Max caught up to him and they fell in step.

"Why, this is a coincidence, Sweetman," Muldoon said jovially. "I was talking about you last night. I was saying you ought to be on the Board."

"Really?" Max asked, smiling deprecatingly. He felt delighted. Even the sunshine and the heat seemed to be just right. He felt suddenly like a happy, confident man with many friends. His only ambition had been to get on the Board of Governors of the University. He had given them many thousands of dollars. He would have given thousands more. His wife had kept whispering that he would never get the appointment because he was a Jew, yet here was old Muldoon bringing the subject up.

"It's time we did something about you," Muldoon said. "I think I'll speak to MacKenzie."

All the way to Peel Street they discussed the subject. When they parted, Max had never had such a sense of belonging. Old Muldoon was a born meddler. He couldn't keep his finger out of anything. "If he wants me on the board it's a foregone conclusion I'll be invited, he'll meddle away at it until he's successful," and he smiled happily.

In his office he whistled cheerfully, he put his wife's package on the desk under his eye so he wouldn't forget it, then leaned back comfortably in his chair with a dreamy smile, his hands linked behind his head. Then his secretary's voice came on the intercom. "It's your wife, Mr. Sweetman." He picked up the telephone. "Hello, Esther. What's on your mind?" he asked.

"I'm downtown," she said. "I'm with Mrs. Silverstein." Her tone was hard and grim. "Have you seen the late-afternoon paper? Well, get it. And for heaven's sake, Max, use your head this time about Harry Lane. It's now a matter of your own prestige. No more of that nice liberal sentimentality. Just get the paper. I've got to go," and she hung up.

Her tone made him angry, but he told his secretary to get him the late-afternoon papers at once. In a little while she returned. Big-eyed and pale, she placed the *Sun* on the desk and withdrew quickly before he could say, "Thank you, Miss Brinsley." Then the headline caught his eye. Sweetman groaned.

BANK MANAGER SUICIDE

This morning Scotty Bowman was to have been taken to the reformatory to begin his sentence, so the newspaper had begun. Mrs. Bowman, visiting him the night before, had noticed he was depressed and had mentioned it to the guard, Frank Summerville, aged sixty-two, who had taken a liking to Mr. Bowman. Summerville had felt sorry for Bowman and had had long talks with him about baseball and fighters. The guard had told Mrs. Bowman he hadn't liked the way her husband had been behaving in the last three days. In the cell Bowman had hardly moved. When reminded that food had been placed in front of him, he would apologize and try to eat. At night time he couldn't sleep; he wanted to keep moving around his cell. When he was rebuked he apologized. Every time he spoke he seemed to want to apologize for something, and the guard, a humble man himself, was troubled by all these apologies. Mrs. Bowman, who was now under sedation, had cried out, "It shocks him, finding himself there. I never saw a man who looked so ashamed. Poor Scotty seemed to be asking me to forgive him," she said. "I told him everybody sympathized with him. After I told him he didn't need to apologize to me, he looked so surprised and humiliated. It all was terribly wrong."

Bowman had shaved and then lain down with the blanket over him, the guard said. When he called and Bowman didn't answer, he opened the door and drew back the blanket. The bed was soaked with blood. The wrists had been cut with a razor blade. Bowman had bled to death.

The rest of the story was about the loan Scotty Bowman had made to Harry Lane, and there was a quotation from the trial judge expressing sympathy with him as a man who had been too fond of his friends.

His heart aching, Max suddenly seemed to get a glimpse of the truth. Gradually it became like a beautiful illumination: there had been a betrayal all right, he thought, but it had come from Scotty Bowman even in his death; he had betrayed a trusting young friend, and knew it. Bowman had been afraid to come out and face the consequences of his deceit. The accuracy of his perception began to disturb Max. But Harry's my public relations director, he thought. A figure of scandal, a public relations director. Impossible! Yet he was still fascinated by the blind and perfect selfishness of Bowman's despair that could let him make Harry his victim again. Oh, the monstrous egotism of despair, he thought, sighing.

Twice he leaned forward to the intercom to speak to his secretary and twice he faltered and sat back motionless and flushed. Then he took his pen as if he were going to make a note on his memo pad. The ink didn't flow immediately so he jabbed viciously at the paper, broke the nib, took the pen in both his hands, broke it and looked at it bewildered. Esther had given the pen to him. "Get Mr. Lane, will you?" he told his secretary.

"You want me, Max?" Harry asked, smiling as he came in, and he had the pleasant easy assured manner of an intimate friend.

"Have you seen this, Harry?" Max said, pushing the paper across the desk.

"What is it, what's up?" Harry asked, sitting down and picking up the paper. "God Almighty," he whispered. His hand holding the paper began to tremble and he was ashen. "I knew . . . well . . . I knew the guy would be tormented— I told Ouimet."

"Ouimet?"

"I told Ouimet the other day how Scotty would be feeling."

"You did?"

"He paid no attention to me. He wouldn't tell Scotty he talked to me."

"Esther was downtown, saw the paper and phoned me," Max said uneasily. "This is a terrible thing, Harry. The other day it didn't worry me so much, but now look how it's snow-balling."

"I know."

"Not just for you, Harry." Sweetman watched Harry stare blankly at the shiny surface of the desk.

"It's terrible for Mrs. Bowman and her boys," Harry whispered. "I know one of those boys."

"Harry, old fellow, I know it's an awful shock. Very poor show. Very poor show for a chap to flack out like that. Probably knew he couldn't face his friends when he came out, couldn't face you. I said I knew you didn't take advantage of that man, didn't I?"

"It was good of you to say so. Let me tell you, Max, I'm grateful."

"Well, we know each other and all that kind of rot." Max cleared his throat, fumbling for his pipe. Leaning back in the chair, he let his chin sink glumly on his chest. The clicking of the desk clock sounded unbearably loud and he moved it nervously, rubbed the side of his nose and shifted around in the chair uncomfortably. "You're in a poor frame of mind now, Harry," he said uneasily. "Why don't you go home and tomorrow—"

"What do you think this is going to do to us, Max?"

"You know the public. It's your job to know the public, isn't it?"

"Are you thinking I might be an embarrassment?"

"That stupid, stupid, crazy, worthless little bank manager," Sweetman said, slumping in his chair. He was getting no help from Harry and it exasperated him. "My wife said—oh, never mind my wife. What a situation for a man with a job like yours. Harry—Harry."

"What do you think I'd better do, Max?"

"I don't know, Harry. The thing is so delicate I simply don't know. I certainly do know that now—right now—you wouldn't be cultivating much good will for us appearing in public. That's plain, isn't it? As a sensitive man I know you don't want us to pretend we're not touched at all—" And then, half believing the Harry Lane he had known might be able to charm his way out of this scandal, he said hesitantly, "Or do you?"

"That's up to you, Max."

"Harry," he said uneasily, for he could see the effect of the shock of Scotty's death, "you know what I'd do? I'd take a two months' vacation. Yes, that's it," he added more confidently. "Take two months' pay now. I'll fix it at once. Go to Florida, stay away till this stupid little bank manager is forgotten."

"I'm not going to run away, Max," Harry said. "I'm not going to have the whole disgrace of Scotty's death pinned on me. Not on your life! I can stand this. You don't think so? That's all right. You say you know me, Max. Well, so do a lot of people."

"You mean you actually want to stay on the job?"

"Yes."

"You'd face the public—just as if nothing had happened?" he asked, truly astonished.

"Yes."

"Harry, you can't do it."

"I think I should do it."

"Harry, what about the distillery?"

"It'd mean they were behind me, Max."

"My God, man, you'd be a target. It's impossible. Have a heart."

"I see," Harry said, and his eyes shifted to the painting of Esther hung after she had redecorated his office. It had been a gloomily impressive office with dark oak paneling, but Esther had had the oak bleached and now the ceiling was painted a pale green, and the draperies were wine-colored with a thin gold pattern. In the picture Esther looked smooth, bold, intelligent and determined. "That's a fine picture of your wife, Max," Harry said. And then he said, his eyes hardening, "All right, Max, have you thought of this? People are unpredictable, you know. When it gets around that you dropped me—wouldn't stand behind me—well, you're not going to win any respect, you know. Loyalties among gentlemen are deeply respected, aren't they?"

"Quite," Sweetman said stiffly.

"I really thought better of you, Max."

"I ask for a little understanding, Harry."

"Oh, quite."

"Now, look here, Harry."

"No need of apologizing, my friend."

"I'm not apologizing, old boy," Max said, but he squirmed. It seemed to him Harry was actually standing there like a figure of moral outrage, being gentle to humiliate him. His eyes begged Harry to get out of the office and let him sit with his head in his hands and wonder if people would say he hadn't been a gentleman. "I'm too sensitive a man," he muttered.

"So long, Max," Harry said, and as he walked out, Max, for a moment, hated him. Grabbing the purchase he had made for his wife he nearly knocked it on the floor, stopped, caught at it with one hand and walked out of the office belligerently, and when he got home he went into the library, poured himself a drink, then picked up a magazine and pretended he didn't hear Esther coming in.

"Well," she asked eagerly, "what about Mr. Harry Lane?" She sat on the couch opposite him and the heat had brought a faint flush to her neck and shoulders. When she crossed her legs he heard the rustle of silk and he stared at the shapely calf that fattened from the pressure of the knee underneath it. Fattened like that, in the rose-beige stocking, and still shapely, it looked like that Polish singer's leg, he thought frowning, the singer his friend Masters slept with when he came into town, and yesterday he had met the gray-haired Masters and the buxom beaming singer coming along the street and had walked with them, laughing and joking; the bold healthy smiling singer had left them at the corner, and Masters, looking after her thoughtfully, had said, "I hate that woman. I think I always hated her. Yet I pound away at her." Max quickly shifted his eyes from his wife's leg.

"Yes, it's done," he said irritably, feeling sorry for himself. "I—I find it hard to cope with the man. Any fool would say that the last man on earth who should be doing public relations for anybody right now is Harry Lane. Does he recognize it? Not him. He took the attitude I was damaging myself, Esther."

"Of all the unadulterated gall. You know I have to admire him," and she shrugged. "As if he didn't know he's to blame for that bank manager's death."

"He wasn't to blame," he snapped at her.

"He wasn't? Well, who was?"

"The bank manager himself. Are you blind, Esther? Have you no insight?" When she only smiled and shrugged he felt all on edge. "Drop it, do you hear?" he said.

"Did you remember that perfume, Max?" she asked, stretching out on the couch, her ankles crossed, her mind untroubled now as she held her drink up so the late sunlight coming through the window would give it a golden glow, and she closed one eye to appreciate it.

"I left it on the hall table," he said, and rose and got the box and brought it to her, and as he put it on the little table by the couch he said, "That heavy perfume again, is it?"

"It's the same perfume I always use. What's the matter with it?"

"For God's sake, why don't you use something a little lighter?"

"Like what, Max?"

"A very light French perfume for a change. Always these damned heavy Oriental perfumes."

"You don't like them?"

"No," he said abruptly.

"Since when?"

"I never liked them."

"Oh, you're a liar, Max," and she smiled to herself.

"I like something fragile, delicate, evanescent. Surely I have a right to have a preference in the kind of perfume my wife uses—" He stopped, for she was laughing to herself, and he glared at her. "What's the joke?"

"The other night you wanted perfume. Remember?"

"It wasn't just the perfume," he muttered.

"It wasn't? Oh, what was it?"

"I wouldn't even try to explain," he said slowly, remembering what had happened the other night.

They had come in early and had been eating some cheese and onion sandwiches, and when they had finished eating and were on their way upstairs she had brushed against him. "How about it, Max?" she said, patting his belly. But she had come into his bedroom too quickly; she had come in with her clothes off and hopped into bed, and as soon as he was undressed she pulled him on her. He hadn't been ready for her. It had all been too blunt and hurried. "Did you even bother to put a touch of perfume on?" he had asked, and she had said bluntly, "Are you interested in sex or aren't you? If you are, come on." And he had felt lonely and far away from her.

"You know something, Esther? I don't think there's a goddamn line of poetry in you," he said now.

"It's not an age of poetry," she said shrugging.

"Bright and all as you are, Esther, you've never been able to remember three lines of poetry. Why is it?"

"Poetry it is now! Are you crazy?"

"No, I've often wondered about it," he persisted irritably. "Why is it you can't remember a line of poetry?"

"It must have been the way it was taught to me at school."

"I see," he said maliciously. "So now you like plays with plenty of guts and box office and down-to-earth novelty about real gutty people, like Mrs. Silverstein."

"You cut it out, Max Sweetman," she said fiercely, and he smiled with savage satisfaction as the bold confidence went out of her eyes. "You don't fool anybody, Max," she said harshly. "All your pretensions with your gentile friends are just so much water off my back. You came out of the same bag as I did."

"I'd drown myself if I thought I did," he said, standing up and facing her, surprised by his own strength, and smiling as he would have done if he'd had on his uniform of the Eighth Army in the desert. Her mouth quivered, neither one could speak, for they both knew suddenly in the stillness that something had ended for them.

"I'm not going to listen to this kind of junk," she said breathlessly. "You're a fool, Max," and fled from the room.

A little puff of warm air from the open window touched his face. It was going to be another hot night. But the temperature had been above normal all week with the heat general on the whole Atlantic seaboard. From that window high above the city Max could see over the streets as far as the harbor. It would be good to be in Europe now, he thought. To be in Italy and see his father with his bald head and the scar on his jaw he had never explained. Moe Sweetman would scoff at him for being concerned about the necessity of getting rid of Harry Lane. "If it's a business matter and it's your own grandmother you can't afford to be sentimental. Business policy is like destiny, Max," he would say.

Okay, but I can't help having some imagination, some insight, Max thought angrily. The more he drank the more aggrieved he became, thinking of Harry sitting as usual at the Ritz bar, proud and calm and refusing to be embarrassed.

Chapter 16

THE late sunlight slanting over the rim of the mountain filled the third-story windows across the street with fire as Harry turned into Mollie's place. He was at the door, he was going in, when a small voice called "Catch," and he turned, startled. A little girl in a pale blue frock and black pigtails with a very white part in her hair, standing on the walk of the house next door, was bouncing a rubber ball. "Catch, mister?" she repeated solemnly, and she tossed the ball to him, and he had to catch it. He tossed it back carefully right into her cupped hands. Then he went in and climbed the stairs very slowly. Mollie's door opened when he pushed it and a shaft of sunlight from the opposite west window lengthened and fell on him, and Mollie came toward him through the brightness. "Oh, Harry, it's awful," she wailed.

"I don't understand it, Mollie," he said helplessly. "His wife and their two boys. The guy had a wife and two boys, Mollie."

"I know."

"I've often talked to the older boy, Philip. I liked the kid. Oh, I can't even think straight. Look, Mollie, maybe Scotty was ashamed to come out, but how could he be such a coward? How could he be so self-centered as to think it would look better like this?"

"It's the way it is," she said hesitantly as if she didn't want to hurt him. "They say he left no note. Nothing. That means . . . well, the impression everybody gets . . ."

"Sure. The wronged ruined man. And I'm to blame. What's happening to me, Mollie?" He walked away, half distracted, then turned, frowning. Something about her that seemed to be different worried him. He didn't want there to be any change in her. She was wearing a black sweater and white slacks, her hair drawn back into a pony tail, making her cheekbones look higher and her eyes bigger. "Why have you got your hair done like that, Mollie?"

"My hair, I—I don't know."

"I've never seen those slacks either."

"I've never worn them," she said, looking puzzled. "I don't know why. When I bought them I was sure I'd never wear them. And how often do I wear a sweater? I came in and I, well, I had to do something. Oh, Harry, what had the man against you?"

"Against me? God, that's funny. Why do you say such a thing?" he asked angrily. "Supposing I made him feel ashamed? Supposing he knew he could never get any respect? Supposing, in his blind selfishness, he never thought of me at all? Why do you ask me such a stupid question?" and he sat down and closed his eyes. In a little while she came and sat down beside him, gentle and apologetic. He told her he was through at Sweetman's and he spoke of Sweetman with bitter contempt.

"What's the matter with you, Harry?" she asked impatiently. "Sweetman couldn't keep you now. Not in that job."

"He believes my story all right, Mollie. Why couldn't he wait? Why does he have to be the first one to give me a black eye?"

"Harry, you're a sophisticated man," she said. "You know you can't do that job for Sweetman now."

"To hell with Sweetman," he shouted. His eyes were wild as he stood and began to walk up and down, struggling to make

126

some savage protest. "I needed Scotty. Good God, you'd think the man did this to mock me because he knew I needed him to come out and clear me. Now he thinks I can't get at him."

"There's no Scotty now, Harry. He's really run out on you now," she whispered, frightened by his anger. "You're all by yourself now," and she came close to him, pleading, "Wouldn't it be better, Harry, to go away for a while?"

"You mean *I* should run out too?" he said angrily. "As if I were to blame?"

"Let the disgrace of the thing die down," she pleaded. "It'll be unbearable, Harry." Her eyes suddenly shifted away and he felt her struggling against her family, her Morris gentility and dread of scandal. "I only mean that people are so cruel," she said, feeling ashamed. "As it was, people were saying you'd never be able to hold your head up around here."

"Cut it out, Mollie," he said harshly. "You forget one thing."

"What's that?"

"Nobody but Sweetman's heard my story. I—and my family —have a position in this town, far better than Sweetman's, and as good as yours. I've had a good life here, and nobody's taking it away from me. Have I tried to tell my story outside that courtroom?"

"No, no, you haven't, Harry."

"I haven't opened my mouth. Well, I've got hundreds of friends," and he stood up slowly, all his confidence returning as he walked up and down, banging his right fist into his left palm, carried away by his conviction of his own innocence. People would listen to him, he said. Who had anything against him? A hundred people would want him to tell his story. "I hate to do anything to hurt Mrs. Bowman and her two boys," he said. "But damn it all, Scotty was a coward, and I'm not going to be left holding the bag."

"It'll be all over town, and everybody'll be against you, Harry. Oh, Lord."

Tears came in her eyes as she walked toward the window, her hips in a gentle sway, her right hand clutching her left elbow, a gesture of hers when she was worried or excited. She was looking down at the back garden. He waited, watching, then moved over to her. In the garden next door were many gay flowers and a pear tree, and two visiting nuns there in the sunlit garden moved in their flowing black robes into the shade under the pear tree.

"I go on my holidays on Monday, Harry."

"Sure."

"At the cottage with my family."

"I know what it means. Just don't argue with them, Mollie."

"You just won't take it, will you?" she whispered, as if his confidence awed her. "Oh, you've got a way with people, Harry, even if they think they're all against you. You just won't take it." She had turned to him and her arms came tight around him, her thighs and her breasts came hard against him too, her hands came up to his head, drawing it down and putting her mouth hungrily against his in some blind and passionate need of sharing a terrifying experience.

His hand, going under her sweater, cupped her full breast; he held it, drawn away from everything into her warmth; they were sinking down to the floor as her tongue came into his mouth; he knelt with her in the one half-falling motion, only half lying on her, feeling the pounding of her heart against him. "Oh, Mollie," he whispered, looking down at her face. It had so much new beauty for him he trembled. Her mouth open, she sighed and her arms came around him. He couldn't get at the zipper of those white slacks, though she lay very still neither helping him nor hindering him. Jerking the slacks off her clumsily, he threw them across the floor. Then he saw the tears coming from under her closed eyes.

"Mollie, what's the matter with you?"

"I don't know."

"Mollie."

"If you want to, all right."

"Don't just lie there then."

"I can't help it."

"What is it?"

"I don't know. It's gone. It's that Bowman making us do it like this."

"Oh my God." As he stared down at her, his weight on his knees, his legs trembling, the desire in him died. It just went dead. Leaning back on his heels, bewildered, he heard the nuns under the pear tree in the garden laughing and chattering brightly, and from the street came the sound of the bouncing rubber ball, the little girl trying to catch it in her cupped hands.

His hand shook as he drew her sweater slowly down over her. One of her shoes lay between him and the slacks and he wondered how it got there. Taking her hand he raised her gently, then crossed the room, picked up the slacks and shoes and held them out to her awkwardly. As she held the slacks against herself, frowning in her thoughts, a flush came on her cheeks. He thought she was ashamed. Her slow glance was hesitant, almost furtive. A tightness came again into his loins as if she had just touched him. "Mollie," he said huskily.

"No, no, please," she said, suddenly fierce. "I'm not a nun, I guess. Not by a long shot. But when I've managed to save something for my wedding night this far— No," and she swung away, striding toward the bedroom with an air of dignity. But the shaft of sunlight was on her shining round buttocks. There were two red marks on them from the floor, and he was glad she couldn't see them. When she had to come out of the bedroom he was sure she would be grim and angry. His own embarrassment grew as he waited.

In a little while she returned, wearing a navy blue dress, her hair combed out, her face powdered. Her cool untroubled calmness so surprised him he couldn't say anything. Smiling a little as if they were a success, had kept what belonged to them alone, for a time of their own, she came toward him and kissed him gently. A sense of happiness and oneness with her seemed to lift him off the ground. "Mollie, my darling," he whispered, his face in her hair, "whenever you're beyond the reach of my eyes I know now I'll feel lonely."

"I'm not going away, Harry," she said impulsively. "I'm staying here with you. It's going to be pretty rough on you. That man's funeral and all. I don't need to go away at all, Harry."

He wouldn't hear of it. Her family would blame him for keeping her away, he said, and he laughed reassuringly. No one needed to worry about him. He would write her every day.

Next morning he went to the station with her. It was a warm bright morning. Before she went through the gate they kissed, and he laughed, and as she turned at the gate, looking back at him, he waved cheerfully, but she had an eager worried smile.

Chapter 17

THE night before Scotty's funeral, Harry couldn't feel like himself at all. It was not the time to start talking—not while they were waiting to bury Scotty. Anyway, as he thought of the letter he had tried to write to him that same wonder about the man began to gnaw away at him again. Of course, it was just because the wretched man was now lying in a funeral parlor.

He wandered out of the apartment, avoiding the familiar places. At about ten he came into the Tahiti, a downstairs place, all gilt and chrome, always in semidarkness except for the strong light over the bar, the faces at the tables half hidden in shadows and smoke, a place where he was not known. Yet there, sitting by herself at the bar, was Annie Laurie, bright and blond in her pretty oyster shade dress. Seeing him in the mirror behind the bar she turned quickly, opening her arms. "Harry, is it really you?" she cried.

"I'm glad to see you, Annie." He didn't like seeing her alone in this room which smelled of cheap perfume and beer. "What are you doing here, Annie? You don't belong in here."

"I was slumming with a man named Mallard, a broker from out of town. We had words, Harry. He asked me if I'd rather be alone, so I said I loved being alone. I'm giving him time to get lost." And then she put her hand on his arm, her face full of indignation. "I hear you're out at Sweetman's. You got a raw deal, Harry."

"It's incredible, isn't it?"

"To put a man like you in that light! It makes my blood boil."

"It'll straighten out. Thanks just the same, Annie." Her unquestioning faith had been offered so quickly he wondered if she really knew the hole he was in. "I haven't seen you around. Where have you been?" he asked.

"Out of town. New York."

"Oh! Well—always out of town."

"Want to hear about it? Sit down and I'll tell you." So he sat on the stool beside her and she asked, smiling, "Do you know Wilkinson, the business manager of the B—— ball club?"

"No—never met him."

"I like having a man who is right off his rocker over me. Well, Wilkinson was. He left town, but he called me late from New York and begged me to come to him, so I did. Honestly, Harry, the guy was crazy about me." Then she shrugged her pretty shoulders, her eyes full of wonder. "A very superstitious man. A real puritan background. Seems he had always been unlucky with women and always felt tortured after he had made love to them. Just couldn't believe in his luck with me. Thought something terrible was going to happen to him because it was easy with me and he felt happy. The guy really felt he'd have to pay off with some terrible bad luck somewhere, see, because he could go to the moon with me. So he started to drink, then he disappeared. Even his ball club couldn't find him. I think he turned up somewhere in Kansas City on a prolonged drunk." Annie Laurie looked thoughtful. "Why do men get themselves all mixed up about women, Harry?" she asked with her charming smile.

"Too much goes on in a man's head, I guess," he said vaguely, his thoughts far away and troubled.

"I'm tired of these men who are all head. I'd like to be a bartender with one of those sticks they use to brush the head off a glass of beer, that way you could see you got your money's worth." Suddenly she touched his arm. "Look, Harry," she said gravely, "you don't need to feel bad about Scotty. Let me tell you something. Scotty killed himself for one simple reason. Terrible disappointment in himself. You're the goat, Harry."

"Wait a minute," he said guardedly. "What makes you so sure you know what went on between me and Scotty?"

"I know something about men. Why shouldn't I? Aside from the act he puts on, every guy has a certain spirit."

"Those steady blue eyes of Scotty's. I'll never know what went on behind them now. I wish I knew."

"Maybe I can tell you. He knew he was slipping, *I* knew he was slipping. On the other hand," she said smiling, "I knew all about you the first time I ever talked to you. Now tell me what really happened between you two."

"You want to know?"

"Yes—please. Go ahead."

He told her the whole story. When he had finished, she leaned over and kissed him gently and it upset him.

"Harry," she said thoughtfully, "one night Scotty walked along with me."

"Did he go home with you?"

"Yes, he did."

"Stay long?"

"I let him come in. Why not?"

"Did he miss his last train?"

"I'm afraid he did."

"Oh, I see," he said, keyed up suddenly.

"Maybe it was the age he was at, I don't know," she said, looking troubled. "It seems to be the worst age for a man when he feels a last kick in him. He had worked hard all his life, his nose always to the grindstone, and he had never realized he had missed so much. A practical businessman, see, hit by the sudden

133

crazy longing for everything beyond him, trying to keep that smile in his shrewd eyes yet letting himself go rather desperately."

"What did he want, Annie?"

"Me, of course."

"Oh, God. Go on."

"Here's the thing, Harry. He seemed to think I was telling him he didn't make enough money, that I was too expensive for him. I felt kind of sorry for him. He said he knew lots of people who came into the bank who could make a quick profit on something for him. Until now he hadn't bothered, he said. He sounded so restless and hungry and apologetic. Yet such a businessman."

"What an eye opener this is," Harry said softly. "The soul of fidelity. In some ways, this is my whole case, Annie. The whole damned case! Did he ever talk to you about me?"

"As a matter of fact he did. That night. On the way home."

"What did he say?"

"As I remember it he didn't think you were very shrewd. You had a kind of weakness, he said. A kind of innocence."

"The son of a bitch," Harry blurted out excitedly. The bartender stared at him. He tried to keep his voice down. "I was an open book to him, eh?" And then Harry put his elbows down on the bar, his head in his hands, and groaned. "If I had only known this story. My God. To get back in that court. What a different picture of Scotty we could give the court."

"I'm afraid the case is closed, Harry."

"No, it's not. It's got to come up again, Annie. It's got to. I'm opening it up."

"Come on, let's get out of here," she said and they went out to the street. "In a little while my broker, full of contrition, will phone me at home. I'd ask you to come with me but I know your Miss Morris."

"One thing, Annie," he said, holding her arm as a taxi drew up for her. "If you get a chance, tell everybody I'm the goat, eh? Tell what kind of a deal I got."

"Don't worry. I'll be your advocate."

"Who could want a prettier one?"

"In some court circles," she said over her shoulder as she stepped into the taxi, "I won't be considered a very persuasive advocate. You'll have others, Harry."

As the taxi pulled away, Harry turned to walk home briskly. At Dominion Square the barouches, with their old bony-backed horses and their patient old drivers, were lined up at the curb, and he heard the trains shunting in the station yard. Everything seemed to be happily in its right place again. He felt no remorse now about Scotty. He just hoped they buried him deep.

Chapter 18

ON THE second day flowers began to arrive at the funeral parlor from bank managers and from St. Catherine Street merchants who had been visited by Mike Kon. Mike said to them all, "Make up your mind. What's the matter with you? Don't you know a tragic figure when you see one? We've all got to make a showing. He was our friend, wasn't he?" And the merchants came one by one to the funeral parlor, and Slocombe, the bank superintendent, came too. Paula Bowman asked Mike to be a pallbearer. She had been afraid they wouldn't have enough pallbearers. All over town there had been sympathy for Scotty, but now he seemed to have re-established himself completely. As he lay with his eyes closed, and a little twisted smile the undertaker had achieved, Scotty made those who looked at him shake their heads and assure each other there had never been such a well-meaning man.

The morning of the burial day the undertaker, Mr. Hampton, who was good at estimating the attendance at rites for better-known citizens, came to Paula and assured her she could have the larger room. It was twice the size of this one, he said; it had been recently redecorated in a soft shade of green, and it had new broadloom on the floor. But he had to back away from her apologetically. A crazy expression had come into her eyes. But Mr. Hampton had been right. The small room couldn't even hold all the flowers. Wreaths were piled one on top of the other and a half hour before the little service there was such a crowd they lined up on the street, although many of them had never seen Scotty.

Paula and her two boys were backed into a corner, and the smell of the flowers and all the strange faces and strange voices speaking to Mrs. Bowman made her ill. Then Mr. Hampton whispered that she and her sons could use the small waiting room. Each one of the mourners who asked to speak to the widow had to identify himself to Mike Kon, who took the name in to Paula.

"I can't think straight about anything, Mike," she said to him helplessly. "I go in there and look at Scotty and I start asking him what to do."

"It's hard, I know, Paula," he said, a lump in his throat. "Things have a way of working out, though."

"The boys"—she looked around anxiously—"where are they?"

"They're here, Paula."

"Oh, God help us," and she started to weep. "Scotty was so fond of them."

"They're big fellows now, Paula. Come on now."

"I don't care how big they are. They're not going to quit school, do you hear?"

"Now look, Paula. It isn't Scotty who should be lying in there. If it had to be somebody, you know who it should be."

"It's all so mixed up, Mike, isn't it? Scotty was so hard to fool. Is there any chance there was a terrible misunderstanding?"

"Misunderstanding?" Her puffed and swollen red face made him choke with emotion. There under his own eyes the faith she had in her certain knowledge of her husband, on which were based all the good memories of their life together, seemed to him to be questioned. He was filled with a terrible compassion. "Misunderstanding my eye," he said harshly, his arm on her shoulder. "I know you're broken up, Paula, and all that seems to matter is that Scotty is gone, but you don't ever need to wonder what happened. That salesman—that phony—just don't forget that Harry Lane's job was to charm the birds off the trees. It was his profession to get around people. I just hope that he's capable of a little human remorse." Then Mike looked around. "Here's the minister. Come on, Paula."

Supported by her two white-faced and startled sons, Paula came out to the main room to hear the minister's few words. He was a thin baldheaded round-faced man who hadn't known Scotty very well, but had no doubt he understood his story. He spoke briefly and movingly about a man of a thousand friends, a man of such established integrity that when he had been blinded and turned in another direction, it had been so alien to his whole life and character he had been driven out of his mind. Considering that he knew nothing about Scotty or Harry, it was a moving tribute. Someone started to sob. It was Scotty's secretary. "I just wish that Harry Lane was here," she whimpered. Then they screwed down the lid of the oaken casket and took Scotty out to the cemetery.

Afterwards the sons and their mother and Mike walked slowly through the cemetery to the car. It was a lovely clear morning. On the long ride to the Bowmans' they all seemed to be afraid of saying the wrong thing. Even when they got to the house and were sitting awkwardly in the living room for a few minutes, it was as if they were afraid to speak. Afraid if they did so they would not hear the familiar voice, the step on the stair. "Well, this is no good," Paula said abruptly. Removing her hat and coat she said calmly she was going to make a cup of coffee. She left Mike with her sons, who sat there watching him uneasily.

This man now seemed to them to know more about their father than they did. It made them ashamed. The younger boy Steve, the fair one, who had nev given Scotty any trouble, averted his eyes, looking at his shoelace as if he thought it had come undone. The older boy Philip, who had admired Harry Lane and who was the image of Scotty sitting there, had been keeping his lonely bitter thoughts to himself. Staring at Mike, he frowned, as if wondering half resentfully how it was that this powerful man with the stitched brows and the rough face, so unlike his father, so plainly out of a different background, was the only friend who was there with them. "My father's friends —all kinds of friends," he said bitterly, "none at the end of things were like him. How did they get into his life?"

"Hell now, wait a minute," Mike said uneasily. "I'm one of those friends."

"I guess I didn't mean you, Mike."

"No, I guess you didn't," he agreed, trying to smile amiably. He felt hurt. In his heart he was sure the boy had included him among those exotic friends who didn't belong in the life of a banker. The deep wrinkles on his brow began to work up and down, moving his hairline a little. Yet he could see that the boy's reaction was partly his fault. When the boys were around he had talked only about mugs and hoods and gamblers and clowns and crooks in the fight mob. Wanting to entertain them, what chance had he given them to see that he was actually a very literate, very thoughtful, dignified businessman, a student of life, a man with rich experiences? They probably thought he was just a stumblebum a jump away from the East End pool-rooms, the son of a funny old newsboy. His vanity never could stand this opinion of him. Just the thought of it—the fancied insult now when he was feeling such grief for Scotty—made him want to lash out at someone.

"I'll tell you something," he said grimly. His hand holding a cigarette trembled and he looked at it, then stood up. The boys gaped at him, startled. They had never seen such a proud, indignant expression on his face. "It's true your father had picked up some strange friends," he said. "I'm glad you're old enough to understand he had no real place in the phony crowd he got into. I'm glad you see it, Philip. Too simple and fine a man for those very insincere people. An amateur. That's what he was. An amateur, you hear? I told him so. I told him, 'Scotty, nobody in that Lane crowd has the slightest concern for you. They're all the same, those easy-money boys. With friends as with money, it's easy come easy go.' I saw it coming." It was true, wonderfully true, he had seen it, he thought, feeling exalted. Right from the beginning, too! The perceptiveness he had shown began to dazzle him. He had been the one who had had the wisdom, the judgment and the moral sense to recognize that Harry Lane was wrong for Scotty. "Ha, God knows I saw it," he said, recovering all his self-esteem. Big comforting words came to him. "That bunch. Cynical, smooth-talking moral illiterates, the lot of them. I hate childish men, see? I hate educated men when they're ignorant."

Lifted out of their loneliness and comforted by his scorn, the two boys nodded, wanting him to go on, but he softened. He saw that they understood now. "I loved your father, kids," he said, choking a little. "I know what went on in him and you don't because you haven't got the experience. Now here's something to remember all your life. Your father was the finest and most loyal man I ever knew, and I've seen a lot of men in a lot of big cities. Yeah, I've seen them all and he was the best, see?" The younger boy put his hand over his face and turned away, but Philip waited, his eyes shining. "Okay," Mike said gruffly. "There's one other thing I know. Your father wouldn't want you to sit here moping. Look, it's a nice day out. Go on and do something. Go on now."

As their mother came in with the coffee they wandered out aimlessly.

"No use them sitting in here not knowing what to do, Paula," he said apologetically.

"You're quite right, Mike. I'm glad you're here with us. I'm grateful," she said, sitting down. "Well, I'm ready to make the best of it myself. You take two lumps of sugar, don't you, Mike?"

"Yes, please."

"He had his faults, Mike."

"Yeah, he had his faults. Who hasn't?"

When she raised her cup to her lips it made a rattling sound against her teeth. All the sensible practical years of her life with Scotty seemed to him to be in that little rattling sound. Some coffee was spilled on her dress. Her eyes had filled with tears. "Cut it out, Paula," he said, getting up and taking the cup.

"I'm sorry," she said helplessly. "I just suddenly get thinking and I can't stop. Nothing's looked after, Mike. There's a mortgage on this house. What will we do?"

"If you ask me, Harry Lane should be willing to do something."

"That man?"

"That man's a human being," he said, putting his cup down on the coffee table, "and he may have a conscience, too. But that's not the thing."

"I haven't heard a word from him."

"We'll wait a while. I know how the mind of a man like him works," he said contemptuously. "Now you listen to me. A man like that can't bear to be in a bad light, and no man was ever in a worse one. By God, that man may come crawling to you on his hands and knees, you understand?"

"I don't know, Mike."

"Well I do. I know the type of man too well. He's got to look big. It's his lifeblood. Right now you drink that cup of coffee." And he sat down in his favorite chair in the room, a big overstuffed one in the corner, where he had always sat on those fine evenings, and as he sipped the coffee, trying to make casual cheerful small talk, he didn't want to leave. Settling deeper into the chair he dreaded getting up, for Scotty had always said, "No, you sit there. We call that Mike's chair now."

Chapter 19

THE story about the funeral was in all the newspapers and when Harry read it he knew he had better wait two or three days before seeking another job. Anyway, he felt he needed a few days to relax and look into his own affairs. He had two thousand dollars in the bank and he sent a thousand to Slocombe with a curt note saying he was making a payment on his loan. For three days he stayed home a lot. It was a week of unseasonably hot weather, the last kick of summer. The heat might last a few days longer, Harry thought, so he walked down to the cleaners to get his tropical suit.

The young Greek, who saw Harry coming in, glanced at him nervously, then went back to the office and returned with a balding older man in a white shirt and a black bow tie, who was carrying Harry's coat. "My friend," said the older man, shaking his head solemnly, "this you won't like," and he opened the coat and spread it out on the counter. The striped-silk lining seemed to have light crisscrossing veins running through it, but these veins were really thin fine gashes.

"See, I do this," the younger man with sideburns said, and he nicked one of the cuts with his finger and it fell open. "You see?" he asked. "All in shreds."

"Good God," Harry said, staring at the lining. "I bring the

coat in to you and you show me you can tear it to pieces, after you've cleaned it."

"Wait. Now wait. Look at the cloth, the rest of the coat. Is it all right?" the older man said, spreading it out on the counter. Getting excited he grabbed at other cleaned coats on hangers. They showed him the linings. "That's a faulty piece of material you got there, mister," they said. "Look, every part of the lining. Now look at the cloth. If it was the cleaning fluid it would have hurt the cloth. No? Take it back. Where did you get it? Mike Kon? It's a gyp. Make him put a new lining in it. Tell him to come to us." They both pounded the counter belligerently, and they convinced him.

"A rotten piece of lining," he said to himself as he went out. "Cheap goods from Mike Kon." All the angry contempt he had felt for Kon at the trial, listening to him, damn him, welled up in Harry again. But one thing about it bothered him. Kon wasn't a stupid man. To walk in on him angrily would be a great mistake. Kon would say, "What's the matter with you? Do you think I did it on purpose?" He walked slowly home with the coat and threw it over the back of a chair and looked at it uneasily.

Finally he decided it would be better to wear it. And when he had put on the suit and was looking at himself in the mirror, he suddenly felt hopeful. Mike, as a tailor, would be bound to be apologetic, and this would give him an opening. Then, too, one of the good things about men in the sports crowd was that they were willing to live and let live, and Mike, the old fighter, facing him in his shop and under a disadvantage, might be willing to relent a little. And since Mike had been so close to Scotty, it would be almost like talking to Scotty.

So Harry walked out in the freshly cleaned suit and moved east in the sunlight, the heat from the hot sidewalk licking at his ankles. Men passing him walked slowly, mopping their necks and foreheads with their handkerchiefs. They all looked cross. But young girls in light summer dresses, cool and gay, passed by looking spotless and immaculate, and the fat man standing at the door of his art shop that had the Picasso print in the window, sighed as he watched the girls and said crossly, "How the hell do they do it? In this weather?"

The tailor shop was there on the other side of the street, the door wide open, and as he crossed he could see Mike sitting on the oaken table in his shirt sleeves. As a dignified merchant now, Mike rarely took off his coat in public.

"Hello there," Harry said calmly.

"You," Mike said suspiciously, sliding off the table slowly, then facing him, stiff with astonishment.

"I want to show you something."

"Show me what?"

"You remember this suit?"

"I do."

"Well, look," and he took off the coat and spread it on the table so all the lining would show. "I just had it cleaned, Mike," he said quietly. "The cleaners tell me it was a faulty piece of lining."

"They do, eh?" Mike said slowly, not looking at the coat but staring at him, his eyes hard and suspicious. He took his time. He had selected the colorful striped silk carefully. He now rubbed a piece of the lining between two fingers, then held the coat up so the light would shine on the lining. "Whoever told you that's a faulty piece of lining is crazy," he said calmly.

"I told you I just talked to the cleaners."

"Ummm. I'm not surprised." He tapped the coat scornfully. "It's the lousy cleaning fluid they're using. You can't pin that on me. Oh, no, Mr. Lane," he said grimly. "You go back to your cleaners and tell them what I said."

"Now, just a minute, Mike," Harry said. "The first thing I said to the cleaners was that it was the fluid."

"You had it right, Mr. Lane."

"Aren't you overlooking something?" Harry said, trying to hold his temper. "If it was the cleaning fluid, wouldn't the cloth as well as the lining be damaged? That's what the cleaners asked me. They're not stupid. They showed me other suits on

144

the rack, suits cleaned with the same fluid and there wasn't a damaged lining in the lot. What about it?"

"Now look. Get this straight," Mike said and he folded the coat neatly, put it on the table, patted it with his hand, then folded his arms across his chest as if trying to pretend to himself he wasn't blinded by his animosity. "I don't put faulty materials in my suits. Any fool would know that what has happened to that lining is the work of a cleaning fluid. Am I to go over to the cleaners with you, is that what you expect?"

"I expect you to put a new lining in that coat."

"Why should I?"

"You won't do it?"

"Why should I? Let your cleaners do it. They did the damage."

"You mean to say you refuse?"

"I'd do it in a minute if I thought I was to blame in any way. I'm not, and I'm not going to have some cheap cleaner pull this stunt on me. Go back to your cleaners. Tell them what I said."

"I see," Harry said, growing pale. "Well, it's not what you'd say to any other customer, is it, Mr. Kon?" And as Mike stiffened and tried to look dignified and contemptuous, Harry smiled and said, "You're bluffing and you know it. What's wrong with you, Mike, that you can't admit to me that you're wrong—even about a piece of lining?"

Coming closer, Mike banged his palm on the table.

"You have only one thing in mind, Harry Lane," he said. "You come around here to try and humiliate me."

"You're wrong, even about that too. I came around here like any other customer, to ask you to put a decent lining in a coat."

"Decent lining," Mike said and he laughed, and you could see he wasn't thinking of the lining at all. "You came around here to make trouble. I saw it in your face."

"Goddamn it. Look," Harry blurted out, wanting to poke him on the nose as he held his coat open. "Are you suggesting I shredded this lousy lining?"

"I don't know what you did. I know you've got it in for me because I was a witness against you."

"You fool. You weren't a witness against me. I wasn't on trial."

"That was your good luck. Have you no shame? Scotty's hardly buried and now you're after me."

"I didn't come after you," Harry said, trembling and wishing he hadn't come. He started to button his coat, taking a lot of time, and then he put his head back with his distinguished air and said quietly, "Well, at least you know what I think of you as a tailor," and he started to go.

"Just a minute," Mike said, following him slowly. One of his rolled-up shirt sleeves had come down, the one on the arm he had banged on the table, and as he rolled it up, looking worried, he tried to remember he was a businessman.

"You bought the suit here, okay," he said grudgingly. Aside from being a witness, and aside from being Scotty's devoted friend, he could see it wasn't to his interest to have any man wearing one of his suits and saying the lining was rotten, no matter how low an opinion he had of the man. "You had your say, I had mine," he said sourly. "I still say it was the cleaner, but if you want me to fix it, bring it in or leave it. I'll fix your damn lining."

"I wasn't asking a favor from you," Harry said scornfully. "I wouldn't waste my time coming around here again. It's not worth it," and he walked out.

Mike took a couple of steps after him so he could stand at the door, just out of the sunlight, and watch him uneasily as he walked away.

Chapter 20

DORFMAN'S wasn't Mike's kind of bar. Patrons who sat in the paneled room had substance, they had families, even the sporting editors who came here were the ones who had wives who had gone to college. But since he had first come here with Scotty the patrons would say to each other, "He's Mike the Scholar, an old fighter, but you should listen to the guy. Go on, talk to him. He's got a fresh angle."

Standing by the bar he looked around to see who was there. Ted Ogilvie and Eddie Adams, the fight promoter, and old Haggerty, the sporting editor, were sitting by the window. A little man with oily black hair, beady eyes and a small heavily tanned face, who certainly didn't belong in Dorfman's at all and knew it, was standing behind Eddie Adams. He was Ray Conlin, who called himself the manager of Johnny Bruno, the fighter, and thought he was big enough for Dorfman's because his picture had appeared in a photo magazine as one of Rosso's henchmen —riding around in Cadillacs and controlling the boxing industry. Everybody who knew the facts had laughed when they read this story. Conlin was merely Bruno's trainer.

"Hi, Mr. Haggerty," Mike said, approaching their table. "Can I sit down?"

"Sure, sure, sit down, Mike," and he pushed out a chair to

him with his foot. "Eddie's going good." Eddie Adams was telling a story about his wife and his row of apartment houses, and how she had cried one night when he came home late and said she wished they were back in the old days when he had driven a taxi. With his sly grin and cold expressionless eyes he made everything on earth seem comical.

"Who do you think came into my store today?" Mike blurted out when Eddie had finished his story. "Harry Lane."

"Harry Lane. He did?" Ogilvie asked. "I'd certainly liked to have been there."

"The bastard's got it in for me," Mike said, feeling sure they would see it his way. He told what had happened. "Naturally I pointed out it was the cleaning fluid," he said. "The lining was a good piece of goods. I examined it, but I saw he just wanted to quarrel with me because I had been a witness against him."

"What are you worried about?" Adams asked, snickering. "Don't you like putting linings in coats?"

"I offered to fix the coat," Mike said grimly. "That guy is in a dangerous mood right now, and he's after me."

"I think you'd better give us all the details of this suit," Haggerty said, mockingly solemn.

"That's it," Adams said, joining in the kidding. "When somebody buys a horse and tries to get a refund I like to get the name of the owner and the breeder."

"Mike's the breeder. Harry now is the owner."

"Give us the details of the suit."

"Maybe Mike's not so good with linings in those tropicals," Ogilvie said, keeping his face straight.

"I wouldn't wear one of those tropicals myself," Mike said.

"What should a guy wear?" Haggerty asked, leading him on.

"One of these," Mike said, grabbing the lapel of his own coat. "A lightweight English worsted. Keeps its press in this weather." Then he asked doggedly, "Don't you get the point? Why doesn't he want a new lining from me?"

"Well, you did put the nail in his coffin, Mike," Ogilvie said. "If you're going to give evidence against a man, you'd better make sure you've given him a good coat lining."

Little Ray Conlin, who had been hovering around the table waiting for a chance to get into the conversation, suddenly saw his opportunity. "Maybe Harry Lane will be too smart to let you touch that coat again, Mike," he said, his little dark face full of mockery. "Maybe he's afraid next time you'll try your own special lining—yellow. You always had a yellow lining, eh, Mike?" And he slapped his knee and danced around, his hard little face full of happiness. It was the only time in his life he had ever been quicker than anyone else with a clever remark. "Ah, ha, aw, ha, aw, aw, ha," he snickered and they all laughed and waited.

"Yellow was never my color, Conlin," Mike said quietly.

"No?"

"No."

"You mean to say those trunks you used to wear in the ring didn't have a yellow lining?"

"That's right," Mike said, smiling disdainfully.

"They didn't?" Conlin asked, trying desperately to hold his audience. "What about that night in Philadelphia ten years ago. Remember? The night you went into the tank for Walters. Wasn't the yellow lining showing then? Ho, ho, ho ho," and as he looked around for approval, Mike, eying him steadily, hated him for reminding them of the days when he had been an illiterate unprincipled washed-up young hoodlum.

"When it comes to tanks, Ray, you'd know all about them," he said quietly. "You and the Rosso mob. The biggest tank industry in the country. How about Bruno's coming fight with the Dutchman?"

"A dirty insinuation. What are you trying to do, hurt the gate? You heard him, Mr. Adams."

"Are you leveling, Mike?" Eddie Adams asked, quietly.

"I only ask a question."

"A yellow question, too yellow to say right out," Ray said, his face shining with sweat as his eyes shifted around. No one was helping him. "Come on outside," he blustered fiercely.

But Mike only smiled lazily. "Oh, go and peddle your papers, Ray," he said, and Conlin, knowing he was unwanted, moved over to the bar.

Through an opened window, rumba music floated in on the night air. Then they all saw Harry Lane come in and Mike noticed that Harry was still wearing the suit. Harry looked over at their table but Mike knew he wouldn't come near them. He watched Harry sit down alone at a table near the bar.

"Is that the coat, Mike?" Haggerty asked, as he looked at Harry and grinned.

"Lay off, Haggerty," Mike said uneasily.

"But I'm an expert on good lining, Mike."

"Never mind the lining. Lay off, I say."

"I want to see what a cleaner can do to a first-class piece of material from a great tailor."

"Keep out of this, please, Mr. Haggerty," Mike begged him. But Haggerty got up, chuckling to himself, and went over to Harry. Mike was sure Harry would show the lining to Haggerty and that everybody would gather around and laugh.

"What's this I hear, Harry?" Haggerty asked solemnly. Taken in by the grave air, Harry looked up. "I'm an old newspaperman," Haggerty said. "I'm trained to get the facts, Harry."

"What's on your mind, Haggerty?"

"There's one thing about me," Haggerty said. "I know a good piece of lining when I see one. Let's see, Harry."

"Don't be silly."

"But Mike says moths got into the cleaning fluid."

"I don't care what that tailor says," and he shrugged as if the whole thing was beneath him. "If that stupid tailor wants to talk to you and is having a good time at my expense, let him talk himself blue in the face. Just don't bother me about it, Haggerty."

"I was only joking," Haggerty said awkwardly.

"Okay. Only I'm not going to be the butt of the joke. Take it up with the tailor."

"Suit yourself," Haggerty said, looking shamefaced as he came back to the table.

"Why can't people mind their own business?" Mike said bitterly. "I told you, Haggerty, I had words with the guy and he won't let me fix the coat. I don't want trouble with him in here." Then he saw Alfred Dorfman come into the bar and stop at Harry's table, where he stood talking, and whatever it was Harry was saying, it aroused Alfred's interest. It seemed to Mike that Alfred looked over at him.

"I'm not going to put up with any slanders from that guy," Mike muttered. "Everybody knows what he's got against me. Just the same, though, I'd give fifty dollars if he didn't have that coat."

"Take it easy, Mike," Haggerty said sympathetically. "You've got a good conscience about him, haven't you?"

"I only told the truth at that trial. I was under oath, wasn't I?"

"Then forget him. To hell with him."

"Have you heard anything about the Bruno fight, Mike?" Ted asked helpfully, and it seemed to Mike they were all with him, trying to comfort him, so he tried to relax as he explained that in his opinion the Dutchman could take Bruno any day in the week, and it shouldn't be called a title fight at all.

Conlin watched Harry get up and go in the direction of the washroom and he loafed along after him. The bare white-tiled washroom seemed to be empty. From one of the cubicles came the sound of a cough. Then Conlin saw the coat hanging on a wall peg.

As he stared at it, his little dark face puckering up in a frown, bright happy thoughts of laughter came to him. He wanted to look at the coat lining so he could tell the others about it and get a big laugh.

All his life Ray Conlin had been ducking and running. When he had been a kid in Brooklyn he had heard himself called a rat of a boy. Around Stillman's Gym he had attached himself to Waxie Rosso. He had been able to get along by doing little things for people, jobs no one else would do, and he had shown Rosso that he could count on him. Even before Rosso put him on his payroll he had picked up a living hanging around the Great Southern Hotel in New York, always ready to do little things for the mob. The way to get along in the world, he had learned, was to do something for the big fellows, something that would surprise them and make them laugh.

Grinning, he took a slow step toward the coat and reached out and unhooked it, full of curiosity to see what the quarrel between Mike and Harry was about. Then he heard Harry moving behind the cubicle door and as he turned quickly the coat slipped off his arm, and when he grabbed it, some papers fell out of the pocket. The cubicle door opened suddenly. He ran. But Lane came charging after him, shouting, "You thief, you dirty little thief . . ." When he got back to the bar he started to laugh, so everybody would see it was a joke. But Lane, right behind him, had him by the shirt collar, jerking him around and tearing his shirt.

"Cut it out," Ray said angrily.

"Stealing my wallet, eh?" Harry shouted.

Ray winced at the strength in Harry's hand and now as he looked at the white angry face with the hard blue eyes he felt scared, as scared as he had felt as a kid when an enormously powerful and coldly superior detective had cornered him hiding behind a counter in a bakery shop. "Lay off," he threatened, scowling viciously. He tried to knee Harry in the groin, then saw Harry's right coming at him and tried to duck, but it caught him on the temple and he fell to the floor.

"I'll get you," Ray whispered, raising himself slowly on one knee as if taking a long count. His long oily black hair fell down over his eyes. He had to brush it away so he could see Harry, who waited, his eyes hard. Ray wished he had a knife.

By now the others had jumped up from the table. Some guests had come running downstairs.

"What kind of a place do you think this is?" Alfred Dorfman shouted. "Is this a cheap little dive where I have to phone for the cops every hour?"

"He was after my wallet," Harry said.

"Like hell I was!" Ray shouted.

"Why don't you call a cop, Alfred?" Harry said. "He's a little gangster. One of Rosso's boys."

It made Ray feel more powerful to be called one of Rosso's boys, so he sneered, "Oh, you wait, brother. You'll be looked after for smacking me. Just you wait."

"You know what I'm going to do? I'm going to have you deported," Harry said grandly.

"You! You couldn't have anybody deported. Your name's dirt around here," Ray yelled, but then he grew frightened. No matter how low Lane had fallen he could ask the police to look into a man's life, he thought. If that happened everything would go, Rosso would turn against him. Rosso knew how important it was that his trainer should be legitimate. "Tell him, you guys," he pleaded desperately with Ted Ogilvie and Haggerty. "It was only the coat. It's a joke. Mike Kon said Lane was going to use the coat to damage his business. I only wanted to see what it was like. You said it, didn't you, Mike?"

"Yeah, I said it," Mike admitted, his face brick-red. The humiliation he had dreaded all evening had come, he was sure, and he turned on Conlin as if he were going to hit him. "Look what you do to me, you fool," he said, as Conlin backed away. "Well, I knew what it meant when Harry Lane wouldn't let me fix that coat."

"I thought I came into your store and asked you to fix it," Harry said quietly.

"I offered to fix that coat," Mike said, hating Harry's cool voice and the way he seemed to be twisting the facts and putting him in the wrong in front of these people. Turning to them all, he raised his hands. He wanted to say, *You know why this*

153

guy has it in for me? I was a witness. But he still thinks he can make people eat out of his hand, see? You know where he should be. But he didn't say it. There was amusement in their faces. Someone snickered and he felt outraged. "What did I say as you left the store?" he asked.

"You mean after you told me to go to the devil and insulted me, then suddenly remembered you were a little business-man?"

It was going all wrong. It was the worst thing that could happen for his shop, and Mike lost his head. Trembling with rage, he thought of Scotty Bowman killing himself over this man, and here he and his business were being damaged and cheapened by the same man, and he grew pale. "Okay," he said, his voice breaking. "I know you've got it in for me. I know a guy who has disgraced himself'll do anything out of shame. But I'm not Scotty Bowman. You could kill him, but you're not going to ruin me too. I won't take it."

All the faces around him now were watchful and tense as he glared at Harry and waited, his fists clenched. The anguish in Harry's face puzzled him, and the silence became unbearable. Yet he had to wait until Harry turned to the others as if expecting a protest, then glanced at the stairs although no one was there, then straightened up, as if he were at bay, and though very pale, smiled proudly.

"If all this is in your mind, Kon," he said scornfully, "and if you think I'd stoop to parading around with a torn coat just to spite you, you're crazy. Here, take your coat. Go to work on it." He tossed the coat contemptuously at him.

"You fling that coat in my face. It's not my coat. What do you think I am?" Mike said, hating him for rising above him with such contempt. "Who do you think you are?" and he wouldn't pick up the coat.

The coat lay on the floor, the torn lining exposed so they could all see it. Shrugging, Harry picked it up. "Good night, Alfred," he said, and he walked out proudly.

Nobody said anything, and Mike looked around uncertainly.

"He had it coming to him," he finally said, his face burning. But now he was watching Alfred Dorfman, who was coming slowly toward him. Suddenly Alfred stopped and he seemed to be remembering. His son, before he had been killed at war, had been a friend of Harry's. Alfred turned slowly and looked at the red-carpeted stairs as if he knew why Harry had glanced in that direction. In the good days Harry's mother and father had often come down those stairs and it seemed like only yesterday when Harry's mother had stopped there, leaning over the banister, to talk to him, the light on her bluish-gray hair, her eyes mirthful and gay. Then Alfred's glance shifted to that place near the bar where Harry had stood at bay, his face full of anguish. Mike saw the sudden hardness in Alfred's face as he took an angry step toward Ray.

"Listen Conlin," Alfred said. "How did you ever get in here? If you come around here again, I'll have you thrown on your face in the middle of the road." Turning his back on Conlin, he looked around and Mike, meeting his eyes, felt himself being pushed out of the place and down the street and back to the cheap neighborhood where he had grown up.

"Look, Kon," Alfred said.

"Mr. Dorfman—"

"I've never had any trouble in here, Kon," Alfred said, reddening. "You're not in that police court now. Nobody's on trial here. You're no witness in here. My family has always been proud of our customers." The pain in Mike's eyes didn't stop him and he went on doggedly. "I like Harry. I don't care what you and the rest of the world have against him. I don't care how deep they buried your friend Scotty Bowman. As far as I'm concerned you've taken a cowardly advantage of Harry in my place. I'd be obliged to you if you'd keep away."

"That's a real insult, Mr. Dorfman," Mike said, the blood draining from his face. "It's not a thing I'd choose to argue about," he added proudly. And as he walked out stiffly, he said to Ray waiting at the door, "You little rat. But they'll deport you right back to 14th Street." The light caught the gray at

Mike's temples and the heavy lines on his forehead and he looked tired and a little wild.

That night he lay awake, twitching in dread of the future, and in the dark he heard voices repeating, *Kicked out of Dorfman's just like a bum.* But the night was long and in moments of dreadful clarity, free of the tossing and twitching, he realized that his silent partner Singerman, of the Textile Associates, would say he couldn't afford to be associated with an old fighter who was an outcast from a place where the best people went. "I'm no outcast. Lane is the outcast," Mike said so loudly that his own voice startled him.

Chapter 21

IN THE morning Harry went down to a little tailoring shop on St. Catherine and asked that a new lining be put in the suit. But that day the town's leading gossip columnist, Tony Edwards, had an amusing story that attracted a lot of attention. The trial of Scotty Bowman was still going on as far as the two witnesses were concerned, he wrote. A suit that Mike Kon had made for Harry Lane, an item of some comment at the trial, was not wearing too well. It was a nice-looking suit, he wrote, and he described it fully. But why should Harry Lane be convinced that Mike Kon would want to put a rotten lining in the coat, and why would Mike Kon be convinced that Harry Lane would rather go on wearing the thing than have it fixed? When Harry read this story, going slowly along the street, he cursed and threw the paper in the gutter.

He went to see Joe Long at the Smithers and Weston Advertising Agency. Perhaps Joe could do something for him. Joe was an old acquaintance—not a close friend, just a man he used to see a lot of in the days when Joe had been a wistful drinker and very charming and sad and given to leaving bad checks in restaurants. Joe had straightened up and joined Alcoholics Anonymous and had become another man; a satisfied smiling and alert man, a little plumper, and a vice-president of his firm, but no one now would think of calling him a lovable wistful fellow. The expression in his eyes was different, too, and as soon as Harry sat down opposite him in the office he wished that Joe had been looking at him with the old expression, not so smiling and so comfortably at ease with himself as he was now.

He talked to Joe. Since nothing was said about Scotty Bowman, Harry didn't want to bring up the subject, but then he got the feeling that Joe thought he wasn't being free with him. "All right, Joe," he said. "I can see you're thinking about Scotty Bowman. Well, let me tell you something. I didn't want to hurt Scotty at the time, but the fact is that calmly and coldly Scotty wanted some of those shares for himself. You see, Joe, he begged me not to mention it. Oh, he was foxy, all right. What a sucker I was."

"That certainly didn't come out," Joe said uneasily.

"You bet it didn't. That's what comes of trusting him. I didn't dream he wouldn't tell the story and how did I know he'd be such a coward? But you can see how it all adds up now, can't you, Joe?"

"Hmm. Yes."

"You've got to get the hang of it, Joe. The bastard let people think I was taking advantage of him. I made a mistake all right, but it was in feeling sorry for the guy. Oh, he knew what he had done to me and himself, so . . . he just chickened out, see?" The thoughtful expression in Joe's eyes encouraged him so he went on telling his whole story about Scotty, while Joe, looking more and more unhappy, studied his fingernails and shifted around uncomfortably in his chair and made no comment. "Is there something you don't see, Joe?" he asked uneasily.

"No, I see," Joe said awkwardly. "Yes, indeed. Oh, by the way," and he brightened. "That witness, the tailor Mike Kon, seems to have had a pretty strong conviction. I heard about it."

"Well, you see, Joe, Scotty set him up in business. They were thick as thieves."

"That isn't the suit you've got on?"

"No."

"It was a tropical suit, wasn't it? A light gray one?"

"That's right."

"So I read," and he smiled broadly. "They're saying around town you're keeping the rotten lining in the coat. People believe anything," and he laughed. "Tell me what happened." Harry told him.

"Well, well," Joe said grinning. "I can see where he'd be a bad guy to have as a tailor."

"How do you mean?"

"If that tailor had a strong conviction about a customer, God knows what he'd do to the suit," and again he laughed, walking with Harry to the door and saying nothing about a job.

Next day he went down to St. James Street and saw a financial man named Hilton who had known his father. It didn't go well at all. That uneasy reticence he had felt in Joe Long, he felt in Mr. Hilton. The gray-haired Hilton, his plump face crisscrossed with little red veins, held back and showed he felt they weren't being frank with each other. "All right, Mr. Hilton," he said patiently. "You're probably thinking about Scotty Bowman. Well, he was a shameful coward." And he told the story from beginning to end and waited. Hilton also looked embarrassed. "You look a little offended, Mr. Hilton," he said sharply. "You know me, don't you?"

"Of course, I do," old Mr. Hilton said, growing flustered. Then a friendlier expression came on his face. "Everybody seems to have heard about that tailor, the witness, and a suit he made for you. That's not the suit?"

"No, it isn't," he said impatiently.

"No, they said it was a light summer suit. A chewed-up lining, eh? Well, well, tell me about it."

"I'm getting a little tired of telling about it," Harry said, scowling. "I don't want to talk about that crazy tailor. Well, keep me in mind, will you?" and he left, and when he was outside, just for a moment he was full of despair—then he remembered there were hundreds of others in clubs and bars and restaurants and on golf courses who had counted on his generosity, who had been with him all the way. So he tramped around, waiting for someone to speak up for him. The thing to do, he thought, was to be just like himself. He came into offices with his splendid assurance. He came into bars with his easy opulent air and bought drinks and acquaintances drank them; then, as he got talking about his case, they all grew embarrassed and resentful. "Pay attention to me," he'd cry angrily. "I've lived my life here. I've injured no man. Is my life to be ruined because a man was a little coward? What was it but a dreadful cowardly betrayal of a friend? Pay attention to me about that man."

No one denounced him. No one said, "Scotty couldn't have been a banker for so many years without having solid integrity." After an awkward silence that infuriated him, they would say, "Oh, say Harry, is that stuff true about you and the other witness, that tailor?" And then they would laugh. It cut him off.

He left each time with his head high, feeling the sting of the insult of their convenient smiles, and he thought of Mollie. A man needed a woman to go to, a man needed a woman to listen to him and make a comfortable world with him, and a man's own woman had a hundred little ways of listening and believing.

Exhausted, he went home after one such frustrating day and threw himself on the bed. It was only eight o'clock, still light out, and he couldn't sleep. He tried to make plans for subletting his apartment and taking a room somewhere. Someone was knocking on the door and he jumped up. A phone ringing, a knock on the door, now made his heart leap hopefully. "Come in," he called eagerly, straightening his tie and hurrying to the door. The plump little woman in the black fall coat came in timidly, but as soon as she saw him her jaw tightened.

"Mrs. Bowman," he said, so surprised his heart took a heavy thud. Then he couldn't say any more.

"Mr. Lane," she said, clutching her purse with both hands, "it's very painful for me to come here."

"No, oh, no, we should talk, Mrs. Bowman. Please sit down."

"Talk! You've been doing enough talking, haven't you?" she said, her voice trembling. "You've been going around town saying my husband was a coward. I want to ask you, is that manly?"

"That's all right, Mrs. Bowman," he said, flushing. "Since you don't know the facts, do you think you have any right to take that tone to me? I've lost my job. I can't get another. This thing follows me around. Am I not entitled to a little justice? I've never had to lie about people, and the truth is that Scotty cut my throat." But her head had jerked back and the glint in her round brown eyes made it hard for him to go on.

"I don't understand you, Mr. Lane. What satisfaction is there for you in keeping after my husband?"

"Mrs. Bowman, I don't keep after your husband. I keep after the truth. I only want the truth about me and Scotty."

"You're an educated, well-known man, Mr. Lane. A thing like this can twist a man's mind. Why can't you see it's your conscience that's bothering you?"

"My conscience?"

"Well then, what's driving you to hurt me and my family, and poor Mr. Kon?"

"Poor Mr. Kon!" Suddenly outraged, he cried, "Are you crazy?"

"Oh, he's told us all about it. He's stuck by us loyally. We know what you're doing to him with your slanders."

"That poor slob," he said bitterly. "That coward. That fraud. That false witness. Why, he's as cheap as the stuff he puts in his suits."

"Mr. Lane—please. Can you honestly pretend you're not trying to ruin him too? Oh, it's shameful. That poor man had to work so hard to get started. How can you be such a spiteful man?"

"You walk into my house and—"

"It's the truth. You know it's the truth."

"The truth? I've had enough of this, Mrs. Bowman," but his voice broke and he turned away. "Look, Mrs. Bowman," he said jerkily. "I don't want to insult you. But I won't take any more. I assure you, as God is my witness, I was not to blame for Scotty's trouble."

There were tears in her eyes as she fumbled with her purse, opened it, took out her handkerchief and dabbed at her nose. "I didn't come here to portion out the blame, Mr. Lane," she said.

"Then for God's sake, what do you want?"

"Mr. Lane, look what's happened to me and my sons, all because my husband was unfortunate enough to like you."

"Mrs. Bowman, because of that husband of yours . . . Look," he said. "I'm moving to a cheap roominghouse. I'm ruined. Can't you grasp what's happened to me?"

"What's happened to you!" she cried indignantly, and again her eyes filled with tears. "Oh my God, don't you understand?" she whispered. "I have two boys. One is fifteen, the other seventeen. Scotty lost his job and his pension. There's a mortgage on our house. In the last months he spent money. Do you know why? He was attracted to the life of men like you. Oh, don't worry, I can look after myself. What's there in life for me now? I've got a job now in a supermarket. But I swear my seventeen-year-old boy is going to go on with his education if I have to work my fingers to the bone. Do you hear? I say he's going to go on," she said fiercely. "He's not going to quit school, do you hear that, Harry Lane? Not for our home or me or his brother. Do you hear me? I'll lose the house. I don't care," and she began to weep angrily. "All right, Scotty is dead, so he suffered, he was sentenced, but you—you escaped scot-free. In the name of all justice, I think it's up to you to do something."

"Up to me? You think it's up to me?" he asked incredulously.

"Don't you think you ought to help us, Mr. Lane?"

"Help you!" he said, shaking his head, his eyes full of wonder. Then suddenly he grew pale, he felt crazy, and for the first time he lost control of himself. "You ask me that!" he blurted out. "That fraud of a husband of yours ruins me and I'm supposed to give you money. Conscience money, eh? Who put you up to this, your friend Mike Kon?" Swinging his arm wildly he shouted, "Mrs. Bowman, get out of here."

"What?"

"What are you trying to do? Drive me crazy? This is a cooked-up job." Taking an angry step toward her, his eyes wild, he pointed again at the door. "I said get out of here, Mrs. Bowman."

"You're a harsh and bitter man," she said, looking bewildered and frightened as she got up and backed away from him. "How humiliating it is for me to talk to you!"

"I don't want to talk to you."

"I came here, I swear, thinking you'd want to do all you could to help."

"You were wrong."

"Why should I be surprised you're throwing me out?" Her eyes blazed. "I thought I could appeal to something good in you because you know in your heart Scotty was the most open and above-board man that ever lived."

"So it's said." Harry grabbed her arm as she turned to go.

"Yes, he was."

"Just a minute. You're as blind about the man as I was."

"You say that to me? His wife?"

"I say you're as foolish about him as I was. You think his life was an open book to you."

"It was. It always was."

"So you think, Mrs. Bowman. Well, supposing in those last months you didn't know what was going on in him at all?"

"What do you mean?"

"Wouldn't you, too, feel taken in?"

"What are you trying to do?" She paled, sudden worry in her eyes.

"What if he kept things in his life to himself?"

163

"But he didn't."

"If you could see it, I'd be in a different light, too, wouldn't I?"

Paula Bowman was a short woman and he was bending down a little, watching her startled worried face.

"I don't want to hear you say anything more about Scotty. Let me go," she said, jerking her arm away, looking up at him with desperate loyalty in her eyes; the whole of her married life was in the way she shook her head, half pleading. He was on the point of telling her about Scotty and Annie Laurie. Suddenly he noticed that her brown dress was much too tight for her at the waist, it wrinkled; then the words wouldn't come. Oh Lord, it's the whole of her life. I can't do it to her, he thought miserably, and turned away.

"You were just going on, weren't you, Mr. Lane?"

"I meant—I meant that Scotty kept you in the dark about me and that stock," he said, fumbling angrily. "He kept things to himself, he kept them from you as he kept them from me."

"It's only your word, Mr. Lane."

"That's right," he cried, grabbing at the doorknob, jerking the door open, sick with humiliation. "Go on, Mrs. Bowman. Good night," he said angrily. "Go on. Good night. Go on, I say."

"I won't forget this," she said, yet at the door she hesitated, an expression on her face he didn't understand at all, her eyes on him a long time. "Mr. Lane, please don't say any more about Scotty. It hurts us. I ask you, please, don't talk any more about him. Please, oh please leave us alone now, Mr. Lane." Then she left. Hurrying to the window he watched her come out of the building, her hand at her neck as she looked both ways; then she lowered her head and walked away slowly.

"God in heaven," he said aloud. Wheeling away from the window in a panic, he started to hurry after her, but stood rooted at the door. "God Almighty, why did I have to do it?" he groaned. "When I could have got at Scotty right in his grave," and he stared raptly at the chair as if Scotty still sat there, his wet rubbers marking the floor, only now he was smiling sardonically, saying, "Don't worry, Harry, I praised you for your generosity. Isn't that what you'd like someone to do now? Good public relations, old boy." It was the tailor too, though. It was his doing. In his wildness Harry imagined that Scotty in jail had talked to Mike Kon, had tipped him off on how to pin him to the wall. The stupid, vindictive, outrageous, mean cunning bastard, how he hated him! "For the sake of the poor woman and her family," he whispered bitterly, "I'm to keep my big mouth shut. Just take it and die." He had to tell it to someone. Since Annie Laurie's name had been on the tip of his tongue, he thought of finding her now. No, someone had told him she was out of town. As Harry walked around the room he felt frantic, for he couldn't get the little plump wife's pleading eyes out of his mind.

Chapter 22

THAT night he walked the streets for hours feeling he was wandering through his own life. It was much cooler. Girls and their fellows on St. Catherine's walked a little faster than they did in the hot weather. A priest coming toward him in his black soutane looked unbearably sober. Under the street light the priest's face was white, his nose pinched. On the city streets there were hundreds of priests and he used to call them the Black Hawks. It was a city of churches and monasteries, bells were always ringing, but Harry hadn't been in a church for ten years. Turning, he watched the priest's hat bobbing along in the crowd. The desire to have someone who didn't know him listen and judge of his right to get at Scotty with the truth, someone with a sense of justice and moral authority, someone who would feel compelled to listen without prejudice, began to overwhelm him. It was a priest's job to listen. His life was to listen, and he couldn't shrug like the others and turn away disdainfully. He began to follow the priest. Soon the heavy stone church, St. Patrick's, loomed up darkly against the night sky. There was a light over the door. An old woman came out, limping painfully down the steps, and he watched her hobble up the street.

He went into the dimly lit church and looked around uneasily. There was a light over a confessional. It was late and only three persons were in the church, a young man and two middle-aged women, all kneeling and praying, and he sat down awkwardly two pews behind the women and watched the curtain at the entrance to the confessional. He didn't kneel down as the others were doing. In a little while a gray-haired, well-dressed man came out. Those who had been waiting made no move, they prayed on, staring at the flickering red altar light, as did the well-dressed man who had come out, all saying their penance.

Harry went into the confessional and drew the curtain. The sound of the grill sliding back startled him. A faint smell of old incense came from the priest. He could see only the jaw of the shadowed face. "I want your advice, father," he said.

"Well, we'll get to that," the priest said. "Go on." He had a raspy old whisper, and a trace of brogue, an old Irish priest with slow old breathing and a faint smell of tobacco. "How long since you've been to confession?" the priest asked. Ten years, he said, and tried to explain he didn't want to make a confession; but they got mixed up. The priest said, "Repeat after me, just repeat after me," and he humored him and repeated the prayer so he could get to his story. "I want some advice, father," he whispered. But the old priest, who seemed to be a little deaf, whispered impatiently, "Well, make a general confession. If you don't want to confess, why are you here? You can always start with the sins of the flesh, my Christian friend. Have you ever committed fornication?"

"Many times," he said.

"How many times?" asked the old priest sharply.

"Well, I can't remember exactly."

"You can't remember?" the priest said sounding worried. "Dear, dear, dear. God forgive you. Were you living with some one woman in a state of sin?"

"No, they were just girls I met."

"Just girls. Were any of these girls married?"

"No, father. But what I want to talk about—"

"I'm sorry," the priest said quietly. "My friend, forgive me for trying to induce you to make a confession. I was blind. You don't want to confess. There's no contrition, is there? But let me help you if I can."

"I have a story I want to—"

"No matter what the story of your trouble is," the priest whispered, and as the side of his face came against the grill he sounded stern and heartbroken, "you can't understand it unless you see that it no doubt is rooted in your carnality. Have you thought of that, young man? You have a story, you say, something is worrying you and you cry out for relief, but before I even hear this tale of trouble I can see that you don't understand that all your sins may be rooted, as I say, in carnality. Don't you see that fornication is the complete and final triumph of all the sins of the flesh? Even the sins of pride and vanity can be traced to a gratification of the senses, and all these great sins seem to flower in your fornication."

"Yes, father," he said impatiently, "but this other thing, my case, it's a matter of justice."

"Justice," whispered the priest taken aback.

"Shouldn't I thirst after justice?"

"You should indeed. Justice for whom, though? If you feel you have suffered an injustice, be very careful," he said warningly. "It's a favorite trap of the devil. He likes to make us think that people aren't doing right by us."

"Wait a minute, father," he pleaded. "Here is the story," and he told all about himself and Scotty Bowman and what was happening to him. "Am I wrong in asking for a little justice? Am I wrong in wanting the truth to be known? Do you believe me?"

"Of course I believe you," he said gently.

"Should I tell the truth to everybody?"

"My dear Christian friend," said the priest in the same gentle troubled tone, "you should be very careful of one thing."

"What's that, father?"

"The great wound to your pride if they don't believe you."

Then his whisper became livelier as he quickened with interest. "These distinctions are very difficult. The more you suffer from an injustice, the deeper the wound to your pride, is it not so? And then to correct an injustice you become like a raging lion doing violence to your own spirit and to others for the sake of the truth. Do you not see this clearly?"

"Then how am I to get the truth known, the truth about this man and me? God sees the truth, doesn't He?"

"God sees the truth but He sometimes waits."

"Waits for what?"

"Till we are ready."

"Father, I can't wait any longer."

"Then you are impatient and contentious and angry as a lion. This is vanity, my dear friend."

"No, I am calm. I assure you I am calm."

"That is good. That is as God would want it and be assured He is waiting and watching."

"Waiting for what, father?"

"Recognition of His truth. We must understand there may be times when God chooses to wait," the priest said sadly.

"Wait a minute, father," he whispered, stiffening with indignation. "Oh, I see," he said cynically. "My case, of course, comes in there."

"Be calm. God may choose to wait until you are ready to see the truth."

"And show it to everybody else, too, I suppose."

"Do you really think it's the same thing?"

"It doesn't fool me, father. Right down the garden path I go again, eh? Naturally my innocence with this man is one of the things even God turns away from, is that it, father?" he asked bitterly.

"Look into your heart," the old priest said gently. "Do you know what is involved in this case? A man killed himself. Surely not to spite just you. What awful egotism of you to think so. So the truth may yet be hidden from you."

"This is double talk, father. All I get anywhere now is double talk. I ask you again— Do you think I tell you the truth?"

"I do."

"Then am I innocent?"

"As any man can be, I'm sure. But it depends on your view of yourself as a man, doesn't it?"

"Oh, this is absurd, father," and in spite of himself he started to laugh. "Excuse me," he whispered. "I feel very foolish troubling you." He drew back and waited. When the priest remained silent he muttered, "I'm sorry," and pushed aside the curtain and walked out. His head felt hot and he was trembling. Standing on the church steps he seemed to see Scotty smiling broadly and pitying him for being absurd enough to think he could get at him in a church.

His knees felt stiff from the unfamiliar kneeling, and he tried to rise above a sense of foolish, endless humiliation. Then he looked up at St. Catherine Street, and up beyond at the row of lights rising around the mountain, so black and solid against the night sky. The rumble of the city's life going on and the winking lights seemed to mock him for thinking he could communicate with someone in the city. He thought he was going out of his mind. In the whole city there was no one who could know what was in his heart. Then he thought of Mollie. There would be no fumbling for the right words with her, no *How do I say this?* It would be felt and known. At this hour there would be a train coming in from the mountains, the last train. In some way she would know what was going on in him. There was a chance she might be hurrying back to him, be on that train tonight.

This thing he wanted became so real to him in his loneliness that he started to hurry up to St. Catherine, looking for a taxi, and when he found one he told the driver to hurry to the Windsor station. There he read the board announcing the arrival and departure of trains and found he had fifteen minutes to wait. So he had something to wait and hope for. The train! It was real. People hurried by him as he waited. Girls carrying bags hurried toward fellows. An elderly man kissed his wife three times and she left, crying. An old woman who had been wandering around sat down wearily and took a sandwich out of a paper bag, still waiting. Over the loud-speaker came the voice calling out the trains. People came and went, they met and parted, and waited to meet and part again, but he kept seeing Mollie coming toward him, a redcap carrying her bag; he could call out "Mollie," and she would turn, that anxious eager expression on her face, crying out, "Harry, why, how did you know?"

The train came in, and she wasn't on it, and he felt foolish as he walked slowly away from the station, his hands in his pockets.

Chapter 23

HARRY had never had any desire to get outside his own life, or even thought about such matters. Until the trial he had been too comfortable. It had been his vocation to make other people comfortable with a handshake and a few words on a street corner, or at his big parties to which he invited everybody. Just naturally he had played ball with people without any real sense of duplicity, just a little good-humored cynicism here and there. That night when he came back to his apartment nursing this strange detachment he thought his head would burst if he didn't tell about it. He went over to his desk and began to write to Mollie. Carried away by the thoughts he had had coming along the street he wrote rapidly and eloquently. He had had a terrible feeling on the street, he wrote. Maybe it was because his position was so humiliating. But he had felt there was no real relationship between his own life and what was happening to him. Things just happened. They had no meaning. Did she ever have such a feeling? Where do you go from there —if things had no meaning? Well, he was no philosopher but he wasn't withdrawing into that sense of unreality. It was a real fact that people were against him. A real fact that Scotty was dead. And it was a real fact that Scotty and Mike Kon had put him in the light he was in. No. No, he wrote furiously. To hell with it all just happening. He could face his conscience, that was the thing. Very soon someone would see this. Someone would take up his case. Someone would come along out of a sense of justice. In these matters you only needed one advocate to spread the word around. Maybe tomorrow he'd be sitting in one of the usual places and someone would come over to him—

When he had got this far in the letter he paused and put his hands over his face. His head felt hot. He got up slowly; he felt sick. As he walked around the big gray room with the yellow chairs, there was a sudden tearing pain in his stomach. Sure now that he didn't have the flu and was developing an ulcer, he went to the phone to talk to a doctor—then couldn't do it. A doctor, smiling knowingly to himself, would imply by his tone that worry from a troubled conscience would lead to an ulcer.

The unfinished letter lay on the desk, and he stared at it and wanted to finish it but couldn't. He went slowly into the bedroom and flung himself on the bed.

At four in the morning, he woke up feeling he was being smothered. The constriction was across his chest and in his abdomen and his heart was pounding. Getting up he took some milk, and as he began to feel some relief he sighed and trembled. Very pale, he moved around the bedroom, stooping a little. Then he went into the living room in the darkness and sat in the chair at the window and looked out at darkened Sherbrooke Street. No one was on the street. He was in his wine-colored pajamas, a slipper dangling from the toe of one bare foot, and when a puff of air came through the open window, he shivered. The cool weather had come. In the western sky a faint streak of dawn light must have appeared, for the window-panes on the upper stories across the street glowed just a little. Suddenly an ambulance came along the street, its siren wailing, its red light flashing and making a fiery path along the dark street.

"All right, Ouimet, you asked me to examine my conscience,

remember?" he said aloud. At this hour in the morning people don't lie to themselves, he thought. The big room was filled with shadows and he began to think it would be wonderful if they could have a court of conscience, a court of justice, not of law. The big city was sprawled out around the mountain in sleep, not silent, of course it was never silent. There was always the low rumble, like the rattle in the throats of millions snoring and stirring in sleep. But some gaunt attendant from the higher court could stand at Mike Kon's bedside, shake him roughly, haul him out of the security of his dreams and make him stand there in his nightshirt. And Ouimet, too. The same court attendant whispering, "It's your turn now, Ouimet."

There in that light, Kon the witness. To be known hereafter and for all time as Mike the Witness. All right, Kon. More loyalty than conscience, eh, Kon? Konscience—that's good. The court has noted it. Do you ever feel like a big fake? Is there an ounce of charity in you? Don't answer. Just stand there. Lots of time here. Now you, Ouimet. You wouldn't let me get at Scotty, would you?

But as the pictures and voices he had conjured up in the shadows of the room soon faded away, he grew deeply troubled, remembering how Ouimet had asked him to doubt his own generosity and kindness in his willingness to help Scotty by suppressing information. Wasn't it selfishness and egotism? Will the witness give a straight answer? No, the witness will answer in his own way for a change. Is one man supposed to act as policeman over the soul of another? Prudence! Scruples! The disease of the Christian conscience. On this—well, call Walter Kehoe. It's quite relevant. The man had joined one of the Christian orders and had become so full of scruples it had been an agony for him to have any kind of a relationship with anyone, and one day at one of the Order's cross-country races he had started out fast, got far out in front and kept on running and they had never heard of him again.

"Oh, no. No," he groaned, standing up and hitching at the loosened cord of his pajamas. . . . The court! It was still gnawing away at him, the same frantic cheated feeling he had had fleeing from the trial court. The things he should have said, the questions he would ask, the mockery he would make of Scotty and Kon and Ouimet if he could only get back in that court again!

Could he sue Kon for slander, for defamation of character? he wondered. After all, in the presence of witnesses in Dorfman's Kon had said, "You killed Scotty Bowman." They would have to talk about Scotty, and he would have evidence, a witness. Annie Laurie would tell about Scotty's night with her and his talk about money. But would any lawyer take the case with just this to go on? No, he was approaching the court the wrong way. He would have to have a better plan. God in heaven, let him think of something soon!

In the faint streak of light touching the mantel he could now see one of the yellow chairs and he sighed, tired out. He went back to bed and tried to dream he was with Mollie. At this hour she would be in her bed, shut off in her sleep and her dreams. Suffering in his mind and body, his thoughts went to her, he was sneaking like a fugitive into her bed, needing all her love. She put her arms around him and kissed him. He said, No, this time I want all of you, and she said, It'll hurt me, it'll hurt me. He had only a little time with her before the city began to rumble and hum. Already car wheels had begun to lick along Sherbrooke. He slept in his dream of love.

In the morning at nine thirty the telephone rang and he hurried to it, his heart leaping.

"Is that you, Harry?"

"Yeah."

"It's Dan Gorman."

"Why, hello, Dan," and he waited, thinking of the Gormans across the river and their two children and Dan going down Peel that day, the rain on his shoulders, looking thin and shabby and beat up, and then he had caught up to him.

"Harry, listen," Gorman said earnestly. "My wife and I were talking about you last night. Naturally we heard about the trouble you got into. Anyway, we just wanted you to know something, Harry. Maybe you've heard it from a lot of people. But we don't believe for a minute you got that bank manager into trouble, and Harry, listen, we don't care how it looks, we just don't buy it, and my wife says to tell you we know there's not a mean conniving bone in your body. That's all, Harry."

"Dan."

"Yeah?"

"No one ever did so much for me, Dan."

"Hell, Harry."

"Thanks, Dan. Give my love to your wife," he said, not wanting to let him go. As he put down the receiver he felt almost weak with gratitude. Old Dan, he thought, the first break in the strange general resentment. The voice coming from the other side of the river. He had to sit down, and he kept staring at the telephone as if he expected to hear it ring again. A little song was in his head. After a while he got up to write to Mollie.

He told her it helped him to have her in his mind all the time, and the funny part of it was he always saw her doing something different. Just a few minutes ago he had been thinking of the way she danced, of the way she came into his arms so easily. Things were looking much better. People were actually phoning him. It was wonderful to pick up the phone and hear someone say he had been wronged. Once a phone started ringing —well, it just kept on. He hoped she wasn't worrying about him.

Late that afternoon he discovered he could drink Scotch in milk without having it stab at his stomach. He was getting back on his feet again. For dinner he ate some custard and felt much stronger. At eight that night he went out to drop into the Ritz bar.

It was one of those cool nights at the end of summer when the city seemed to hum with the life of the new fall season. The leaves were still thick on the trees with the lights shining through them, and the great faces of the apartment houses, glowing with light, hid the mountain behind them. After the summer, people were back and strolling along and at that hour debs were meeting their brothers in those little bars along Sherbrooke.

Harry came into the Ritz and went downstairs to the Maritime bar. Those who had dined late were having their coffee. The waiters lit candles under the coffee containers, and in the dim light of the flickering candles the tablecloths gleamed softly. The faces at the tables all looked warm and friendly, the blond head of Mrs. Stevens, who just naturally dominated any committee she sat on, had a golden gleam, and the face of her dull sandy-haired husband, the motor dealer who tried so hard to keep up with her, had a candlelight ruddiness. In that light Eddie Mathews the alderman, who always went where money was, was always eating someone else's cold cuts, and was always so grateful for a case of Sweetman's fine old rye at Christmas, had a flickering warmth in his face too. All by himself, in his own candlelight, was the philosophy professor who took a little cash on the side acting as consultant for the Sweetman Foundation scholarships. He was getting a lot of sympathy these days from his friends, for his young wife had run off with one of his brilliant students. They all looked up when Harry came in. No one asked him to sit down. Then he saw Ted Ogilvie at the bar with old Muldoon, the baggy-eyed economic adviser, and Harry approached Ogilvie with his old cheerful air of well-being and asked if he had been at the fights last night. He had, and Bruno showed no signs of developing a real punch, Ted said.

Lowering his voice, Harry said, "You know something, Ted, people are starting to see I'm getting a raw deal. They're phoning me now. Once that phone starts ringing— Today I heard from Dan Gorman."

"Who's Dan Gorman?"

"Just a guy I know."

"From around here?"

"Not exactly," he said uneasily. "He's across the river, an old friend."

177

"Look Harry," Ted said impatiently. "All right. He's across the river. It's around here you've been talking. For God's sake, why don't you stop? People want to run from you. Don't go by this guy across the river."

"I see," he whispered. The hope Dan Gorman had given him vanished. He felt utterly deflated.

"I only mean you may be too sincere about it," Ted said awkwardly. "I'm an authority on sincerity." He led a terrible life with his wife, who was always trying to cut him down intellectually and now was asking people if they didn't notice he was becoming an alcoholic. "Take my wife," he said. "She's so magnificently insincere in so many directions there's a certain sincerity about her insincerity."

"Look, Ted . . . never mind your wife. The thing is you say shut up about Scotty. What is this? Mrs. Bowman implores me, please, please leave the poor man alone. Am I to accept the fact that nobody believes me? What's the matter, Ted?"

"Harry, Scotty's six feet underground."

"And that settles it, eh?"

"It's a peculiar position you're in, Harry," Ted said uneasily. "With Scotty not here as he was in court, well, maybe people think that in trying to get at him now you don't come into court with clean hands, see?"

Then old Muldoon, who had been listening, cleared his throat gruffly and gave his gray mustache a little pat. "And you don't either, you know, Lane," he said grandly. "You don't give Bowman much of a chance to have his say, do you?" Swinging off his stool he shook his head pityingly. "Of course, you must have a pretty thick skin, Lane," he said. "Well, well, well, I suppose I'm old-fashioned about these things." He sauntered out.

"The pompous old fool," Harry said, glaring after him. "If he was twenty years younger I could punch him on the nose— That old scamp a figure of moral grandeur? Excuse me while I vomit."

"You know Muldoon, Harry."

"What a fraud. The old phony just strings along though," he said scornfully. Then he pondered, toying with his glass, the other question still in his mind. "I think I know what the trouble is, Ted. It was my job. Isn't that right?"

"Your job . . . Now look, Harry," Ted began awkwardly. "We're all in the same boat, aren't we?"

"No, I was the big flossy public relations director."

"Not just the job, Harry. Don't forget it was Scotty and the way the facts lined up against you."

"I know," he whispered. "But now—a man like me—people expect me to put the best face on everything. An old expert hand at cultivating good will, eh?"

"Nothing wrong with cultivating good will, Harry. It's our job. We're all just making a buck, aren't we? And people understand it. I'm behind the scenes and you're out in front. That's all." He laughed a little, but his sudden uneasy apologetic glance worried Harry. He considered Ogilvie a cynical man, but not an embittered one, a man who seemed to have discovered long ago that the mistake people made was in thinking life had some meaning, whereas he knew it only had the meaning you wanted to give it, and sometimes he seemed to feel like an amused and adventurous artist about his own life. "Now don't get sore, Harry," he said with his friendliest smile. "I think you've been handling your case all wrong. If I were you I'd handle it just like I'd handle a television account. As I see it, we con people. It's our job. But they know we con them and they don't care as long as we're nice guys. And aren't we?" he asked, smiling. "We're taking baths all the time and looking nice and smelling nice. Who cares about my ethics, and my nice points of honor, and my goddamned integrity if they know I'm in the great American image? The nice guy making a buck. Nobody cares about these other matters. It's the age of the slobs." Shrugging, he went on earnestly with his charming smile. "If I were you what I'd be doing now is letting people see I'm really one sweet guy. Generous to a fault and I must have let myself be conned into this mess! I'd stick to my best helpless boyish smile. And listen, Harry. The last thing on earth I'd be doing is annoying people by arguing angrily with them and being earnest about the right and the wrong of it. Nobody cares. I'd only be making them remember it had been my job to con people. See what I mean?"

"Of course, of course," he said, laughing, his eyes too bright now. "My God, how a man can get carried away though. An occupational hazard, I guess. But . . . well . . . I mean, how can he always remember that everything he says or does is taken with a grain of salt?" Turning slowly he looked at those who were sitting at the tables. A bewildering feeling that he was unknown to them struck him; all along he had been a stranger in his own town. He stared at the blond Mrs. Stevens and her stupid husband, at the alderman and the others, with such a strange smile no one met his eyes. Free loaders all, he thought bitterly, a city full of free loaders always cynical about their cynical host, and he whispered, "Yeah, to them I was always just Sweetman's bum boy."

"What's that Harry?"

"Nothing, nothing, Ted. Say, you're not wearing that hat I gave you."

"I wear it. What's the matter?" Trying to change the subject, Ted said, "At least give old Muldoon credit. He didn't ask about that lining Mike Kon put in your suit."

"Cut it out, Ted," Harry said fiercely.

"What?"

"Don't switch to that subject, you hear?"

"Well, I was only—"

"A man can take only so many humiliations," he said, his voice shaking. "I try to talk about Scotty and like everybody else you switch good-humoredly to that son of a bitch of a tailor. That meat head . . . that presumptuous clown. . . . The Witness. . . ." His face was contorted with rage and hatred. Ogilvie was startled. "I'm sorry, Ted," Harry said after a moment, and he tried to laugh. "I've lost my sense of humor. Yes, it is funny. I should be able to see how funny it is." Now, oddly, Harry did have an amused expression on his face; he did begin to chuckle. "I try to talk to people and they say, 'Don't bother us, see Kon. He's looking after it.' Who's this boy? This great civic burden bearer? Why, my tailor. What the world needs is more cheap tailors with a sense of moral grandeur. What about it, Ted? Come on, I'll buy you a drink."

"No, thanks, Harry. I've got to get home." Ted said uneasily, and he slapped him on the back and went.

Harry sat there alone, finishing his drink. His face was flushed but he went on smiling to himself. There was so much amused derision in the smile that Mrs. Stevens, looking over, nudged her husband. She thought Harry was trying to get drunk.

Chapter 24

It was then Harry started wearing the light tropical suit that had been described so fully in the newspapers. At first no one noticed that he never changed it, for at first he wore it with that splendid sense of well-being that people had always so much admired. From these same people Harry now began to attract a different attention simply because he had been a fastidious dresser, a man who never wore the same suit two days in a row. Furthermore, no one else in the downtown places was wearing a light tropical suit in late September with the weather so much cooler. People began to whisper about him and snicker. The same meddling gossip columnist wrote, "Why won't Harry Lane take off that Mike Kon suit? Or haven't you noticed?" And so it was all over town.

After Harry had turned up alone at the stadium among the fans watching the pro football team working out, Eddie Adams, the fight promoter, said to old Haggerty, "If I go over there and speak to Harry I'm afraid I'll start laughing."

"You know something, Eddie? It'll be a big laugh all the way round."

"How so?"

"I said to him, 'Jesus Christ, Harry, take it off,' and I laughed in his face."

182

"So?"

"Nothing. He just laughed along with me, as good-humored as hell about it. It was a . . . well, I don't know . . . very frustrating."

"Frustrating?"

"I mean, since he was laughing with me, the question is what the hell were we both laughing at? See what I mean?" Haggerty asked profoundly, and as Eddie started to snicker, he snickered too. "Guess I'll have to take it up with Mike Kon," he said.

Then one night Mike came into Mother Martin's down by the station, a place where he felt more at home than he did in Dorfman's. When he saw Harry wearing the suit, sitting all by himself, he drew back, not wanting any trouble. Mike saw Ogilvie and Haggerty, who were sitting at the bar, watching him alertly. Others at the nearby tables had also looked up expectantly. Mike wasn't going to let Harry drive him out of this place, too, so he sat down at the bar and waited nervously.

Showing no interest in him at all, Harry went on reading the newspapers. There was no trouble.

Next night Mike came back grimly again so no one could say he was afraid to show up. He couldn't believe what was happening there under his eyes. Harry Lane had become a joke. Even the waiters seemed to feel free to kid him about the suit. . . . Everybody passing his table appeared to feel compelled to make a snickering derisive remark, and the odd part of it was that Harry seemed to know he wasn't entitled to take any offense at all. He answered each one with a jovial laugh. An infectious laugh it was too, like that of a clown grateful for any attention, and Mike really despised him. "The poor fool," Mike said, leaning along the bar to Ogilvie. "How can any man so lower himself? Is he just driven to it? Well, I can't say I mind. The pathetic clown. I suppose he'd rather people laugh at him than despise him openly, eh?"

"Lay off him, Mike," said Ogilvie, and he got up and went over to Harry's table. Keeping his head down, yet watching out of the corner of his eye, Mike listened.

"Harry, listen to me," Ogilvie pleaded. "As an old friend, I'm telling you you're doing a ridiculous thing. There's no excuse because you've had a lot of experience dealing with the public. Have you gone mad? What are you trying to do? Offer yourself as a slap-happy martyr?"

"Martyr, my eye," Harry said exuberantly, a little flush in his face, a bright wild glint in his eye. "Actually, I'm a great public benefactor. I seem to bring out the wit and humor in people. Come on now, Ted, what is it everyone wants to be? Funny. Very funny. Well, I seem to bring the bright cracks right off the top of their heads—even the dumbest guys. Come on now, don't be so stubborn. You know you want to say something funny."

"It's a farce, Harry," Ted said, smiling.

"Of course, it's *all* a farce."

"Even Mike Kon is laughing at you. Look at him over there."

"Oh, you mean the Witness?" Harry asked mildly.

When he heard his name Mike turned, ready to meet Harry's eyes grimly; he couldn't; he didn't seem to exist for Harry Lane. It upset Mike. As he looked around uneasily little things that had given him satisfaction began to take on another meaning. He heard a tall thin stranger in a charcoal-gray suit ask Whitmore, the drama critic of the *Sun*, "Who's the guy in the light summer suit?" Whitmore began to tell the whole story, keeping his voice down. When the tall man turned and looked superciliously at Mike, he felt angry and belittled.

From then on Mike hated to hear anyone say "There's the guy still wearing that suit." He hated it because he understood now that no one could look at Harry without thinking of him, Mike, and no one could think of Mike Kon without remembering Scotty Bowman. Somehow it frightened him.

One night Eddie Adams, on his way out, stopped at the bar, "How's the Witness tonight?" he asked, going on his way then with his little smile of derision. My God, so now they're calling me the Witness, he thought. Now I'm just part of this joke, too.

Looking around in anguish, Mike wondered how far this be-littlement might go. The same night an advertising man he didn't know, having a drink beside him at the bar, said, "Hello there, Mike," and smirked. "Still making the sackcloth for martyrs?" Next day Ogilvie, shaking his head sadly, said, "Mike Kon vs. Harry Lane, a piece of matchmaking even Eddie Adams wouldn't have thought of," and Ogilvie snickered. Mike looked at Harry sitting by himself with that untroubled fixed smile, complaining to no one, and realized at last what Harry was doing to him. Flashing him a look of hatred, Mike got up and tried to saunter out, knowing he couldn't come back to Mother Martin's, either.

The new attitude to Mike had already got around even in his own neighborhood. "What's this we hear about you being told to keep out of these places?" the merchants would ask, and Mike would tell his story. "It's the clown's psychology now," he would say angrily. "Do you think for a minute Harry Lane is really complaining about that suit? Not on your life. He's looking for an excuse to damage my business reputation because I stood by Scotty at that trial. Don't you get it?" When people shrugged and looked amused, Mike began to feel they didn't believe a word he said. "Okay, Mike," they would reply derisively. "Take it easy. It's all right to hate the guy for what he did to your friend Scotty, but you don't look so good yourself, you know, taking it out on him in your own shop."

Mike knew the merchants were talking about him, but he wouldn't have believed that one of them would go out of his way to speak to Harry. Yet the man who owned the little Peel Street shirt shop, standing at his door, watched Harry come down the street and called "Hello there, Harry," feeling entitled to be familiar now. "Hello there," Harry answered cheerfully. The grinning round smooth-faced fat man, with the full red lips, took a good look at him in the summer suit. "Everybody seems to know the facts about you and Mike Kon but me, Harry," he said. "Is Kon just a lousy tailor or was he taking something out on you? Would you mind telling me?"

"Why don't you ask him?"

"He takes your money then tells you you've lost your rights as a customer; because of that trial, huh?"

"I'm a bad boy, I guess," Harry said, smiling.

"It's no way to treat any customer."

"Don't tell it to me."

"I'll tell it to him. He went too far," the fat man said profoundly. "A man in business shouldn't go too far in his attitudes. If he does there's no business. Well, thanks for filling me in, Harry."

The fat man did tell it to Mike, and Mike lost his temper and called him stupid. From then on the fat man had a story to tell. He was a born storyteller, and he was one of the first to say Mike was a snide and ridiculous tailor who carried his vendettas into his tailoring and maybe oughtn't to be in business at all.

Then at noontime, right on the Peel corner, near the tobacco shop, Harry had been talking to Little Ambrose, a runner for a bookie, and Ambrose had given him an envelope containing fifty-two dollars. Harry had won a daily double. He had picked the two horses blindly because he liked the sound and feel of their names. So he was elated as he gave Little Ambrose five dollars and put the envelope in his pocket; his luck seemed to be changing. Then Mike, coming east on the way to his shop, saw him and half stopped, his hand going up slowly to his chin as if he were trying to bring himself to speak to him. Glancing full at him, Harry waited. It was an odd awkward moment. They both wanted to speak, reach a peaceful settlement. But they were so far apart now that neither one trusted the first words he would have to use, or any words needed to tell what was in his heart; they shared for the moment that helpless angry feeling. There was no way of communicating, nor showing any recognition of what they felt almost furtively as a desperate need. There was nothing left to say. Then sullen fury came into Mike's scarred face as if he couldn't forget all the jibes and mocking questions he had been enduring. They were just ten feet apart, the two witnesses, facing each other, with passing people getting between them, and then Mike's eyes shifted from Harry's cold gray eager eyes. Mike walked away pondering, walking with a slow heavy stride.

Chapter 25

MIKE couldn't admit to himself he had become ashamed to encounter Harry. Nor could he believe that the uneasy angry embarrassment he now felt in Harry's presence was a feeling of guilt. Mike told himself he didn't want any trouble and the way to avoid it was by keeping away from those places where he might meet Harry. Dorfman's and Mother Martin's were already out. He had always gone to Slitkin's and Slotkin's little bar at midnight; he was a convivial man and he had always liked the rowdy good humor of the patrons of this place. One night old Jimmie, the bartender, whispered, "Harry Lane is coming in here a lot now, Mike. He'll be in soon." Then the bartender laughed. "Why don't you get with it, Mike?"

Snorting contemptuously, Mike finished his drink and quietly withdrew. He didn't go any more to Slitkin's either. On Stanley Street with its night clubs and little bars and the pale-faced girls in sweaters and the bearded boys, and the jazz joints, he still had friends. At the Blue Jade, there was round-faced little May Kovacs, the singer. She said to him, "That clown Lane is starting to drop in here every night. He's attracting attention, too, Mike. What about it?" At some time or other Lane was dropping into all the bars and restaurants on Stanley. Even in the cafeterias on St. Catherine's, and in the upstairs bars, and the small restaurants. And at Joe's place, and Tom's Spaghetti House, and at the Danube Steak House they told Mike, with bright smiles, that Lane now came in every night for a drink, and waited around. Soon there wasn't a restaurant or bar in the whole Metropolitan neighborhood Mike loved where he could be sure he wouldn't meet Harry. It was as if the "clown" were trailing around after him like a cop on a beat to make him a laughingstock in all the places where he felt at home; to humiliate and provoke him and drive him away. Well, he thought, he wasn't going to have another humiliating scene with Harry.

He was consoled a little to remember he was called Mike the Scholar. So he finally began to stay home at night. He took to his books again. As he sat down in his big overstuffed green chair beside his father's wheel chair he would take out his handkerchief, wipe his reading glasses and say, "You notice one thing, Poppa? They make their stupid jokes about my tailoring, but have you noticed that so far no one has had the gall to come and say I was wrong about Lane?" He talked confidently to his father now, sure that he had a good listener. A wonderful thing had happened between them. The old man, with his wisps of gray hair combed neatly back and the big brown liver spots large on his forehead, sat there most of the time with his one good eye pretty vague, yet Mike, before he sat down himself, would always put the pencil carefully between the fingers of the right hand, hold the hand, then move it on the pad. Sometimes he massaged the old man's arm and the fingers very gently. The skinny fingers always moved, twitched a little, with an intermittent life of their own, making those little pencil scratches on the pad. Smiling, Mike would pat his father on the back. The main thing was that he saw that his father's good eye was following him around the room. The light of intelligence, the light of a man's character and soul was in that eye; all that concern and affection for him of the old poverty-stricken days was there too. It was a very beautiful thing, Mike thought.

He didn't bother telling Mrs. McManus about it. She was one of those nurses, all enthusiasm, hope and interest at first, massaging the old man's arm, talking to him and laughing. But she had come to some silly unobservant half-baked professional conclusion about her patient. Now she just did her job. The old man would never recover his speech, she said. There was more to the world than words, Mike told her. He would be satisfied if the old man was able to communicate with a word or two on the pad. The real communication between men was often in the silence they share. On these nights when he seemed holed up, feeling like a fugitive, Mike began to read aloud to his father, a poor man who had never had a chance to read. Mike tried to talk to him about the books he read.

Having his good simple religious father there seemed to calm and restrain Mike. He read about the Spanish conquest of Mexico. Strange big new words on a page used to fascinate him; he used to say them aloud, liking the sound of big words, and tried to use them in his speech. Now he just skipped these big words. His mind wandered. There was a paperback book that had had a big sale—a discussion of the great philosophers which, only a few months ago, had given him a sense of power and wisdom, a gratifying feeling of superiority over old friends. Sitting with this book on his knee now, Mike suddenly cursed. "Who am I? What am I?" he said violently. "I'm cooped up here, hiding like a thief. I can't go anywhere in peace. That man won't let me live my life." As he met the old man's wondering and worried eye he waved the book and tossed it away. "Words. Just fine calm words. Just fancy thinking, Poppa. What good is all this when you've got a man on your back? They're nice calm thinkers. Nobody can talk to this Lane. He's all hate. I couldn't talk to him. He'd laugh in my face."

The old man's fingers twitched. He was trying to say something. What was the old man trying to say? Mike wondered.

At the end of that week, one noon Mike went into his office and took out his books so he could compare this week with the week before. Just as he had suspected! Business was very bad. He was frightened. From the back room came the sound of Willie moving around. Balding Willie's impassive face as he stood there, the tape measure around his neck, offended Mike. Willie had once said bluntly, "What's the matter with you, Mike? It couldn't have been the cleaning fluid. Anyway, Bowman is dead."

Then a short broad man with a paunch and glasses came into the store. It was I. J. Singerman himself. He had just dropped in, being in the neighborhood, Mr. Singerman said, and he talked about the textile strike and the "goddamned union." Mr. Singerman had been a very affable man in the days when Mike had first met him, a rich man with a big house on Pine, two children, a beautiful wife, and a place in the country. But just when he was learning to play tennis his wife began an affair with Ozzie Benjamin, the broker. For three months now he had been trying to catch them in bed together, and couldn't.

Looking out the window Mr. Singerman asked what was this story he had heard from Max Sweetman about faulty material in a suit of Harry Lane's.

"Mr. Singerman, I told your man about that piece of lining," Mike said.

"Mike, I've got money in this business."

"So have I, Mr. Singerman. All I have in the world."

"So why make a big production out of it and humiliate the man? Is that good business?"

"Damn it all, the man flung the coat in my face. What would you do?"

"I don't understand this, Mike. Why should he fling the coat in your face?"

"Because he hates my guts," Mike said bitterly. "Because I was a witness for Scotty Bowman, see. He won't be satisfied until he ruins me too. He's maneuvered me into this position."

"Look Mike, you're a tailor, not a police court judge. You went too far. Nobody sympathizes with a man who goes too far. People talk."

"Who talks?"

"How did I hear it then? From Max Sweetman? Were you thrown out of Dorfman's, Mike?"

"Alfred Dorfman is a friend of Lane's. Don't you understand?" Mike said angrily.

"I understand that everybody knows that my partner is invited to keep out of well-known places. Is this good for business, Mike?"

"Of course it isn't good for business. Oh, I hear all the stories, too." Excited, Mike raised his voice. "I just wish you'd tell me one thing. Tell me why people would be crazy enough to turn against me on account of a guy they turned against themselves."

"I told you. You went too far."

"I went too far. Ha," Mike scoffed. "I didn't go an inch further than everybody else in town." But his knowledge of Mr. Singerman's basic stupidity suddenly depressed him.

"A businessman has to be well liked, Mike," Singerman said quietly. "Are you well liked now, Mike?"

"Of course I am. This is all just a little kidding from people who fundamentally are with me."

"Fundamentally. That's a big word, Mike," Singerman said grimly. "I want you to get that guy off your back."

"Just how do I do that, Mr. Singerman?" Mike asked and he was pale now. "You tell me, please."

"What would any businessman do? Make an adjustment with the customer, of course."

"An adjustment?"

"Go out of your way, Mike. Fix it up with him. People will hear about it. Be big. Say you want to make a handsome adjustment. You've been a fool. Smarten up. Get hold of the guy and offer to make him a new suit. The very best, hand stitching on the lapels and whatever else he wants. Make it look big. And get right to it," he said quietly. "With a bad reputation, you're no good to me, Mike. There, I've laid it on the line."

"I understand, Mr. Singerman," Mike whispered.

"Good. Then it's settled." Singerman said sourly, "I'll be in and you tell me."

At the window watching him get into his car, Mike thought, How quickly he'd drop me—and he tried to think of himself calling on Harry Lane but he couldn't. With all his heart he wished suddenly he wasn't in business; then the unfairness of his position began to enrage him. No one was going to send him crawling to Harry Lane. He had a case, he had right, he had legal weapons. "Look after things, Willie," Mike called, and he rushed out looking for a taxi. His own lawyer was Louis Applebaum, but it was Ouimet who loomed up in his mind now. He had seen Ouimet handle Harry Lane very deftly.

In the lawyer's office an elderly woman was waiting to keep an appointment. The big-breasted secretary told Mike he would have to wait for some time, but she would take his name in. When she returned and said he could go right in, he felt important.

"Sit down, Mr. Kon," Ouimet said gently, leaning back in his desk chair; and the sympathy and respect in his manner consoled Mike and put him at ease.

"Well, it's about Harry Lane. Have you heard how he's been going on, Mr. Ouimet?" he said, wanting to sound like a conservative businessman.

"Why yes, I have heard something."

"It's a campaign of slander," Mike said. "The bum is out to ruin me. My partner, Singerman, is on me now. My business is being damaged by that jerk's clowning. I'm a laughingstock. Can't the law protect me, Mr. Ouimet? I want to sue him."

"Of course he's trying to bait you," Ouimet said and he got up and walked slowly to the window, looking troubled himself. "Is he unhinged? Or is he clever and imaginative too?" he said half to himself, and then he turned. "You see, Mr. Kon, we can't very well sue a man for wearing a suit we made for him, can we? No. And I imagine, yes indeed I do, that this man would like nothing better than to get us in court again, eh?" Mike nodded. The lawyer's concern soothed and dignified him, made him feel they were in it together. "To know the right thing to do is very difficult," Ouimet said and he walked back to the chair, sat down and linked his hands behind his head, pursed his mouth and stared at the ceiling and pondered. So Mike sat down across the desk from him and waited. There was a long silence.

"All this clowning of Lane's is embarrassing and injurious to your reputation. Of course it is," Ouimet said suddenly. "It could ruin you, too. There certainly seems to be some kind of tort here," and he was so interested that he got up again and walked around a little, pondering. "And you say Singerman is taking Lane pretty seriously?"

"Well, he says I've got to stop him. He'll drop me, Mr. Ouimet."

"A little patience and you yourself may not have to stop Lane, you know. He'll do it himself," Ouimet said, coming back to his desk. "What we've got here is simply the spectacle of a man deteriorating rapidly. Soon he'll start drinking heavily and insulting people and getting sick and dirty, making more of a fool of himself in public places. They go downhill pretty rapidly, you know. And there's another thing—the Morrises. I wonder what that Morris girl has to say? They're a fine old family and immersed in conventional morality. I understand they don't even like to see their names in the social columns. The daughter is young, but to a girl of her stamp Lane's kind of public clowning must be simply shattering. They're a sedate family, Mr. Kon, incapable of wild extravagance about anything. I could tell you some stories about that fine old judge. Well, they say he dotes on his beautiful daughter." Again he smiled. "Why don't you wait a little, Mr. Kon, and let the ones Lane can't stand up against do the job for you?"

"Yeah, why don't I?" Mike said softly, and he leaned across the desk on which Ouimet now had his elbows, and they nodded, and he believed in the shrewdness he saw in Ouimet's eyes.

Chapter 26

It was late in the afternoon when Mollie returned, all golden from the sun and the water, and the first thing she did was call Harry. He wasn't in. Later, from the newspaper office, she called him again and got him. "Are you all right, Harry? Are you all right?" she asked. Of course he was all right, he said, laughing. Mollie asked him to come to her place for dinner, then a little later she called him again and told him not to come till early in the evening, her mother had just telephoned to say they were coming down with some draperies and dishes they wanted her to have so that her place could have some of the touches of her own home.

Mollie knew, though, why her parents were coming; they had been talking to her Cousin Sarah. Sarah actually came down to the *Sun* to see her. She told Sarah she had been getting letters from Harry; he was all right, just a little wild and lonely; but she wouldn't be scandalized.

Sarah was into everything in the city, and the young wives, her friends, were live wires too, all on committees; one ballet, one symphony, one arthritis, one opera, and one muscular distrophy. Their graying husbands who made the money usually stood around, smiling and tired, with little to say to their brilliant wives. "Somebody should grab him with a butterfly net," Sarah said sympathetically. "Mollie, you're a lovely girl. You can't put up with that ruined man. You might as well face it, he's absurd now. Simply an absurd man." A flush on her face, her eyes shining, Mollie said in her best slow-measured cultivated tone, "You see him as a shameless deteriorating man, but I know what he's been through. Maybe his imagination is a little twisted, but he's an interesting man. How many men do you know, Sarah, who have any imagination at all?"

She had hurt Sarah's feelings, but on the other hand, Sarah had put a chip on her shoulder. Mollie didn't want to have to hurry to the studio and make dinner for her father and mother, yet she felt she had to. She felt cross and nervous.

When she heard them on the stairs she opened the door and called out cheerfully. They were coming up slowly, her mother leading the way, her thin nervous face with the lonely eyes flushed from the climbing, with pride and affection in her smile. Two steps behind, carrying the draperies and the china, was her father in his black Homburg, his big nose looking bigger as his face got redder from the exertion. Fluttering around them she took their hats; she chattered and gossiped. She sat them down to dinner. All through the meal she talked brightly. Yet she knew they were waiting nervously as she was waiting.

"Well, have you heard from Harry Lane?" her mother said finally.

"Well . . . just on the phone."

"Take my advice, Mollie," her father said. "Keep away from him. You have no idea how people are talking. Why, he's a laughingstock, Mollie. That man has no brains and no shame now." He snorted. "Is my daughter going to hang around with a man people snicker at? Just yesterday your Cousin Sarah said—"

"I don't care what Sarah said," Mollie began. Then her sudden embarrassment left her desolate. She had counted on defending Harry; she had thought he would tell his story with dignity and grace, and now she felt lost. She got up and took some dishes from the table and carried them into the kitchen. When she came back she blurted out vehemently, "Just the same, Daddy, if I were Harry and that tailor humiliated me the way he did him, I'd march right down and break all his windows."

"Now look, Mollie, sit down," her father said patiently. "You know what Harry's doing, don't you?"

"No. No, I don't know at all."

"Well, he's simply wallowing in his disgrace."

"I don't think so. I don't think so."

"Now look," he said sternly, and he glanced at his wife who was listening too quietly. "You seemed to have had some doubt about him ruining that bank manager. Well, you shouldn't now. It's on his conscience. He just can't let the thing die. Well, a man's sense of guilt can take some peculiar forms." His tone changed suddenly. "That silly fool of a man. The very thought of him counting in any way on the sympathy of a respectable girl like you . . . It's out of the question."

"Oh, stop," Mollie cried.

"Mollie—"

"Please, please, *please* stop talking," she said and got up, walked away, then turned, her eyes moist, and as she shook her head, distracted, she thought she heard Harry's step on the stairs, and thought she would die if he came in now. "I've heard all about this and I don't know what to think. He's warped, all warped now, I can see that." And then her whole face felt warm and she said ardently, "I know one thing though—Harry was never an exhibitionist. He has a lovely manner. He is the most available man alive. That's why he's in all this trouble. And of one thing I'm sure—even if he's making a fool of himself, I know he's trying in some crazy way to be honest with himself."

"Honest with himself?" asked her mother, who until now hadn't said a word, sitting with her hands folded in her lap, her eyes turned inward with a wistful half-melancholy expression. "Yes, it's a hard thing to do, isn't it, Mollie? I don't think we could live if we came face to face with things. Unless we changed, I suppose it would be the end."

"The end of what, Mother?"

"Well, when the illusions go— Haven't you lost your illusions about Harry, Mollie? Aren't you really ashamed of him?"

"I'm bewildered at the way he's behaving, if that's what you mean."

"Of course you are ashamed."

"I mean it's just not like him to behave so badly," Mollie said, worried by her mother's gentle smile.

"You know the whole thing reminds me a little of Harry's father," the Judge said, sighing. He had pushed back his chair and linked his hands over his stomach. "In his way he, too, was quite an exhibitionist, wasn't he, Helena?"

"Well, yes, he was," Mollie's mother agreed with her bright nervous laugh. "And I suppose his mother was a bit showy too. I mean nothing about her was ever subdued."

"A nice woman, but an opinionated one."

"It does shape a boy's life, you know, Mollie."

"Oh, Harry's father and mother," Mollie cried as she started to clear the table, feeling lonely and unhappy. "How people should behave and who they are. Oh, how we agree."

"Really, Mollie," said the Judge. "Shouldn't the members of a decent family agree?"

"It just strikes me though that we've always agreed about everything," she said nervously. "The perfect quiet family understanding. Oh, it's beautiful. But most families bicker and quarrel, then they apologize, and then they know they're fond of each other."

"Aren't we fond of each other, Mollie?" the Judge asked.

"Fond of each other? Of course, of course," she said irritably, watching him raise his eyebrows. Now his hand would go nervously to the crown of his head, she knew, and it did, and he patted the few strands of hair, and she wanted to shriek. His little habits! She could foretell them for any occasion so accurately it was a joke. He seemed to be smothering her. She was drowning. The food he would like, the effect of a new strange dish on his stomach, the wry face he would make, the socks he would wear, the people he would automatically dislike. And that time three years ago when he had taken them to Italy. Why did it come into her mind now, the picture of them standing in the Sistine Chapel, a catalogue in his hand, giving her the excellent correct researched view of Michelangelo, and herself, annoyed, wandering away from him, longing to have some fresh spontaneous reaction of her own. His lawbooks had got into his blood, all his tastes were now codified too. Then the cry in her heart, *Nobody should ever know anybody this well!*

In his eyes, now, there was some alarm, a rebuke, a lonely plea, as if he knew she was pulling away from him wildly. She was trembling all over; she had to get away from him quickly, she thought desperately, or she would be blinded to Harry when he came in. Then the flicker of pain in his eyes seemed to stab her and remind her how she had been able to sit on his knee and get anything she wanted from him, and how her complete knowledge of him had given all the security in her life. "The last thing on earth I'd wonder about is whether we were fond of each other," she said.

"Here, let me help you with the dishes, Mollie."

"No, you sit down, Mother."

"But I want to help you."

"Please, please sit down."

"All right— You know, I was just thinking, Mollie, you're a lucky girl. I've never heard you say you were really in love with Harry."

"I don't know what you're talking about."

"I mean if you were so unfortunate now as to be in love with him, you'd have to follow him through all this disgrace, wouldn't you?" With her head tilted to one side, a faded dreaming eagerness in her eyes (although she would be the last person

199

in town to put up with Harry's behavior), she said, half to herself, "Some women are so glad of a chance to risk something. . . ."

"Risk something?" the Judge asked uneasily.

"What are you trying to say, Mother?"

"What did I say?" she asked, flustered.

"Risk something."

"Heavens, I don't know what I meant."

All on edge Mollie took the dishes into the kitchen. She had never felt close to her mother; now she wondered if she knew anything about her life at all, and it was a bad upsetting feeling. She wished they would go home. A monastery bell chimed somewhere. The ticking of the clock in the kitchen sounded unbearably loud. They were waiting for her to come back from the kitchen.

"Anyway, let's drop the subject of Harry?" Mollie said irritably.

In the general embarrassment that followed they could only sit there uncomfortably. In a little while they went home. It seemed to be ages before Mollie heard the step on the stairs.

"Harry," she cried, running to the door. He came bouncing in, wearing the suit Mike Kon had made, and with a big smile, as if the world now was full of good news. She didn't know how to take him.

"At last. Thank heavens," he sighed. Then he grabbed her. Whirling her around until she was dizzy, he laughed, he gave her a little kiss, then a big warm greedy one, then he bent her back and drew her hard against him, his hand going over her body so lovingly she shivered.

"No. No, let me look at you," she pleaded, freeing herself. "You're thin. You've been sick. I know all about it, Harry. I know you feel driven to the wall."

"Driven to the wall? Yes, they nearly got me. I was looking for a hole to crawl into." Then he smiled. "Not now, though. Oh no, not now, not by a long shot." The way he said it stabbed Mollie with anguish; yet he sat her down on the sofa as if he thought she was the one who needed to be comforted, and she felt confused. "Now look, Mollie," he said quietly. "I'm off the wall. I've got that tailor and everything he stands for on the run. It's working out splendidly."

"Harry, Harry, are you serious? What is this? Oh please be serious."

"Of course I'm serious," he said, taking both her hands, so quietly confident she had to listen. It was like this, he said. No one had wanted to pay any attention to him. Okay, after all, why should they? Look at the competition. Hundreds of thousands of others in the city imagined they were stories and were begging for a little attention to them. People turn desperately to each other, or burst into tears, or break the furniture, or fake a suicide. Anything to become news. Smiling now as if he were on top of the situation, Harry made it sound a little droll. But Mollie couldn't get used to him. Her mouth open a little, she watched him stand up to tell about his adventures. His blue eyes sparkled as he paced up and down. His strange buoyancy held her. He was wound up.

"It's ridiculous, simply ridiculous," he said, smiling. "Sometimes I feel like a cop on the beat," and he started to laugh. In restaurants, hotels and bars in the neighborhood everyone was so jolly. They'd say Kon hadn't been in. It made him laugh to himself because they were like a lot of stool pigeons working for him, watching for the tailor. Maybe warning the tailor he was coming.

"Oh no, *no*, Harry," she wailed, thinking of the affronts and insults he suffered without caring. Tears came in her eyes and she thought her heart would break, yet he made it sound so amusing. As he talked on Mollie started to giggle hysterically. Carried away, she didn't know whether she was laughing or crying, or just savagely satisfied that in his heart he had got up off the ground and was not the wreck her father and mother had imagined. "Don't go on, Harry," she pleaded. "I'll get you some coffee. I'll get you something to eat." Anything to try to break the spell.

But as they went into the kitchen his arm coming around her waist made her feel she was wildly with him. "You see, Kon'll have to sue me," he said, sitting in the kitchen. "What choice has he? Can he keep running from me? Of course he can't. What happens to his business? And there you are—we'll have our court case, Mollie."

"Our court case?"

"Back to the court we go."

"Kon is to get you back in court?"

"What choice has he?"

"No, it's mad, it's mad," Mollie protested. "I shouldn't laugh." Yet there he was looking so pleased with himself, and while he had that glint in his eye and his air of assurance any wild quixotic thing seemed possible. If she had cried desperately, "To see you like this, Harry," she knew he would laugh and then in spite of herself she would laugh with him and feel his elation. He had to get something to do, he said. It was costing him a fortune drinking in all the places. Anyway, he was giving up his apartment, he added.

At one thirty she told him he simply had to go. At the door, after he had kissed her, he said huskily, "You're different, Mollie. You don't belong in this whole ridiculous setup."

"There's a circus in town," she said suddenly. "Let's go tomorrow night, Harry, and look at the lions and the tigers."

"You're wonderful," he said, taking her face in both hands and kissing her again, and he left.

Close to tears and not knowing why, Mollie hurried to the window, listening to the sound of his step on the quiet street. It was a lonely sound, but oh, the splendid wild defiance in him; the fight in him! In the houses across the road was one lone lighted window. She stood there thinking of Harry and the tailor, wondering why they couldn't talk to each other about Scotty Bowman. Why couldn't they say, "Why are we like this because of our understanding of this man we both tried to help? Let us talk about that man, not keep away from each other, full of hate." Then Mollie imagined that in those darkened rooms across the street, many people lived their lives cut off from each other, never really meeting intimately and revealing what was in their hearts because they couldn't communicate. No one had the words they trusted themselves to reveal, and it seemed to her that Harry had become one of them, cut off and alone, unable to find the right believable words. He wanted to say something; he was trying desperately to say it to the whole city with a coat. To say it as if it were a piece of new conclusive evidence that disqualified the tailor who had made himself Harry's judge before a whole city.

"Oh, the poor dear man," she whispered, "to let himself get so carried away as to think that man will take him to court." She was so sorry for Harry she wanted to weep. The lone light across the road went out. Suddenly, as she pondered, she grew apprehensive. Harry would keep after the tailor. Stalking him through all the lighted places he would try to shame the tailor from bars and restaurants, till his life became smaller and smaller. Suddenly Mollie felt a chill of uneasiness, as if the night breeze from the open window had touched her with some new and terrible disgrace. Then she thought of how Harry's arms came out to her, how his hands groped for her, of that terrible need he had for her. Standing there in a trance, her thoughts seemed to flow out to the streets of the city around the mountain to the little places where Kon would never go. She saw herself waiting for Harry to meet her after work. She saw them going to obscure little restaurants in the East End, sitting and sampling the wines and speaking only in French, she saw them going into darkened movie houses night after night, just two people in the shadows whom no one knew. It would all start with the circus tomorrow night. Always they would come back here to her place where he could be what he should be, and she would keep herself sweet and lovely so he would always come hurrying, and with her there would be no Mike Kon, no Scotty Bowman, no advertising men and television people and actresses. She would share with him good humor and affection and respect, always respect till she gave him back his self-esteem and his dignity and he came to his senses. Nursing this dream Mollie turned away from the window and went to bed. . . .

For the next week she did all the things as she had planned them, but she couldn't budge Harry in his attitude. His quiet unshakable passion began to worry her sick.

Miss Jacoby, the middle-aged spinster in the ground floor apartment who sat in the dark at her window, watching the houses, who went in and who went out, lighting her life from all the other doors and windows, used to see Mollie and Harry coming up the street at all hours. He came in with her and didn't leave till hours later. Miss Jacoby always fell asleep listening for his step on the stair.

All that week as far as Mollie knew, for she couldn't be with him all the time, he didn't catch up with Mike Kon. And he didn't ask her to sit very long with him in the bars and restaurants, just look in and maybe have a drink.

But on Friday night she was with him at El Morocco, but it wasn't a routine call in Kon's territory; it was a kind of sporting event. Everyone was there to see if the half-crazy singer Denise La Coste would make a heartbreaking fool of herself again, or show she had really come back.

Chapter 27

AT ONE time, the whole town had been proud of Denise's continental fame. There wasn't a capital in Europe in which she hadn't sung her Latin love ballads in a husky voice. She had been such a darling! The mayor had had a reception for her in the City Hall. No one knew what had eventually caused her breakdown; perhaps too much love, too much alcoholism, too many relatives sponging. Anyway, one night Denise had been picked up in the gutter and taken to a mental home with bars on the windows. There had been stories since that she was dead. Denise had died from neglected syphilis, they said. She had had a lobotomy, others said. Last year, just three months after an operation, when Denise had tried to sing in a beer hall in the East End she forgot the lyrics. In a rage she had screamed foul and filthy curses at the audience and had been dragged off. Now they said she was all right again. Tonight, following the regular floor show, El Morocco was giving Denise La Coste another chance.

A little waiter came up to Austin Spragg, the handsome, pock-marked master of ceremonies, whispered to him, handed him a slip of paper and pointed to a table directly in front of the platform. In a minute a spotlight was put on this table where four middle-aged and self-important men sat drinking.

Holding up his hand for attention, Austin Spragg called out, "Ladies and Gentlemen, we are honored to have with us tonight . . . will you stand up, sir . . . that famous writer . . ." As he glanced at the name on the slip of paper, each of the four men rose diffidently, looked at each other, laughed in their embarrassment, and sat down slowly. "Joe, Joe," Austin whispered, "Get all their names quickly. What the hell are you doing to us?"

Not far away from the writers was Ted Ogilvie, with a tall silver-blond girl, another "cousin," and at the next table was old Haggerty with his sweet and dignified wife who rarely came out to the night places. "Listen, Hag," Ogilvie said, half turning his chair so he could snicker with Haggerty, "Levine gave the waiter five dollars to have it announced that he was here. What the hell, nobody ever heard of any of those guys."

"All is vanity. As I get older it's the one thing I'm certain of. These writers are all the same," Haggerty chuckled, hitching his chair around. They were neglecting their ladies, who smiled self-consciously, separated by the two tables.

"By the way—I saw Harry on the street with Mollie," Ogilvie said.

"The guy offends me," Haggerty said. "Don't ask me why. And I thought that girl had more brains. You can't tell about any of these women, can you?"

"Me, I feel sorry for her. There she was coming along the street with Harry, people gaping at him, and him looking straight ahead untroubled. She's so well-groomed herself, a proud girl. That girl is suffering."

"She's old enough to know suffering never did anybody any good," Haggerty said, disgusted. "I have no sympathy for her. Why doesn't she put him in the booby hatch. I hate childish men."

"Is he so childish, though? I told him points of honor were out of date. But come to think of it, for ten thousand years men have been willing to die for the sake of their self-esteem. How about it?"

Jerking his head back, Haggerty whistled softly. "Look over there . . . across the floor. I'd know the line of those shoulders and the set of that head anywhere. It's Mike."

"So it is. Who's the broad with him?"

"That Kovack girl. She goes for him."

"So he's come out of retirement. Well, well, well. What does it mean?"

"I hope it means he's had enough. That shop is everything that he's got in this world. Well, good. I was beginning to feel ashamed of Mike."

"I think he's ashamed of himself," said Ogilvie, then he turned hastily. His neglected "cousin" had kicked his ankle under the table. It really ached. He was furious. He was a stubborn man himself. He continued to look at Mike, who was just a shadowy figure leaning over a patch of white tablecloth.

Mike, dressed sedately in a blue suit, a white shirt and blue tie, was feeling more at ease than he had felt all week. When he had come in with May Kovack he had looked around warily to see if Harry was trailing him. When he didn't see him he was certain he wouldn't come in at all; for this he thanked Mollie Morris, he congratulated himself on the shrewdness of his judgment in counting on her unasked support. He had been sure she would start working for him as soon as she got back, would have to because of what she was, and because she had dignity, taste and charm; had been born knowing how to behave; and with her prominent family, he thought, she would be putting all the social pressures on Harry. He had told Singerman point-blank that he didn't need to go running to Harry with an adjustment; wait and see, he said. What a relief it was, he thought, to be out in the world again enjoying the pleasures of life with his Miss Kovack.

"I like the way you've got your hair done, honey," he said, stirred by her hard bright handsome little face and the shrewd blue eyes. "I go for that kind of cut. Negligent but smart."

"It's the Italian style," she said, patting her hair. "I cut it myself, and it's a better job than the professionals do. More like I wanted."

"Ladies and gentlemen," the master of ceremonies called out solemnly, holding up his hand for silence. Then he said simply, "Denise La Coste."

They gave her a big hand. She was a small dark lean-faced girl in a white sheath dress with something lithe and wild in her movement. As her eyes glittered in the spotlight there was an apprehensive hush. No one knew whether or not she was close to insanity. "Oh Lord, I hope she doesn't blow her top again," May Kovack whispered.

"Don't say such things, you hear, May?" Mike scolded her. "Have only positive thoughts. Let her feel them."

Denise began to sing one of her Latin-American love ballads. She had a husky voice with deep chest notes, and to everyone's relief she finished the lyrics without any trouble. There was a vast sigh which she must have heard, for she threw out her arms and laughed, then, stunned by the roar of applause, the faces of people standing up happily and toasting her, she looked frightened. "Bravo, Bravo," they shouted exultantly. "Good girl, Good girl." Two of her old admirers, now middle-aged, embraced each other. She held up her hand; she wanted to sing again. This time she was like herself as they had known her in her good days and those deep warm erotic notes came out huskily and exultant, one shoulder strap falling off, and she went on singing, her face aglow with pride and happiness, letting them see she could have sung all night. In the end they had to let her go. She kept backing off the stage, throwing kisses.

"This is a wonderful thing," Mike said huskily. He laughed and threw up his hands in jubilation. "To see a girl come back from the dead-house. All that guts and heart, right from the girdle. Ah, it's wonderful," he cried, really moved.

As the lights came on, Mike was still applauding wildly. Then his eyes, wandering across the floor, fell on Harry and Mollie at a little table in the corner by the band. They had come in fifteen minutes before Denise appeared, but in the dim light he hadn't seen them. Mollie wore a black dress, cut low at the neck, and her black hair gleamed in the strong light, and there was Harry in the summer suit. "God Almighty," Mike said, his jaw falling, and he sat down and slumped in the chair, staring at them.

Mollie's elbows were on the table, her hands clasped, her face raised in enchanted surprise at Denise. She was talking to Harry with the same happy animation she would have had if he had been wearing white tie and tails.

Grabbing his glass angrily, Mike drained it.

"You told me you were ignoring him, Mike," May said. "Come on now."

"That girl's with him."

"All right. So she's his girl."

The applause for Denise was dying down, though many were still calling out her name.

"Where's her pride? Where's her self-respect?" Mike said, deeply hurt. Then he couldn't believe his eyes; he saw Harry jump to his feet. Standing there in the summer suit, so incongruous, so wildly conspicuous, he shouted, "Denise, Denise. Here, over here." As her head appeared again in the wings, he beckoned wildly as if he really expected her to come and sit at his table as she might have done in his happy opulent days.

"The ham! The contemptible ham! Look at him," Mike muttered viciously. He couldn't believe that Harry was simply sharing his jubilation in the resurrection of a girl who had been low in the gutter and the madhouse. "To choose a spot like this for his malice," he said with loathing. "Oh, the phony bastard."

"It's his own shame," May said. "Let him stand on his head if he wants to. He's not bothering us."

"Are you stupid? Why do you think he's clowning and dancing around up there? Everybody knows what he's doing. See how he's got their attention."

Across the floor from them, Ogilvie had again swung his chair around to Haggerty. "Poor old Harry," he said smiling.

"Look at him there in the spotlight. What is it about his act that's so wrong? So terribly wrong."

"I snicker at him, sure," Haggerty said. "Just the same he embarrasses me. I think he embarrasses everybody. Still, it's up to Mike."

"I'm beginning now to wonder if Harry's got something on him."

Then a young advertising man with a pointed beard called out derisively, "All right, Harry. We see you're here. How can we miss you? Now what?"

"What's that?" Harry asked, startled. At that moment, indeed, he was innocent. He had been lifted out of himself, his heart sweetly free of all the mind's pride and cunning. The needling seemed to bring him back to where he was and what he was now, and there in the strong light, he stood chalk-white, a flicker of anguish in his pale blue eyes. Only for a moment though. Recovering himself magnificently, he laughed. "After Denise there should be a little comic relief," he cried. "Come on, where are those hecklers?" Still standing there he took the kidding remarks hurled at him, tried to top them, and he did it with a goodhearted charm.

"Let's all take up a collection and rush Harry to a tailor," Haggerty called out.

"Fine," Harry said laughing. "Can we do it now? Is my tailor here?"

"I'm right here," Mike called out belligerently, his jaw thrust out as he stood up. "You want to see me?" he jeered.

Now there was only the little dance floor between them, and as Harry, his eyes suddenly bright and fierce, took a challenging step, Mike's heart leaped exultantly. This was it. Out in the open at last, and he looked around. Some of the patrons had stood up, craning their necks. The bright intermission lights shone on their heads and on the snow-white tablecloths, and in the awful silence it seemed to him that they had seen the mask of laughter slip from Harry. They could all see him there, rotten with spite for having been named the criminal he was.

"All right, now's your chance," they seemed to say, "Go get him." *With me all the way,* and Mike's heart pounded. Wild Biblical phrases he had learned as a boy from his father sang in his head. "Something you want to lay on the line?" Mike goaded him.

Harry started to answer, but Miss Morris reached out and touched his arm and he turned to her.

"No, goddamn her. No," Mike whispered. He thought Mollie would at least stand up as an outraged, disgraced woman and take Harry out. Mike couldn't take his eyes off her. Mollie was drawing Harry down to the chair beside her. Offering no rebuke to him, no embarrassment, no change of expression— she even smiled, her white teeth showing. It was a lovely smile; and there Mollie was, starting a conversation, treating Harry Lane with a grave respect. Mike slumped down slowly himself, his jaw dropping in dismay.

"It's disgraceful," Mike said hoarsely. "Look at them, May. They're actors. Who does she think she's kidding? What a lousy act." Suddenly he guffawed. Then he started to clap his hands as if he had witnessed a burlesque performance. All by himself in the silence he sat there applauding. But Mollie and Harry didn't even look over at him. Miss Morris said something quietly to Harry, making him smile. Under the spell of the sweetness of her magnificent composure he gave no sign he was being taunted and mocked, and Mike slowly stopped clapping his hands. The color drained from his face, and he didn't know what to do; he felt terribly embarrassed. Folding his arms across his chest, Mike looked around for some further sign of support. Those nearest to him who had stood up expectantly were now sitting down with a shrug. There was a little relaxing laughter. "The man's a contemptible coward," Mike muttered to May.

"People are gaping at us, Mike," May answered. "I don't like to see you in this position. It's not like you, and it hurts me. We shouldn't stay here."

"Don't you dare move." Mike gripped May's wrist angrily. "I'm not budging from this place."

"It's you, Mike, I'm thinking of. To hell with all these long-necked turkeys. Let's go home, please."

"Not on your life," he said grimly. "What's the matter with you? Where's your loyalty? Look at that clown's girl over there. Is she running out?"

Her feelings hurt, May said bitterly, "You want I should not give a damn like her, no matter how you look?"

"Don't worry. I look all right."

"I can't sit here and see you belittle yourself. If you let me walk out of here by myself, I warn you, don't come near me again."

"That's not fair," Mike said, a catch in his throat. As he tightened his grip on May's wrist, Mike was suddenly aware that she belonged in a secret part of his life even Scotty hadn't touched. He had never told Scotty that he had often talked to this girl about marrying her. She had a bedroom done in pink and gray, and she was neat as a pin, and had a talent for drawing. She drew strange comical little pictures of people she saw on the street; he kept them in a folder. He brought her books to read; she was reading a book a week, and he had never known a woman who got so much pleasure out of sleeping with him. "Yeah," he said, his hand suddenly gentle on hers, "You've got some pride, May. You've got some real self-respect. By God," he said huskily, "I'm glad somebody has."

Yet as he beckoned to the waiter he looked around uneasily, all on edge. At the next table was David Witherspoon, the plump hotel man, with his good-natured wife who had a nervous tic at the corner of her mouth. Seeing that Mike was leaving, Witherspoon stared at him thoughtfully, then shook his head.

"Something the matter?" Mike asked, threatening.

"Nothing, nothing at all," Witherspoon said hastily. "I used to like watching you in the ring, that's all."

"I think the guy's disappointed in me," Mike said sarcastically to May. "I shouldn't disappoint such lofty-minded people, should I?"

"Where's that stupid waiter?" May asked nervously.

"Here he is." Mike took his time counting his change; he tipped the waiter elaborately, and as he stood up he tried to give the impression of unhurried opulence. As they began to walk around the dance floor the band was playing a new arrangement of an old song, "That Old Black Magic." The lights had been dimmed again. Mike had assumed an air of vast scornful superior dignity. The blue and pinkish lights floated over his rough strong face. No one spoke to him. When he looked around, people seemed to be embarrassed, as if they knew he felt cheated. He trembled. Taking May's arm he made a show of being concerned only with her sensitive feelings so at least they could see he was with a woman who had enough self-respect to be revolted by a vulgar scene.

But when he got to the door, in spite of himself he had to look back at Harry, longing for him to drop his guard again. "Tell me how to get that guy out of my mind," he said savagely, his hand tightening on May's arm as they went out.

Harry hadn't even turned. His eyes were on Mollie.

"I'm sorry," he whispered. "I'm terribly sorry."

"It's all right," Mollie said, but her lip quivered, and he saw the suffering in her eyes and he felt stricken. "You make me feel half demented. You make me hate myself. Look, darling, when I stood up calling to Denise—"

"I know, Harry."

"I don't know why you insist on coming out with me."

"I guess I have to."

"You don't have to."

"Yes, I do," she said, fumbling with her purse, her head down so no one could see the tears in her eyes. "I don't know why I have to. These places are all places of terrible indignity. They tear me to pieces. But any place you go . . ." She had a hard time controlling her breathing. "I can't stay home, Harry.

213

I need to be with you. It's a terrible gnawing need. If I'm not with you, it's worse. I wonder where you are and the unhappiness leaves me so empty. It's all right, Harry."

"Look, you saw him there. He can't go on."

"Next time he won't run, Harry."

"So much the better."

"Harry," she said hesitantly, "when you told me you thought he might sue you . . ."

"I remember."

"I thought it was a wild hope, a crazy understandable dream."

"I know."

"Now I don't think you're dreaming. It means terrible trouble. The common police court. Is that what you want?"

"Of course he can always come and see me if he wants to," he said, with his new bright smile. "Maybe he'd rather appear in the police court."

"Oh, Lord," she said, fascinated that Harry could think he was working his way day by day back to the court, that he was bringing the tailor against him, crazy with violence. But to get Mike into court, anything for another chance in court, the whole case aired again. She still couldn't believe it. She wanted only to get him back to her place. In the big room with the white walls, the yellow draperies, the Italian-marble mantelpiece, he was always so different, so peaceful, so yielding; in her place they still seemed to have much of their old happy life. "Let's go, Harry," she said gently. "Do you mind?"

"Not at all," he said, calling the waiter. When he had paid his bill he said calmly to the waiter, who was trying not to grin, "How did Denise take her triumph?"

"Right in her old stride, Mr. Lane. She went off with that wrestler, that new guy in town."

"I'd better go speak to her," he said grandly as if he owned the place. "Yes, I should have a word with her." Then he took Mollie's arm and she found hope in the way he said, "Let's go home."

Chapter 28

"It was mainly Mollie Morris's fault," Mike said, sitting in May Kovack's pink and gray bedroom watching her powder her nose before she went out to work the next afternoon. "The more I think about it, the plainer it is. Look, the guy says 'Is my tailor here?' Remember? Okay, I shouldn't have said a word. I should have got up quietly, walked around that dance floor and with one punch broken his nose, then quietly walked back to our table and sat down and gone on talking to you. It would have had great dignity, May."

"Well, why didn't you?" she asked impatiently, the powder puff suddenly held rigid against her cheek.

"Like I say, it was that Miss Morris, I think," he said, worried. "The way she sits there so dignified. Another thing," he said uneasily, "way back in my mind now is the idea this guy in that suit is not the real Harry Lane." As she put her hands on her hips impatiently, he said, "I'm not crazy, May. Look now, isn't this why it's hard to get set for the right punch at him? The guy Scotty fell for, the guy he admired so much, had such a different style, butter wouldn't melt in his mouth, see. Doing all the phony right things, trying to look good, the charm boy always holding somebody's coat with his eye on the gallery. The way he is now—this guy—he don't seem to have the same set of feelings as the guy who came into my store or the guy at the trial. How in hell then can I feint him out of position? He doesn't come at me right. If Harry Lane, the guy we knew, behaved like this, would a girl like Miss Morris sit with him, would she?"

"You're crazy, Mike," May said, her feelings wounded. "You sound like a flunkey abashed by one of those rich bitches talking through her teeth. Can't you see she's just teaming up with her guy against you? If she doesn't wash her feet they stink just like mine. Come off it, will you?"

They quarreled. Mike felt alone and misunderstood. Coming out of her place, he happened to look up at the mountain there in the sunlight, the slopes banked with the rich red and brown of autumn, and green too. A great deep drift of white clouds in the blue sky, full of shadowy vaults and long avenues, rising into cliffs and mighty turrets, was so low on the rim the slopes were like a garden hanging from a city in the clouds. It looked all wrong to him. A guy had to pinch himself to remember it was still the old mountain and the sky. Things were beginning to look wrong and out of place all the way down the line.

From then on Mike's breath began to smell increasingly of liquor. When he had had a few drinks in his own room he could rise above the situation; he seemed to see he was in a frivolous society in which people had no sense of justice. Then he would laugh to himself, sing bawdy songs, forget about his father in the next room, then fall asleep and look awful in the morning. He was uneasy about meeting new people. If he was standing at the window and saw someone he didn't know coming in he'd walk away, leaving the customer to Willie. He no longer felt at home in his own store.

Willie was worried about him, and one day he took him aside. "I say, Mike," he began in his English accent. "I wish we had never heard of Scotty Bowman."

"What?" he asked, startled. "That's an awful thing to say."

"Just the same, Mike, it's a pity, you know."

"Why, I wouldn't even be in this store without Scotty."

"Don't get sore, Mike."

"Then don't say such things, Willie."

"But it's not just that fellow Harry Lane."

"How do you mean?"

"It's the bank manager that's on your back."

"Scotty on my back? What is this? Are you crazy?"

"Take it easy. Look, why don't you take a little holiday? Go down to Miami."

"Let that bastard drive me out of this town? Who'd look after the store? You're a lousy salesman, Willie. What is this? Is everybody waiting for me to blow my top?"

"Right now why don't you go over to the gym and watch Bruno training? I can look after things. Go on, Mike."

It was a normal thing for him to do so Mike went. The gym smelled of dust, sweat and men. Bruno was in the ring with a Negro sparring partner who had very heavy shoulders. Little Ray Conlin leaned against the corner post, a towel over his shoulder, watching Bruno carefully. There were only a few folding chairs for spectators. Three of the sports writers stood together near the office door, and off by himself, sitting on a chair on the other side of the ring and wearing the suit, was Harry Lane. It was normal, too, for Harry to be there because he used to talk in his big opulent manner about buying a piece of Bruno's contract. Their eyes met. This could be a God-given second chance at him, Mike thought. Oh, he wouldn't miss it this time.

Harry's stare was detached and cold as if Mike were some kind of a disgusting bug. "Hello, Tiger," Haggerty called out to Mike. The sports writers, winking at each other, threw glances across the ring at Harry. "Tiger" they were calling him now, and he longed for one little taunting gesture from Harry, even one word about him to the others. With his eyes he begged him to make a little provoking gesture, just one smirk, just one laugh. After a few moments Harry got up lazily as if the simple pleasure he got out of watching Bruno was spoiled by the bad company, and he sauntered out. Yet no one could say he was driven away.

Old Haggerty called out to little Ray Conlin, "By the way, Ray, when Harry Lane has you deported, where are you going?"

"Who are you kidding, Haggerty?" Conlin said, turning away from the ring where his boy Bruno had started to slug with the heavy-shouldered Negro. "You know that guy couldn't get anybody deported."

"No? What about his big friends?" Haggerty said solemnly as he and his two colleagues joined Conlin at the ringside.

Mike knew they were needling Conlin just for the laughs and hoping to draw him in on it too. In spite of himself he said bitterly, "That guy's got his face so deep in the mud, Conlin, not even a lavatory attendant would listen to him."

"Well, I don't know. The Witness here is prejudiced, of course," Haggerty said shrugging. "Where does your lawyer say you should go, Conlin? Mexico, Panama? Where do you go when you're deported?"

Conlin, who was really worried about his record, started to curse Harry and dance around. Then one of the handlers shouted, "It's Bruno's nose. Look, it's bleeding." The Negro and Bruno had been slugging while Conlin had been distracted. Jumping into the ring, Conlin sat Bruno down on the stool, put his head back and applied the towel to his nose. It was a bad nosebleed. Conlin looked pale and stricken. The fight was only two days away.

Forgetting that he despised Conlin, Mike turned savagely on the sports writers. "See, you guys, see," he shouted. "Just because that clown Lane is around here you lose all sense of responsibility. You feel you got to make stupid irresponsible jokes, and get everybody demoralized. You turn this here poor little guy's work into a joke and look what happens." Pleading with them angrily, Mike stammered, "Don't you understand? A man's life, his work, is bigger than a joke. Pay attention to me, you hear? Have some respect for a man."

He was so moved they all were embarrassed, and little Conlin, who had been working on Bruno's nose, looked up at him in wonder. A heavy dull flush came on Mike's face. "Well, so long," he said abruptly, and sick with shame and anger, he got out.

As he walked slowly along the street people brushed by him. It was four thirty in the afternoon, and a pleasant day. People were coming out of the shops, hurrying, intent only on getting home before the rush hour. People going home after shopping at this hour usually have an absorbed expression on their faces. Mike was sure not one of them, if he had stopped him, could understand a word about a justified man. If he had tried to explain to any one of them he would end up doing some crazy thing that would make him stutter with humiliation. As they came hurrying by in the sunlight it seemed to him they knew nothing about each other and didn't care; they weren't people, they were hardly even faces.

This loneliness only deepened his terrible anger and he couldn't bear to go back to the store where he would have to talk to Willie or a customer.

In his thoughts suddenly he was in Scotty's home with Scotty's wife and her boys, sitting in a comfortable chair, having a beer, making some kind of a plan with her. As he passed a drugstore he stopped, pondered, then suddenly turned in. He went to the telephone booth, called Mrs. Bowman and told her he would like to come out to see her; he wanted to talk to her about an obligation Harry Lane had to her, there were angles to the case they had never discussed and they ought to. Her voice, as they talked, was full of sympathy and respect and gratitude. In the narrow closed-off phone booth he had the wonderful feeling that he was not really alone any more. Trembling, he wiped his brow with his handkerchief, stepped out of the booth, then saw Mollie Morris standing at the counter, a tube of toothpaste in her black-gloved hand.

She looked so cool and untroubled with so much pretty fresh-

219

ness in her face that he lost his head, went over to her and blurted out, "I want to tell you something, Miss Morris."

"I beg your pardon?" she said, startled, backing away from him.

"You don't need to back away from me. I always had a high opinion of you, Miss Morris, figuring you didn't have that guy's number."

"Are you out of your mind, Mr. Kon?"

"I'm not out of my mind," he said bitterly. "I'm just telling you. I had you wrong. I thought you were too fine and respectable a girl to put up with it. I thought you were taken in by the guy. Now I know you're not, you can't be. You just don't care, do you? Everybody knows now you just don't care what he does. I thought a woman like you . . . well, I didn't think a woman like you could be so common about a man. You're a pair. That's swell. Okay," and he grinned and strode to the door.

Her face burning, she took an angry step after him, but his contemptuous grin, and the violent way he pushed the door open, frightened her. The clerk in his beige-colored dust coat had his mouth open waiting, and she looked at him, shook her head as she put the tube of toothpaste slowly down on the counter, and trembled as she turned and went out.

Chapter 29

IT HADN'T occurred to Mollie that she herself might be showing scant respect for Harry in just going along with him.

Now Mike had put a doubt in her mind. When she was with her friends, she was watchful, ready to defend herself, and coldly superior; yet short-tempered, too. At the newspaper office they began to lose sympathy for her, for she came in late and had a chip on her shoulder, and something of Harry's mocking air. One day when she came late to the office the women's editor, Miss Thorndike, rebuked her. All week Mollie had been impatient with this plump alcoholic little newspaper-woman. She seemed to want to hurt Miss Thorndike cruelly with her eyes, with her laugh and the tone of her voice. Miss Thorndike, who liked her, was bewildered. Nor could Mollie concentrate on her work.

At ten o'clock Mr. Moss, the city editor, called her to the desk. "Miss Morris," he said, and she couldn't take her eyes off his red forehead which was usually so pale against his florid cheeks. "If you don't mind my using a very nasty deplorable phrase, what the hell is the matter with you?"

"Nothing at all, Mr. Moss."

"Look at this story you've written. Was that a party for hats?"

"Why, no. Of course not."

"Was there nothing else there but hats?"

"Women are interested in hats, Mr. Moss."

"Just hats moving around, eh? Nothing but hats," he said grimly. "What are you trying to do, make us or these prominent women look ridiculous? Do you want to work here?"

"Of course I do," she said, feeling close to tears. "Mr. Moss, I seem to be washed up on the women's page. Couldn't I work in the city room, Mr. Moss?"

"You surprise me," he said slowly. "Anyway, you're off the women's page as of now." Then he added gruffly, "That's a good mocking story about those hats. I enjoyed it. But I'm not going to frame it. It's in the wastepaper basket. Here's a story for you," he said, meeting her eyes, and he wrote down an address. "Go to this address and see the girl and the fellow. They were in a car and some guy came along and slugged the kid and raped her. It's the woman's angle I want."

She took a taxi to the address, a small apartment building near the Forum. A big man in a light brown suit, a detective, opened the door. A middle-aged newspaperman named Grant, from the *Star*, was sitting beside a young man in a blue sport shirt and gray slacks. His name was Boychuck. He was a lean healthy-looking boy weighing about one hundred and forty pounds. He looked about twenty-one and had a badly swollen black eye which wasn't quite closed. Breathing slowly and heavily he leaned back in the chair as if he had been running. His good eye shifted eagerly to Mollie. An older gray-haired man, the girl's father, was sitting by himself on the other side of the room. Again and again his hand went to his head and he rubbed it as if he had some great pain in his skull, and there was contempt and hatred of the boy in his eyes.

Boychuck was explaining that he and his girl had liked sitting in the car out on a country road with the moon coming up and shining on the mist over the tall grass. Then last night his girl had said nervously, "Who's that man there? What does he want?" and Boychuck had looked out. A heavy-set man was standing only two feet away from the car door. He stood there motionless and so still he didn't inspire any fear at all. Maybe the guy was sick, something the matter with him, Boychuck had thought, and he'd opened the car door.

Then the man hit him on the eye with a blunt instrument and knocked him over and everything went black, till he heard the man say, "I'll kill him this time."

He tried to get up and the man kicked him in the stomach. He couldn't see what it was he held in his hand. It was some kind of a blunt instrument, and anyway the kick in the stomach made him sick and he thought he was going to vomit. He heard the man tell Ellen to take off her clothes and hurry or he'd break her guy's head this time; then he must have fainted. When he came to, he saw Ellen standing beside the car naked but for her shoes and stockings and crying. He wanted to jump at the man but he fell to his knees. "Try and follow me and I'll kill her," the big guy said. "Sound that horn and she gets it." And he had this blunt instrument and Ellen was naked.

He was afraid the man would hit Ellen if he yelled. As the shadows closed over them he felt crazy from not knowing what to do. They had turned off the road into the tall grass where it was waist-high. In his excitement he must have run out past the place, and when he turned back he couldn't find it and he looked at the tall grass and listened. Then he realized Ellen would be afraid of being killed if she cried out, and he ran back to the car. Ellen's clothes were on the road in a little pile by the car and he picked them up and put them on the front seat and got in and drove further along till he found another parked car and he jumped out and banged on the window. The guy inside said he would go back with him but the girl said, no, they'd get the cops, and they drove away, and he got into his car and turned it around.

Then he saw Ellen fifty feet down the road, coming toward the car lights, naked and white. All she said was, "Where are my clothes?" Then the police cruiser came along.

"That's just how it happened," he said, putting his hands

over his face, as if the silence in the room seemed to be an unbearable reproach. Dropping his hands helplessly, he turned to Mollie. "You believe I couldn't do anything else, don't you?"

"Don't—don't ask me," Mollie whispered, her heart beating heavily. It was too horrible to picture that naked girl walking through the tall grass.

"A car wrench would cut your eye a lot more than that blow did, son," the detective said.

"It was a flat and heavy thing."

"I see," the detective said, looking at the boy's eye. "Now look, are you sure it wasn't just his fist?"

"It was a blunt instrument. It knocked me out. Look at my eye."

"It was only a blow from his fist, my God," the *Star* man whispered to Mollie. "The guy just poked him in the eye and scared him stiff."

"How terrible," Mollie whispered, twisting her mouth. Then the boy's pleading eyes shifted to her again.

"You weren't there, miss," Boychuck said. "That big guy would have hit Ellen the same way he hit me."

"What with?" the *Star* man asked quietly.

"The blunt instrument," the boy said angrily.

"I'll say something," the girl's father said bitterly, taking a step closer to the boy. He was a big man and Mollie thought he was going to hit the boy, for his mouth was twitching. "I think you're a little coward," he said harshly. "That man only used his fist on you. If I'd been your age and out there with a girl, I swear to God I'd have tried to kill the man even if he beat me into a pulp. What about my daughter?"

"Yes, what about me?" came the voice from the hall and they all turned, and there was the girl, Ellen, in a pale blue print dress, a pretty girl, plump and round-faced but very pale now and big-eyed from the shock of her experience. Behind her stood the doctor, a short man in a brown suit.

"Oh, the poor kid," Mollie said to the *Star* man.

"Who are you?" the girl asked, staring boldly at Mollie, and then, "Why don't you mind your own business? . . . Oh, Gerry, your eye. It's terrible!" she cried, turning to Boychuck. She sat down beside him and held him against her. Weeping, she lifted his head in her hands so she could see the bruised eye, and tried to comfort him.

"Good heavens," Mollie whispered to the *Star* man. "She never expected anything of him." The little fat-faced empty-eyed girl's whimpering, and the weak way the man, like a wounded dog, licked it up, revolted Mollie. "The woman's angle," she whispered cynically. "Mr. Moss wanted the woman's angle. Well, there it is."

Yet, as she watched, Mollie grew uneasy. Was this also what a real man wanted of a woman? she wondered. Did nothing else in life matter? That poor little thing there, accepting that man in his shameful role, didn't she care how she was belittling him? Maybe she was just one of those little soft women. Rising and shining only when a man was in the gutter. Get him into bed, make him need that warm darkness. Just pillows they were. That soft little thing there, it would never break her heart if a man wore a white carnation on his fly, or a straw sailor hat in winter, or how he ruined his life, if it made her feel more needed. "Oh God, I've had enough of this," she muttered, bewildered by sudden anguish. "I'm going."

That night there were so many stars out that the sky came down to the narrow dark street behind the apartment. From the open window of a house across the road floated young laughter and lovely cool jazz. A taxi, whose driver had seen her, was making a full right turn at the corner, the headlights swinging around to her in a wide arc. She got in, went back to the office, wrote her story in a hurry under the impulse of her strong feeling, and again found herself hurrying home to her studio to wait and listen.

She sat in the kitchen having a cup of coffee, her head in her hands, and as she listened to the night sounds of the city she wondered where Harry was at that hour. Again she asked herself if her attitude to him was all wrong, if the destruction of all dignity and respect could come from love as well as hate. Was she doing to Harry—in her own way—what the girl Ellen was doing to Boychuck? Harboring him and destroying at one and the same time?

She was angry, ashamed and restless, yet she felt again a terrible need to be with Harry wherever he was. Going into the bedroom she put on the pale blue nightgown he had given her for her birthday. It was almost indecently short, coming just halfway down her thighs, and he had laughed when he gave it to her. Sitting at the mirror she began to brush her hair. If she could only do it in a new way, she thought restlessly. Slamming the comb down she got into bed. Soon she fell asleep, but she had a bad dream. She dreamt that the girl Ellen was chasing her naked through tall grass, trying to catch her and show her how to do her hair. She woke suddenly, full of some dreadful apprehension. She couldn't lie there. She went to the window. The street was quiet, but her mind went racing along street after street. What if it was the night when Mike Kon, flushed out, came after Harry? She remembered the look on his face in the drugstore; the tailor had had a frantic anger in his eyes. And he was a powerful man, his neck was thick, an old fighter. Tonight he might have lifted his head slowly and looked around, astonished that he had been sitting back, letting his tailoring be treated as a public joke. It was two o'clock, there wasn't a light on the street, but she went to the telephone and called Harry's place. When he answered sleepily, she was so relieved she could hardly speak.

"What's the matter?" he asked.

"I just wondered why you hadn't called me."

"I did. They said at the paper you were out on an assignment."

"It was a crazy assignment," she said, and she tried to laugh, wanting him to go on talking.

The next night, her night off, they went to a movie. Afterwards, they started off for Mollie's. It was a fine night, one of those clear nights with a real touch of fall in it. They were coming up Peel, by the lighted hotel entrance. Some men were there, one of them little Ray Conlin, in his light brown suit, his blue shirt open at the neck. The little brown-faced oily-haired man with the light hard eyes was trying to get in on a conversation with four well-dressed men. He often stood at the hotel entrance so he could say hello to people he looked up to who were on their way to Dorfman's. When he saw Mollie and Harry he grinned happily. "Look who's coming," he said.

Frozen-faced, her arm in Harry's, Mollie walked serenely by the lighted entrance. "Hey, Lane," Conlin jeered, sure of himself at last. "You still got that cheap Kon suit on, eh? Well, you should wear it, it becomes you," and he burst out laughing. The other men, who were embarrassed, turned away to hide their snickers. Furious, Mollie half stopped and looked at Harry. She couldn't imagine him taking this cheap street insult. But his face under the street light was stonily impervious. He stared straight ahead at the mountain, or maybe the night sky above the mountain, and he walked her along silently.

When they got to her apartment and he sat down on the sofa, she said she would make a cup of coffee, but she went over to the window instead, pulled the yellow draperies together, tucked them in at the sill, then turned, quivering. "For God's sake, Harry. . . ."

"Come on, Mollie. That guy's a little creep."

"I've been humoring you, parading around as if I had no pride. Am I nothing, a nobody?"

"Now take it easy. Take it easy."

"I'm not a buffoon, even if you are. Now we're being laughed at on the street."

"I could see this coming," he said, terribly agitated as he started to walk up and down, keeping away from her, not meeting her eyes. As she waited, she thought he was ashamed, she thought she had him. He was staring raptly at one spot on the floor, then that grim stubborn expression she hated came on his face. "Well, why shouldn't they laugh?" he asked doggedly.

"Me, that tailor . . . isn't the whole thing laughable? Why shouldn't we laugh too?"

"You poor proud silly wretched man," she blurted out, half crazy with exasperation. All the indignation from the weeks of secret humiliation she had suffered filled her with rage and hatred of his blindness to the thing in him that was so alien, so destructive of everything she thought she loved in him. Her rage made her dizzy. She had to put her hands to her head to get control of herself so she could try and reason with him.

"Listen to me please, Harry. When a man clings to his suffering, he violates all human sympathy and without that human sympathy what he does has no meaning. All you're doing with your antics is cutting yourself off . . ." Her voice broke because he looked so pale. "Think of me, Harry. How can I go on? Oh Lord, where's your self-respect?"

"Self-respect?" he said, pouncing eagerly on the word and trying to smile. "Now this is very comical. I don't fit into this social pattern they've made for me. I don't act like a respectable black sheep, praying that no one will notice me. I don't, do I?"

"No, you don't," she cried. "The awful light you put yourself in. This is the worst public relations job in the history of the world."

"So it turns out I'm a lousy public relations man. I'm in a bad light, eh? Would you rather I stayed in that phony light I've been in ever since that trial?"

"That's it. The trial. I know what's in the back of your mind. You think you're going to get back into that court through that tailor even if it means driving him to half kill you."

Suddenly his patient, tight, unprotesting smile outraged her, and she grabbed him and tried to shake him. "Oh, you fool! That cheap tailor.. The condemnation of that one mean man!" she cried. "What is he to you? If he were some great figure of justice . . . But no, he's a little creep two jumps out of the gutter. A self-righteous little creep, you hear?"

"I know what he is."

"It's like talking to a brick wall," she wailed, blinded by tears. Moving away to the window, she clutched the yellow draperies; her black hair was half buried in them. Then she caught a glimpse of his hand fumbling with his cigarettes as he watched her. She had always loved his hands, it was the first thing she had ever noticed about him; she had always felt his need of her in his hands touching her so secretly; now she imagined them reaching out soothingly, touching her and telling her that if he could only feel her shiver under his caress, ready to open up to him in warmth and oneness, nothing in the world would matter to him as much as his need of her. "Oh, Harry darling, darling," she said. "Why are we like this?" and she went slowly over to the sofa and sat down looking up at him helplessly. "I feel so lost, Harry. I'm alone, I'm without you. I don't think you need me now at all."

"I love you, Mollie, more than ever."

"I don't think you even want to kiss me now."

"I'll kiss you," he said huskily, yet he didn't move. He only stared at her, and the suffering in his eyes seemed to accuse her, and she blushed and explained desperately, "I'm a woman, Harry. And when it comes right down to it, a woman doesn't care about anyone's fine sense of honor, or the righting of great wrongs, if it sacrifices all her hopes of a decent life. Just think! We were going to get married. After this terrible thing happened to us I still wanted to try and make the best of it, didn't I, Harry?"

The light from the table lamp was on his face and she had never seen him look so torn, and he seemed to be trying to find the right honest words to explain another need in him, but he fumbled awkwardly as if he no longer trusted her to understand his words. "The way it is with me . . . well, I know how you feel," he stammered. "To put it in words, I haven't . . . I . . . I can't explain. I just know what I'm doing is right."

Then she said the wrong thing. Sighing she said, "Oh, Harry, imagine you of all people not knowing how to behave."

"Me of all people," he said laughing bitterly. "I was an expert on the subject, wasn't I? Nothing ever the matter with me except that I smoked too much and coughed a lot after I laughed too loudly. You know something?" he asked ironically. "On certain occasions even Sweetman used to ask me how to behave."

"Please don't clown with me now, Harry. I'm not the public."

"Wasn't I the most accommodating man in the world?"

"Harry. . . ."

"You should ask old Scotty if I wasn't the most available and accommodating of men. The real nice guy. As Ogilvie said, 'One sweet guy.' Why, it was the only thing about me everybody believed in. Oh, hell," and he laughed at himself and it seemed to tell her how smothered he now was by his passion. "You know something, Mollie?" he went on, carried away, his eyes shining. "I used to be quite a different person. Oh, a hundred years ago. I had a view of myself. How unique that is now, eh? Another thing. You won't believe this, but when I was a boy my mother used to tell me I was too aloof from people. You know why? I wore my heart on my sleeve and was protecting myself, she said. I was so shy I actually used to stutter. Imagine, me, as they say now, the glib talker. I stuttered! I remember how my mother had me sit with her and read poetry aloud, intoning it, the speech getting carried along by the rhythm. We used to sit and read together. What a wonderful, patient woman she was. I overcame the stutter. I overcame my shyness too. With a bang! My God, even in the air force I still had a life of my own, Mollie. We had fine Athenian conversations—till dawn —about everything . . . everything. My imagination was young and alive."

As he paused to light a cigarette he noticed his hand trembling, and he threw the cigarette down angrily. "A thing like this happens to me. . . . For the first time in years I'm forced to open my eyes again and look around. Well, it's a pretty agonizing experience. It's the damndest thing, Mollie. The whole world in false face. No one quite in the place he pretends to be.

I don't mind at all. Everyone looks so amusingly phony. I feel a power in me, Mollie."

"I don't understand you, Harry," she said nervously, staring at him. "You've changed. Your whole personality has changed. This . . . this exploration of your innocence. I think you're out of your mind." She stood up slowly. "God in heaven, the truth is I've been ashamed of you."

"No!" he said, shaken. "You're my girl."

"I mean it, Harry."

"I . . . I don't think you do," he muttered. "No, not you. It's the others."

"The others?"

"Sure," he said bitterly. "That social-climbing Cousin Sarah of yours and her fatheaded husband, and all those respectable friends of yours in their porcelain pants. Yes, and your ponderous father with his dog-eared lawbooks. Why not just tell them I'm drunk all the time? That they will understand."

"More and more you hate everything I stand for," she whispered. "It can't keep on. If you won't quit—"

"I can't quit, Mollie."

"Then keep away from me."

"Mollie, I need you."

"You don't need me. You need Mike Kon."

"Mollie. . . ."

"Don't touch me. It's Mike Kon you need more than anything else in the world." She walked grimly to the door and opened it. "Good night, Harry."

They looked at each other, both waiting, pale and tense, neither one believing the other wouldn't yield. He took out his handkerchief and wiped his mouth. He had a foolish awkward smile. Then he turned and looked out at the stairs, hesitating as if he knew that as soon as he went down those stairs he would be really alone. He seemed to be so shaken and wretched and proud, so angry he was half crazy, yet he went and Mollie let him go.

Chapter 30

THERE was a question she hadn't asked him, a question any sensible person would have asked long ago, and on the way home, wretched though he felt, Harry asked it of himself. It was this: Aside from any court scene, supposing Mike Kon, thinking it over, came to see him and wanted to do all in his power to make amends. What then? What would he do? What would happen to him in this town? Could it ever be the same again? He had to face the fact that it couldn't, and Mollie was stupid not to see that it couldn't. After all the days of belittlement, how could he ever offer himself to any businessman as the old agreeable Harry Lane? Even Max Sweetman, full of sympathy and remorse, wouldn't be able to touch him. No employer could dream of passing him off as a plausible ingratiating public figure again. Who could ever be sure of what he would do next, after watching him destroy day by day the last shred of respect for the old Harry Lane? "No one, no one at all," Harry said to himself, and when he had said it he felt a fierce satisfaction.

His step had quickened as he came along Sherbrooke. Somewhere a guy was playing a horn. A stooped old woman, in old-fashioned clothes, came hobbling by him, chuckling to herself. Ahead was the unlighted bay window of his apartment. The place was so often dark now, he thought, yet in the old days someone else had so often been there, using the key. He went in and looked all around the big handsome front room as if expecting to feel some pang of regret that he was moving. Yesterday he had rented the apartment to a middle-aged broker named Jackson, and given his car to the garageman to sell. In his pocket he had the key to the furnished room he had taken on Mountain Street. As he looked around now the apartment seemed to fill with faces and voices; men with red indulgent faces, crowding in, holding pretty women from nowhere by the elbow, looking for a drink and food; the frantic chatter, no one listening; lots to drink, plates of good food, and the smoke curling heavily to the ceiling. *"Do I know you?" "No, I know Harry. We both know Harry." "Sure, everybody knows Harry. Where's Harry?"*

He felt he couldn't stay there even one more night. Rushing into the bedroom he got his bag, then his haste began to embarrass him, so he took his time; he packed the bag, poured himself a Scotch as if assuring himself there was no hurry. He drank it sitting in the chair by the window, looking around the big room where he had once been so comfortable. Then he put the bottle in his bag, went out, and got a taxi. In two minutes he was at the roominghouse. It was a decent enough place operated by two spinsters named Lacey, of Irish-French-Canadian origin. The old house had the right situation for him in the neighborhood, close to all the old haunts.

The front door was open and he went in and along the dark narrow hall and unlocked the door to his own room and turned on the light. The windows overlooked the street. There was a dresser, a desk, a comfortable chair, and the bed. The faded carpet had only one badly worn spot. Yesterday he had brought over most of his personal things. Opening his bag now he took out the bottle of Scotch and took a big drink. It didn't taste right. It only made him feel more lonely and despondent. For the first time in his life he felt truly despondent, and as he sat down on the bed and sighed he thought, What am I doing here so far away from all the pleasures of life?

Mollie was in his mind. Suddenly he could see himself going over to her place and waiting, and giving in to her; forget everything and be nothing—anything she wanted—as her arms opened and she comforted him. But he told himself, desperately, that if he valued anything good in himself, any truth about himself, he shouldn't let her shame him. She could break his heart but not shame him. Just as though she had passed through the room he suddenly caught that faint lovely scent of her skin under the perfume she wore. Was it the liquor he had gulped down on an empty stomach? he wondered. He should have eaten something. His beautiful nibbled-at virgin seemed to be pulling him out toward the door. He had to get up, as if he were struggling with her and losing. The small room with its faded wallpaper seemed to give him back his strength. He was glad she didn't know where he was. The room was miles and miles away from all the other places in her life. That was good. He was safe.

Utterly exhausted, he got undressed, went to bed and lay listening to the other roomers coming in one by one. They rushed for the two toilets, which began to run steadily. Somewhere a girl was crying softly. It was coming from the room overhead. At last the house was quiet. A patch of light flickered and flared on his door; it came through the window from a big neon sign across the street. Trying to sleep, watching this outside light on the door, he seemed to hear Mollie say, "You don't know how far down you've gone, Harry Lane. Look at you there. Who are you kidding? You're not just ruined by Scotty Bowman and Mike Kon."

"So what?" he answered. "You're a little late with it, honey. Nobody's buying that comeback bit. Nobody at all." It made him strangely hopeful again to think of it. The patch of light on the door flickered; it went on and off. It put him in a trance. He seemed to see the last shreds of old disguises dropping away from him; the last of all the old stuff that hung on him and hid him. It would all go when Mike Kon cried out an apology to the world, or assaulted him and the whole case was thrown into court again; and Kon would. And soon, too, because who held all the winning cards? Half asleep now, half dreaming, he muttered that trapped men always had to help each other.

It was nearly noontime when he woke up. He went out to a little hamburg joint for something to eat and then returned to the room. All afternoon he stayed there. At nightfall he would go out on his rounds again. But when the darkness came, he couldn't force himself to go out; it wouldn't be safe feeling so lonely, so exiled now from his own little world. The whole place reeked with the smell of cooking food. Sometimes he went to the window. It had been raining. The neon lights from the cleaning establishment across the road threw a pinkish glare on the wet black pavement. He sat there watching and waiting. The light quick step of a woman made him crane his neck eagerly. When she came into the light she didn't look like Mollie at all, and his heart sank. With all his soul he protested: when you're in love you don't say it must be like this or like that; turn it on or turn it off; if it's there you go down with it, and there's nothing more to say. A little later he heard a man's heavy deliberate step and he stood up slowly, his heart thumping. The step turned in to another house. The idea of Mike coming to him became so real it filled the emptiness in his heart. He tried to believe he only needed to sit there now, enough had happened —now Mike would come—he had to. If Mollie came around she would find him sitting there calmly waiting for Mike. If only he could be as sure of her as he was of Mike coming after him.

Leaving the door open to go along the hall to the ground-floor toilet, he bumped into a curly-haired young fellow who had come running down the stairs. As the fellow cursed, Harry said, "What are you so sore about?"

"Nothing," he answered, looking surprised. "I'm tired waiting for advancement, waiting for buses, waiting for my girl, waiting to get into toilets," and he hurried upstairs to try for another one.

Along the hall there was a room with the door open. An old

French Canadian with a deep warm laugh lay there reading. Farther down the hall was the sound of hammering, like someone working on furniture, and he went along and looked in. The Lacey sisters, in big old-fashioned aprons, were hammering on an upturned sofa. "Here, I'll help you," he said. His name had meant nothing to them. Whom did they know who counted?

The big heavy solemn sister, Rosamund, had great and sober dignity, believing they were descended from William the Conqueror by way of a Norman knight, DeLacey, in Ireland. The sister Louella, fragile and bright-eyed, asked him if he had read the poetry of William Butler Yeats. He had? She had been waiting for years to talk about Yeats, and they talked while they showed him how to nail webbing on wood. His suit seemed to interest them, they thought he must be out of work and asked him how his French was, and when he said it was excellent they were delighted; they had a cousin in the insurance building at Dominion Square who was looking for someone to translate letters. They would get the job for him tomorrow. A translator! Translators were as good as anonymous, and he wondered if those pigeons were still on the path in the Square as they had been that day when he walked there with Scotty. At midnight the sisters gave him a cup of tea and he went to bed.

With a little strangled cry he woke up, struggling fiercely with someone, his heart pounding. It was a dream, all the details vivid in his mind. A policeman was struggling with him at the door of the courtroom. It was that same cop who had stared at him that awful day as he had mopped his head in the corridor; only now the cop had been pounding and choking him. "You fool, Harry Lane is dead," the cop shouted. Over the cop's shoulder he could see, just a little, the white-plumed Judge Montpetit on the bench, see all the familiar faces of the spectators, and the figure in the dock—only it wasn't Scotty. It was Mike Kon, his head going back proudly as Henderson with his dissipated face asked, "Did you kill Harry Lane?" and Kon

236

said, "I did and I'm glad I did," and at the door he himself cried out, struggling with the brutal cop.

He lay there waiting for his pulse to stop racing, the sunlight falling across his bed. Then he fell asleep again, and slept all afternoon.

That night, ready to go on his rounds, he started out. "Mr. Lane," Miss Rosamund Lacey called to him. "I don't think you locked your door. In a roominghouse you should always lock your door, you know."

"That's all right," he said. "I left it open on purpose. I'm expecting someone. Maybe a girl named Miss Morris. Maybe a man named Mike Kon. If I'm not here, ask them to wait in the room."

"Friends of yours?"

"Yeah, they'll be around," he said.

Chapter 31

THE Press Club was a big lounge with a bar in the basement of the Mount Royal Hotel. One night, some weeks later, it was, as usual, crowded by ten. The editorial writer everyone called the Brigadier, reeking of brandy, was lecturing two city hall reporters in a toothy British accent about the situation in the Middle East. Reporters came in with their girls. The man who did the saloon beat for the *Sun* came in, smiling complacently and with an air of grandeur as he led the blonde who was the hotel's attraction in the Normandie Room, to a table. At another table nearer the bar Joe Long, of the Wesson Advertising Agency, was sitting with the Young Lion. More newspapermen and their friends, the public relations men and the advertising men who always hung around, came in. A fat red-faced man, who had got himself a drink at the bar, sat down at the piano and began to play.

Mollie came in with Jay Scott, a young lawyer she had known for years, who had been pestering her all week. His family was highly regarded by her parents. An intelligent, slim man of thirty-five, with a wistful smile, and a little alcoholic, Jay kept telling Mollie he had had his eye on her for years. She was just the girl to straighten him out and give him ambition. These words hurt her though she didn't know why, nor why she let

Jay paw her, leading him on, then laughing and hurting him. They sat by themselves in a corner alcove. He began to bore her, telling about a real estate deal his clients were making for a giant skyscraper on Dorchester that would alter the whole appearance of that old neighborhood. "Hey, Mollie," he said suddenly. "Look who's here."

Harry Lane was coming in. With his distinguished air, Harry acted as though he were bringing a little class to the place. Approaching the bar he got a drink and sat down at a corner table. As on every other night, Harry was making himself available to the newspapermen if they wanted to take up his case. With sublime indifference he opened a magazine, unaware that he showed the effect of the many drinks he had already had.

The Brigadier called out to him, "Ah, Prince Harry, you are paler tonight."

"How strange, my lord," Harry replied with his charming smile. "It must be the light. I'm in the very pink."

The man at the piano was pounding out some Dixieland jazz.

The Young Lion, weaving his way to the bar for another drink, said jovially, "Man, keep this under your suit, but I got it on the grapevine the Witness has been tipped off you're waiting here."

"Me?" Harry asked shrugging. "Man, I'm just waiting for a streetcar."

He was deathly pale, and Mollie, staring at him, knew how much he had been drinking. His tie had been pulled away from his collar, and in spite of his smile he seemed to be deteriorating there under her eyes. *For heaven's sake, Harry, don't let them see you like this,* she wanted to beg him. *Fix your tie and go. Just do this one little thing. Give me a chance to respect you.* Then Harry turned; his eyes met hers, then shifted furtively. Out of simple respect for everything she had once meant to him, Mollie was sure he wouldn't be able to bear to clown in her presence, and would leave soon.

"You know, the guy has courage," Jay said thoughtfully.

"You've got to give that much to him. But he's certainly got a very thick skin."

"Yes, I'll give that much to him," Mollie said bitterly.

"Of course you know what he's doing, Mollie."

"Ruining himself forever around here. He's mad."

"No, not mad at all. Harry Lane's thumbing his nose at the world."

"Oh—is that what you call it?" Mollie said.

"Look out. He's coming over here."

"Oh, no," she breathed. But Harry had got up and was coming toward them slowly with an embarrassed smile. A fine flush appeared low on Mollie's throat, just at the collar line of the white blouse she wore with her black suit, and it spread slowly to her face. She whispered to Jay, "I've got to go. You stay here. Please, *please*."

As she got up Harry stopped dead in his tracks. For a moment Mollie faltered, held by the terrible loneliness in his eyes. Then she fled with everybody staring at her. She hurried out of the hotel and down the street, dabbing at her eyes with her handkerchief until she had to stop, blinded by her tears and pretending she was looking in a shop window, ashamed that anyone should see her crying so bitterly. "It just isn't Harry any more," she said to herself. "That absurd man isn't Harry. There's no Harry at all any more!"

The sound of hurrying footsteps made her turn. She saw him just as his hand came out to her arm. "Don't touch me," Mollie cried. It was as though he were a stranger, and in her panic she swung the back of her hand at him, striking him on the face. Again she ran, and now she kept on running.

Chapter 32

CONFUSED, he stood on the pavement watching her turn the corner, his hand up to his face. But the sting he felt didn't seem to come from the blow; it was the sight of her twisted face, her tear-filled, fierce protesting eyes. His cheek was burning, yet as she vanished around the corner the blow seemed to have been a light touch, almost a gentle caress, making him feel desolate.

As he wandered away he felt a touch of panic. He thought he would continue on his rounds. He couldn't keep track. He couldn't even feel drunk. A sense of futility was overwhelming him, and now he knew how desperately he needed Mike Kon.

At midnight he was a solitary figure passing under the rash of neon lights on old Dorchester Street. On the corner where construction work had been going on, workmen had left red lights on the road. The whole dark old neighborhood would soon be gone, and as he looked around he was frightened. His life couldn't go on like this night after night, the life of an actor playing a part he hated. Supposing Mike had the strength and the calmness to take his losses to his prestige and his pride and go on ignoring him? Keep to his store, keep holed up somewhere at night, no hand out for him, no "What right had I to judge you?", no court case at all, letting him go his way, letting him fade into the limbo of the city's lost causes, another amiable eccentric with the burden of some half-forgotten bank manager's death on him. If this happened there would be nothing left for him; he would be nothing; he would be really lost. "Goddamn you, you stiff-necked arrogant righteous son of a bitch. You can't keep it up, you hear? You know Scotty's driving you to me," he said aloud furiously, as if he were talking to Mike. A little later, when he was at the Windsor Hotel, he whispered bitterly, "My God, how I need him." He didn't notice that he was thinking of Mike not as a man he hated, but as someone whose support he needed, as if he had some blind wild knowledge, some faith in Mike's anger, his rage, his conscience, his torment as a fellow human being, able to give him what he needed if he was to go on, and he tried to think only of the almost uncontrollable frantic eagerness he had seen in Mike's eyes at the Bruno workout.

"Harry," someone called from the hotel steps. It was Annie Laurie, in a long, golden silk coat the color of her hair, looking fresh and happy. As she came hurrying to him her expression changed. "My God, you look awful, Harry."

"I feel fine," he said.

"Yes, I guess you do," she said gently.

"I haven't seen you around," he said as she took his arm. "You were going to be my advocate, remember?"

"I tried it. But I told you I wouldn't help your case. The court wants to disbar me," she said smiling. "Anyhow, I've been away, Las Vegas with my broker friend." And then she laughed as if they were both themselves. "It's a funny thing. There was a big party in the hotel there, and I heard a man looking at me say to a woman, 'What does she do?' And the woman after thinking about it, said, 'She goes around the world.' Imagine! How's your Miss Morris?"

"We've broken off."

"I see. The ride got too rough, eh?"

"Maybe."

"I thought she'd break a leg before she broke with you,

Harry. Come on, we'll get a taxi and go to my place and I'll make you some coffee."

"Maybe if we walk my head'll clear."

"It's quite a walk, but I'm game." She had a nice new place on University, she said, which was reasonably cheap because she was going to decorate it herself. As they walked along, her arm tightened on his, and she didn't mention that he was wearing the suit. It worried him. Didn't she even notice it? They turned up Sherbrooke, and there was the campus with a heavy moon throwing a pallid light on the roofs sloping up to the mountain, the trees stark and still. Across the street came a dirty little terrier that circled around them, then trotted behind, then stopped and watched them go into the house halfway up the hill.

Annie Laurie had the ground-floor apartment, and on the bare living room floor were two cans of paint on a spread-out newspaper. A stepladder stood near the end wall, which she had already painted a shade of pastel green. "I'm doing it all myself," she said proudly, standing with her hands on her hips, a cigarette hanging from her lips. "Who could do it any better? I think I'm a great natural painter, don't you think so? Hey, watch out for that paint." His foot had bumped against one of the cans. He was standing on the women's page of the *Sun*, and he thought of Mollie. Gliding around the room Annie pointed at cracks in the wall she had mended neatly with plaster of Paris, and he watched her, fascinated.

"Annie Laurie," he said softly, "you're a fine honest woman."

"Don't say that, Harry."

"Why not?"

"When you say something like that I feel as cold as charity."

"It's the simple truth."

"No, the truth is that when I'm with you, Harry, I'm always wishing I wasn't such a high-class bum. I've got no guts. You've got courage. Oh, I've got the class, but I know I'm a bum."

"I like being here with you."

"I always admired you, Harry, so I'm lucky tonight."

"I used to think I was lucky, Annie."

"It's easy to handle, Harry, when you get the hang of it. Just don't care."

"That's me, Annie. Ask anybody," he said with his cracked forced grin.

"I play strictly by ear now, Harry. All the trouble comes for people who are bent on using their heads. They look for angels in people, they always expect people to be better than they are, and they have their little schemes for them. Not me. I don't care. So I don't get outraged, see?"

"That's right. The laugh's the thing. Don't I know it. You're wonderful."

"No, I'm just a vegetable. See what's on the radio while I make some coffee, eh?"

While they drank the coffee his head began to clear, and he tried to take on an air of unruffled good humor. Chalk-white and haggard-eyed, he tried to joke with her so she wouldn't see he felt driven to the wall and lonely, desperately anxious to talk to her about Mike Kon, but ashamed. He thought she would look at him pityingly, for she didn't seem to have noticed the suit he was wearing. Kon would mean nothing to her. He wasn't sure whether she was just playing along with her bantering. She always had had that playful, amused expression with a man. She kicked off one shoe and wiggled her toes. The bright birdlike flirtatious jerk of her blond head began to trouble him. Did she really not care? None of Mollie's lofty self-regard. None of that pitiful embarrassment over what other people thought. Yet that unspoiled glow in her! There she was, thirty at least, many lovers, drinking a lot, having her fatalistic acceptance that all she could give a man was very brief love, yet having that enormous self-possession that sustained her and kept her loyal to her own heart. And a beauty, too!

"Harry," she said mockingly, "I make you feel so serious, don't I?"

"I was just thinking," he said awkwardly, closing one eye. "There's nothing common about you, Annie."

"Of course there isn't. I was brought up to be a lady. Everything is in the way you're brought up. I went to good schools."

"There's something I never asked you."

"Go ahead."

"What were you like when you were a kid?"

"Knock-kneed."

"They certainly straightened out."

"They're not bad, are they?" she said, stretching out her legs. "Even if I do say it myself."

"Talk to me, will you?" he said. "For God's sake, just talk to me."

"What about?"

"Yourself."

"Everything I am I owe to my mother," she said lightly to make him smile, to let him recover his aplomb. "I'm just here complete. Why does nobody ever ask me for my story?" Her eyes were on him, gentle with compassion, and he tried to smile brightly.

Her father, a schoolteacher, an interesting man, had felt he was overlooked; he had become a secret drinker in his room at night, she said. A terribly expensive sport. Her mother, old before her time, had worked her fingers to the bone, feeling she had never had a chance to be a woman. Her mother had sent her to a convent school, to a dancing school, to an art school, dramatic classes too, polishing her up.

"What for? Well, one day she pointed to my breasts. 'You be different,' she said. 'Remember, while you have these you can get anything out of life you want. See that you do.' My poor beat-up mother. Isn't it an immoral story?" she said. "I shouldn't laugh, should I?"

But he was groggy. Why didn't the corners of her mouth turn down when she talked about her life, as the mouths of so many women did? he wondered. "I'm just taking it easy," he said, and then he didn't notice that she had stopped talking. He was asleep.

For a long time she listened to his heavy breathing, then she got up, looked down at him gravely, kissing him gently on the head. She got a blanket from the bedroom, put it over him, and went to bed.

In an hour he woke up and sat there listening. It was dark. A patch of moonlight fell near his chair. Getting up, he went into her bedroom. The moonlight slanted across her bed. She was asleep. He got undressed quietly, then he lifted the cover off her. She was naked, lying on her side. Waking, she looked up at him, then drew him down to her. It was no good. He couldn't do anything. One arm behind her head, she lay there, then her arms came out to him and she whispered, "Take it easy, Harry. . . . I understand. When you really feel like it we'll get around to it. Don't worry." Pulling the covers over them, she put her arms around him and drew his head against her breast.

But at four in the morning he was awakened by piping whistles from the canal boats. He heard rain against the window. Still half dreaming he seemed to see Mollie beside the bed looking down at him to make sure he was asleep; then she put her hand under his pillow, then she went to his suit and quickly rifled through the pockets, and he struggled to wake up to see what she would steal from him if she could. He was so disappointed in her he couldn't move. He was really wide awake now, lying in the dark. He put his hand on Annie's breast and turned her over and she sighed: her arms came around him. After a minute she gave a little snort of delight.

He woke up smelling new paint. The sun was trying to come out after the rain. He heard a brushing noise, got up, and there she was in the living room standing by the window in a pale green print dress, a small brush in her hand, delicately dabbing at the white window trim.

"What time is it, Annie?"

"Two o'clock. I just came in."

"Oh Lord, is it that late?"

246

"I don't think you've really slept for weeks. You slept the sleep of the just."

"It was about time," he said.

She put on some coffee and some bacon and eggs for him, and while he was taking a shower he wondered why he didn't want to go on his way. "I'm going to help you with the painting," he said when he had finished his breakfast.

"Harry, I just can't see you with a brush in your hand."

"I'm a master painter."

"I'll bet you are. All right. I'm going to be the foreman," she said. "I may not be an honest woman but I'm an honest painter, and I'll tell you why. The great trick is to keep the brushes clean," and she showed him two brushes thoroughly cleaned and wrapped in damp paper, which he inspected critically. A little breeze was coming through the open window and she looked young, happy and elegant.

"Well, let's get going," he said.

"This is comical," she said. "Harry Lane painting my place. Gosh, I should sell tickets."

"In the next few days I'll help you paint the whole damned place. Come on."

"I've tried everything a guy and a girl can do together. I haven't tried this. Let's see where it leads," she said. "Come on."

She wrapped an apron around his waist, and around her own blond hair she put a handkerchief, then took off her dress and put on a paint-smudged smock, and he got up on the stepladder and she worked from the floor. He would stare at an area he had painted, then touch a few spots lightly with the brush.

"You know something, Harry? I like the way you paint," she said gravely, holding up her brush. "Like this. You paint twelve strokes down like this, then twelve strokes across the downstrokes like this. Where did you learn that?"

Got it with my mother's milk. It gives the right texture."

"And then you lean back and stare at it so attentively."

247

"With me everything is feel and texture. That's what my father used to say. Make sure of the feel and texture, Son."

"An old family of old housepainters," she said, smiling up at him, a little smudge on her nose.

In the room there was the clean smell of new paint; the cleanness seemed to be all around her with the newness of the room. It added to her strange compelling freshness. Her smock was open, and from his perch on the ladder he could see her breasts and her legs. "You're really something, Annie," he said.

"I wondered how long I'd be able to keep my gentleman admirer on that ladder," she said, making a face at him. "Whether a man paints a town red or a wall green it leads in the one direction. Get on with your work." Then she hesitated. "By the way," she said quietly. "I didn't tell you last night, but I ran into Mike Kon yesterday."

"You did?" he said, coming down the ladder quickly. "Whereabouts?"

"On the street at noontime. I had some words with him. Only one thing in that guy's mind, Harry. You," she said uneasily. "Honestly, I think he's just about off his rocker. He's got a funny hard look in his eyes. He's going to pieces. Not that it doesn't serve him right."

"You're damn right it does."

"Maybe it's what happens to all those hard-nosed righteous guys out of the Old Testament. Anyway, I might as well tell you. He knows you've moved."

"No kidding?"

"The guy has actually been over looking at your place."

"Go on. What did he say, Annie?"

"It was the way he said it. Like a man trying to get some kicks out of watching you go downhill, only it's not happening fast enough. You in that run-down roominghouse, he said. That cheap crummy joint. A jump from the gutter where you know you belong. All you need is a little push. Boy, it's real hatred, Harry. It frightened me a little."

"So he really keeps track of me," he said exultantly. "I knew it. I knew it. Now he comes around to the house."

Putting the brush down on the paint tin he stood in a trance, then he looked at her, saw the worry in her face and tried to smile. Hiding his restlessness he went over to the ladder; then, as if he had just remembered something, he said that the mailman was bringing him some stuff from the insurance company; he was doing some translating for them, he had better get right back to the room; tomorrow he would help her with the painting. And he took off the apron.

She offered to come with him. No, he said, he wouldn't wait. She could come down later and they could have dinner together.

"Watch yourself, eh, Harry?" she called to him as he went out. "And look, don't drink. Please stop drinking. Okay?"

The streets were still wet and the sun hadn't quite broken through the thin clouds, and the sky was all of a gray uniform lightness. Going down the hill he started to whistle. The lower part of the city all the way down to the harbor was a valley of mist. As the sun gleamed behind the overcast, many-colored streaks of light shot across the misty valley, tinting all the wet roofs and spires.

Chapter 33

It HAD been a quiet day in the store with hardly anyone coming in. And just before closing time at six Mike, sitting at his desk in his office, had been trying to write some checks in settlement of his accounts with the textile people; he had trouble concentrating. All day long he had been having bad moments and he blamed Mrs. Bowman. When he had gone out to see her, she had told him she had been thinking of Harry. The man had a good face, she said; the man had seemed to be so desperately sincere. It was enough for Mike. Though he was furious with her, he knew now he was alone. There in his office he would put down his pen and seem to be looking at Scotty thoughtfully, in the company of Mrs. Bowman, and he would wonder about Scotty's silence at the trial. Then he would remember uneasily how he used to want to be as shrewd a judge of character as Scotty was, and how Scotty, in spite of his good-humored smile, had never once been taken in by anybody. Catching himself in these thoughts, he would feel sick with shame that he was asking himself questions about his old friend; yet he seemed to be under some terrible pressure, as if he were being grilled on the witness stand. Unable to concentrate on his clerical work, he had been trying to figure out what he would do. Suddenly he slammed both palms down hard on the desk. The big glass ashtray bounced on the floor and rolled against his foot.

Willie came to the door, white-faced and worried. "Mike," he pleaded. "I was selling a woman a jacket for her boy. What's the matter?"

"They mustn't be able to say I didn't try everything first."

"Try what, Mike?"

"It's a terrible thing, Willie. Look—I'm asking myself questions about the best friend I ever had. It's come to this, Willie."

"Now look, Mike, if you've got a good conscience—"

"Conscience!" he shouted so angrily that Willie quickly closed the office door. "I'm the only one around here who's got any conscience. What a stupid thing to say to me. Well, out of my way, Willie."

"Where are you going, Mike?"

"Just to make a call."

"Take it easy, Mike."

Willie followed him to the door, then stood at the window watching him going west, walking slowly, a grim hard expression on his face. He had forgotten his hat. Mike always wore a hat even in the hottest summer weather.

The street was crowded at that hour with people going home from work. Some who knew Mike started to speak, but he paid no attention. Just as he turned up Bishop Street, the late sunlight vanished in a heavy bank of clouds forming over the mountain. There was no breeze at all. He watched the numbers of the houses, then turned in at Mollie Morris's place, and he rang her apartment bell and kept on ringing when no one answered.

Going back to the street, he began to walk up and down. Then he stood under a tree, and two leaves came floating down from the branches, and one struck his shoulder and fell at his feet, and he stooped over and picked it up and put the stem between his teeth.

In a little while he saw her coming up the street. She came

on slowly, wearing a little flat white hat tilted forward on her head, and a black suit, and his knowledge that she had broken with Harry gave him hope; it seemed to put her on his side where she should have been in the beginning, and he was sure that if Harry had loved this girl he still would have this love, because you couldn't get such a girl out of your mind; just look at her coming up the street.

A shaft of sunlight suddenly broke through the heavy clouds. It came streaming through the one break in the dark in a slanting path of light on the trees and the street, and she came walking against the sun, her hand up to her eyes. Something about her puzzled him. Her walk was so slow and indolent, so full of discontent she didn't look like herself.

"Just a minute, Miss Morris," he called.

She turned and stiffened, then quickened her step, trying to brush by him angrily. "No, I don't want to talk to you," she said. "It's no use. I won't listen to you."

"You have some responsibility," he said, keeping in step with her.

"I have a responsibility! Oh, go away. You're impertinent," she said haughtily.

"As a decent woman, you have," he insisted. "He's moved, you know."

"It's not my business."

"Some cheap roominghouse on Mountain Street." He gave her the address. "Just a jump away from the gutter he is, but what does he care as long as he can go on damaging me? You can help, Miss Morris."

"I won't be drawn into the stupid business," she said jerkily, and tried to pass him.

"Look, I'm giving him a break, speaking to you," and he blocked the way. He kept his voice down, but his cold hatred showed in his eyes. "They call me the Witness now, a comic, see. I'm the funny tailor who plays jokes with his suits. I know you can laugh down anything. Laugh off a trial, laugh off a courtroom. Maybe a woman knows she shouldn't do something, but how long does she have scruples if her friends keep laughing at her? There's no longer a crime when it's a big laugh, Miss Morris. And what happens when people laugh at justice? A man's whole life, his business, dies under a laugh. Even when I was just a tough kid in the East End nobody laughed at me."

"Am I laughing at you?"

"Miss Morris," he said grimly, "I know you're the only one he'll listen to. Just make this one thing clear to him. If he shows around here again in that suit I'll beat him up. I'll leave him a bloody mess. Will you tell this to him? As a decent person will you see what you can do?"

He watched her face hopefully. All her changing emotions made it lovely, and he saw she believed in his anger and his strength, and he was so moved with such a strange ache in him, he wanted to draw her toward him. Suddenly she laughed.

"What a cry baby you are. A really big man. Why don't you talk to him yourself? Go and talk to him like a human being."

"I don't trust myself, Miss Morris."

"Is that what a man's innocence does to you?"

"I was not a false witness at the trial. I won't be one now. Am I the only one left who has a sense of justice?"

"Justice. Oh, that pompous word."

"It's not a dirty word, Miss Morris. Your own father . . . justice is his business."

"I'm not my father," she said angrily. "I don't think there's an ounce of Christian charity in you. Rather than go to Harry and say you made a mistake, you come running to me."

"Cut it out, lady," he said fiercely. "You know why I come running to you. Innocence! In that style? You too have contempt for this man's behavior. I come to you because you're on my side."

"On your side," she whispered.

"Aren't you ashamed of yourself, Miss Morris? Why the phony attitude to me?"

"You fool."

"Fool, eh? Okay, Miss Morris, I tried something."

He shrugged, and she watched him going down the street, the man who had helped steal Harry's name and now would rather kill him than help give it back to him. His shoulders looked almost too heavy as he rolled a little in his slow-measured proud angry stride. And a torn newspaper page, lying in the gutter, was picked up by a sudden gust of wind and tossed crazily as high as his head.

Chapter 34

RUNNING upstairs, Mollie went to the window to see if Mike Kon was out of sight. The street was in heavy shadow now because the sun had gone. It was darkening rapidly. She looked across the road at the row of windows in the limestone houses. Lights had come on. A young woman came to one of those open windows and looked out, the curtains blowing around her head, then she closed the window. In the excited state of her imagination the woman's gesture had some worrying meaning for Mollie, as if she herself had been doing the same thing night after night while some duel went on in the street. "I told you, Harry. I told you," she said aloud. Everything she stood for seemed to be outraged. She blurted out, "Damn you, Scotty Bowman. Oh, you wretched little man." Then, trying to think about it clearly, she saw that she ought to warn Harry. But what good would it do? He wouldn't be frightened at all, he would laugh and maybe his eyes would light up as if he were close to some absurd triumph of his innocence. Her lower lip started to quiver and she bit it hard, feeling the pain of knowing he would rather go his own absurd way than be with her. She felt so weak she had to sit down. Oh God, why wasn't he there with her? she thought. Where was the failure of love in bringing him to his senses? Why couldn't she make him need her more than he needed that tailor and his day in court.

Picking up her purse, she looked at herself in her hand mirror, put on some more lipstick, very carefully, moistened her lips, straightened her hat, repeated to herself the address of the roominghouse as Mike had given it to her, and went out and walked down the hill. When she got to Mountain Street, which was only a few blocks away, she moved slowly, looking for the number. Never before had she wondered who lived in these old houses. When she came to the right one she looked up at it blankly. It was a shabby old house. A light was in the hall and lights were in the upstairs windows. Across the road was a cleaning and pressing establishment. She wanted to cry out in protest, "What are you doing here, Harry? Why don't you come home?" She stood by the lamppost for a long time looking at the house, then she went to the door and rang the bell.

Miss Lacey, the big one, answered. She had her glasses on. She had a book of poems in her hand. "Mr. Lane, miss? Well, I don't know whether he's in. I'll see. Who'll I say?"

"Mollie Morris."

"How do you do, Miss Morris. I'm Miss Lacey. Just step in here. His room is right here," and she rapped on the door. "Unless he's sleeping I'm afraid he's out. I'll see." She opened the door and glanced in. "Yes, he's out," she said, and then apologetically, "You see the door is always open. It's an odd thing. I tell him to lock his door. He's the only one who never locks it, no matter what I say. Will I tell him you called?"

"What?" she said vaguely, staring at the room's door. It was dark and old and painted brown. And why did he leave it open, always open? she wondered. Open to whom? Was he waiting for someone to come to the room? Who? Max Sweetman? Or Mike Kon? Was he really waiting for Mike Kon? Or did he ever think that she herself would come walking in on him? Or was there some strange hopefulness in him that kept him thinking the door should be open because he hadn't really cut himself off from the world.

"Could I wait for Mr. Lane?" she said.

"Wait where?"

"In his room. It's all right, I assure you. He's expecting me."

"Well, it wouldn't do any harm, I suppose," she said doubtfully. "Not for a while anyway," and she led Mollie into the room, hesitated, then left her alone.

But the room now didn't seem to Mollie to be Harry's and she began to poke around. On the dresser there was nothing to remind her of him, the desk had nothing of his on it. Then she saw a dark blue tie hanging on the doorknob of the clothes closet and she grabbed it eagerly, held it in her hand and let it run slowly through her fingers. Feeling comforted, she sat down and listened to the roomers coming home from work and climbing the stairs. Overhead, shoes were dropped on the floor. Somewhere a girl was crying softly. She suddenly got up and closed the door which Miss Lacey had left open a few inches and didn't know why she did it. When she was sitting down again her eye caught a pair of Harry's shoes just under the bed. She kicked off her own shoes. Snuggling down in the chair she told herself she should relax and doze a little. Again and again she glanced at the bed as if the chair wasn't comfortable. It got dark in the room, the street lights had come on, but she didn't turn on the lamp. Finally she walked over to the bed and stretched out, feeling a strain in her whole body as she watched the door. A flickering pinkish light coming through the window from the neon light over the cleaning and pressing establishment across the street played on the door. The sound of a step on the street made her heart flutter as she waited to see if it was Harry coming in to find her there on his bed. The next step would be his, she thought, and in her mind she began looking anxiously for him on the corner as people streamed by; she looked for him in the taxicabs and the bars and on the streets. Her head was on Harry's pillow, and the fragrance of her perfume and the sweetness of her odor that was, he said, like the faint taste of honey was there too, and as she buried her head in his pillow Mike Kon's threats, Harry's disgrace, the way he was carrying on, became unimportant, she was there on his bed waiting for him, making him need her. Abandoning herself to her deepest longings, she told herself nothing and no one was going to put her out of his life again.

Then she heard a cough at the door. The light came on. Miss Lacey stood there, the fingers of one plump hand twisting her heavy blue necklace. "I thought you didn't know where the light was," Miss Lacey said. She had an odd accusing expression in her eyes.

"I was tired," Mollie explained. She knew her face was burning and she was angry at herself, but it was as if Miss Lacey, looking at her in that way, was telling her she knew why she was there and what she had been planning. She got off the bed and crossed the room and picked up her shoes and tried to hide her embarrassment with a bright smile. "I can't wait any longer," she said. "I may see Mr. Lane on the way up the street."

"I hope so," Miss Lacey said primly, leading the way quickly to the front door. "I'll tell him you were here."

"Please do."

"It looks like rain, doesn't it," Miss Lacey said politely as she opened the front door, "though it's still all on the mountain."

"No, not just on the mountain," Mollie said. "Well, thanks. Good-by."

The silly woman, Mollie thought, coming in on me like that. If only it had been Harry. Why wasn't it Harry? As she went up the street slowly, she watched the corner hopefully. Again Mike Kon began to loom up close and threatening in her mind. At the corner she waited, growing more nervous; then she went along as far as the pastry shop and its lighted window. A warm rich smell of freshly baked bread came from the opening door.

A customer in the store, a big plump cheerful woman, the sales-girl beside her, was pointing at a plate of Napoleons in the window. People were hurrying by.

Then she saw Harry coming along in the silly summer suit, and he was with Annie Laurie, who held his arm as she chattered and smiled up at him. He looked as if he had been drinking. A little moan of pain came from Mollie. She tried to force herself to go toward them proudly, but suddenly she went weak. She dreaded the look she might get from Annie, the amused pitying smile coming out of the pretty woman's secret cynical knowledge of love and its satisfaction. She shivered. The force of her jealousy bewildered her. Then the sight of him walking along in that summer suit with Annie infuriated her; it seemed right that he was with Annie; it showed how low he had fallen. Annie was a loose woman who didn't care what he was, and like a drunken drifter he sought refuge in her bed.

Mollie rushed away ahead of them. She knew they had seen her, were following her with their eyes, and she tried to go faster and faster as if even their eyes on her touched her with the sordid grotesqueness of their lives. Whatever he gets from Mike Kon, she thought fiercely, it serves him right.

Chapter 35

LATER, Mike was in Ben's, the cafeteria behind the hotel, having two hot pastrami sandwiches. At the next table were three young fellows in black leather jackets, their long oily hair in duck cuts, and three little girls in pony tails and jeans. The boys looked pale, sad, and defiant, the girls in their tight sweaters bored and restless; they were like young actors waiting for a scene. Their utter inertia began to bother Mike and he got up and headed for home.

It was cooler out. Far down over the harbor there was a light streak in the sky but the rain clouds were so low on the mountain you couldn't see the rim, so that side of the city was like a dark wall with lights in it. Climbing the stairs slowly he went into the front room and sat down beside his father. Absorbed in his own dark thoughts he was as stiff and still in his chair as the mute old man was in his. They were both staring straight ahead at the wall; then Mike turned. The old man had just had his face washed and his hair combed. His face had a pinkish glow.

"There's something wrong with my life, Poppa," he said. "There's something wrong or I'd have someone speaking up for me now. Someone saying out loud things that everybody could hear— Like you would say them. Willie says I'm the one driving people out of my own store. He says it's me now—the fool. Me!" The good eye blinked at him sympathetically, so he got up and began to walk around. "You know something, Poppa?" he asked bitterly. "There's no such thing as a public conscience. It's one thing today, something else tomorrow. It's like an old piano. Who's the player, that's all. Is there a man in the world who wouldn't understand my position? I have a business and a spiteful, backbiting, crazy man is out to ruin me. Why don't I talk to him? Why do you think I don't try it?"

Mrs. McManus came from the kitchen to fix his father up for the night and he wondered uneasily if she had heard him. It wouldn't matter; no one believed anything he said now anyway. Familiar street sounds came through the open window, the voices of passing people sounded loud, then the purr of the cars. It all sounded so normal. All he wanted was to be wonderfully normal. Right under the window a happy high-pitched woman's voice: "When I remember the name of the book, I can't remember the name of the author, and when I remember an author's name I can't remember the name of the book. Isn't that odd?" And then, in a moment, three lazy indolent young men, laughing: "A very good day at the track." . . . "So it was. All short figures. No long ones." Just fine normal people.

"Oh God in heaven," Mrs. McManus cried out, startled. "Mr. Kon! Mr. Kon!"

"What is it, Mrs. McManus?" he asked, frightened, she was so pale.

"I think he tried to write something."

"He what?"

"I think he tried to write something," she said, trying to smile. "There on the pad," she said. "I was fixing him up and there, the marks like letters—"

Grabbing the pad, knocking the pencil from his father's fingers, he tried to make sense out of the wavering scrawling line.

"Yeah. It's words," he said exultantly. "What's this?" His own hand was trembling badly now. "It's . . . it's . . . could

261

it be— Does that look like judge to you? yeah, it does to me. And this, trailing off— Not— It could be Judge not."

"Do you think so?" she asked incredulously. "Oh, Mr. Kon, you're imagining—" Then she gave him a strange embarrassed look as he stared at the old man sitting there lifelessly, his bright eyes fixed straight ahead. "Well, if you think that's what it is," she said soothingly.

"I . . . I don't know. He used to say religious things," Mike said.

"Of course, of course," Mrs. McManus said, humoring him. "I knew a woman in his condition in the hospital. All she would say was 'Hail to the Lord's Anointed. And the heavens shall open.' That's all."

"His mind isn't gone," he said angrily. "I tell you, he knows and thinks, and he was trying to write."

"In that case, we'll have to watch what we say, won't we, Mr. Kon?" and she went back to the kitchen.

Feeling uneasy and embarrassed he followed her into the kitchen, where she had begun to iron, and he straddled a chair, watching her. There was a smell of steam as she moved the iron up and down the board with slow rhythmic strokes, her plump face getting red from the steam.

"I guess I was just seeing things," he said uncomfortably. "Maybe it was just a scrawl. I don't know. Maybe those words, judge not, just popped into my mind on account of you hear them so much."

"It's true, it's a saying, Mr. Kon."

"Not much of a saying either, when you come to think of it, Mrs. McManus."

"Now I don't know about that."

"Well, I do. Now that I think about it," he said, trying to smile. "It's all right for God to say 'Judge not.' That's from where God sits . . . not you and me. We're sitting here in this kitchen. Do you know something? You couldn't live if you weren't using your head every day about people you meet and things you see happening. Look. Supposing you see a guy's

262

a crook or a phony or a murderer. What are you supposed to do? Just let him get away with it? I'm not God, Mrs. McManus. I have to do the best I can."

Putting down her iron she looked at him strangely, for he sounded so wrought up. "I wouldn't let it worry you, Mr. Kon," she said soothingly. "People say such things, meaning it's the way it should be. Maybe there's got to be a 'should be.' Of course everyone knows it can't be that way."

Smiling, she picked up her iron, so he went back to the living room and sat down beside his father, still shaken, and he lit a cigar and puffed steadily. His poor father, he thought; buried in the old man was the hopeful belief in people. The good man, if he understood at all, couldn't believe a man like Harry Lane wouldn't listen to a little sense, wouldn't accept a gesture offered in a nice way. For half an hour he sat there pondering, feeling his father's eye on him. Just the same, maybe nobody should be able to say he didn't try, he thought uneasily. Suddenly he stood up, patted the old man on the shoulder and walked out.

It was sticky and hot without a puff of air, and a few drops of rain fell. Going up Mountain Street Mike watched the heavy clouds gathering and rolling together in a monstrous threatening black weight settling on the mountain's summit; then it started to rain heavily. The rain came lashing at the trees and thunder rattled off the mountain and came bang, banging right down at Mike and he rushed to get under a tree. A young mother and her little boy had also taken shelter under the tree, and the thunder rolled down the mountain, right down the sloping street at Mike and the mother and her boy. The boy cried, "It's like big guns shooting in the dark at us," and the mother said nervously, "Don't Son, don't." Mike had never been able to get used to thunder low on the mountain; it wasn't like a thunderstorm in any other city he had been in, and he was glad when it stopped just as suddenly as it began. His shoulders and pants were soaking wet but he went on up the street.

A light was in the ground-floor front window which was

Harry's room, and he turned in eagerly, but a young fellow and a girl, standing on the step making love, blocked the way. The girl's head was lifted, she was very young and she let her head fall back and her mouth opened ecstatically, but the young fellow had his mouth buried in her throat; his hands were under her open blouse. Blocking the doorway, they didn't even turn. Mike went up the street a little way, then hated himself for retiring as if he didn't want anyone to see him. Turning back, he brushed by the boy and girl. "Excuse me," he said and he opened the door and walked in.

"Who's there?" Miss Rosamund Lacey called from the head of the stairs. "Why don't you ring? What do you want?"

"Mr. Lane."

"The door right there," she said, coming down the stairs a few steps, her hand on the banister. Then her head came thrusting into the light so she could get a look at him, "And ring the next time, will you? This isn't the Windsor Station," and mumbling to herself she went back upstairs.

Mike stared at the door uneasily, wavered, took a deep breath, knocked. . . .

"Who is it?" Harry called.

"Mike Kon." Opening the door he saw him lying on the bed in his shorts, and Annie Laurie, kneeling on the bed, seemed to have been kneading the muscles on his legs as he lay on his belly. Gaping at them, startled, Mike muttered, "I thought you were alone."

"Ah, so you've come," Harry said. "It's good. I've got my lawyer here," and he laughed as he swung his legs off the bed and jumped up. He looked washed out, tired, his hair mussed, his body bare except for the shorts, yet his pale face had come alive, his fierce blue eyes were shining with crazy satisfaction. Tightening up, Mike stammered, then was glad Annie was there to make it easier, someone he could smile at, and he did, and she smiled a little, nodded encouragingly at him and stood up too. "Take it easy, Harry," Mike said. "I only wanted to talk to you." He raised his hand in a peaceful gesture, but he couldn't go on. The change in Harry bewildered him. The taunting hardness, the grim satisfaction, were going out of Harry's face, as if he grasped that this was really a peaceful visit; now there was wonder in his eyes. A flush came on his face.

Harry started to speak, then looked at Annie, trying to hide how much he was moved. Almost awkwardly, and he never had been awkward, he glanced at his bare body. Quickly he smoothed his hair, picked up his blue silk dressing gown which was on the end of the bed and put it on as if he were now embarrassed by his appearance. Then he smiled, taking on an air of courtesy and great dignity. "I know this is an embarrassing scene to walk in on, Mike," he said apologetically. "It oughtn't to be like this for us. I'm not drunk, though. It's a strange thing, but if I drink in the afternoon now, the nerves of my legs twitch after dinner. After they've been rubbed a little they're all right. Excuse us, Mike, won't you? Annie seems to be a born nurse. Eh, Annie?"

"I do seem to have that talent."

"She certainly has, Mike," he said, with his polite smile. The effort at friendly dignity, the kind of respect Harry was showing him, as if trying to convey that he knew he ought to be his best for this occasion, baffled Mike. Yet it gave him hope. He tried to take the same apologetic, respectful tone. "I'm sorry to barge in like this," he began. Then he stammered again for he couldn't get used to the grace that was offered to him; he couldn't quite believe in it. "Do you mind if I sit down?"

"I'm sorry. What's the matter with me? Here," Harry said, getting a chair for him. It was done so easily, so apologetically, that Mike became uneasy.

"Thank you," he said stiffly. Crossing his legs with an elaborate dignity he didn't feel at all, he wondered warily if he was being set up for some piece of mockery by all this sudden gentle helpful respect for him. "You see," he said bluntly, "I made a mistake."

"A mistake . . . you made a mistake. . . . Well, I . . ." Harry began. He looked at Annie; he started to speak, then there seemed to be a catch in his throat; he just shook his head. The silence was painful. "Well, I guess this is it," he said huskily.

"The fact is I'd like to rectify my mistake," Mike said awkwardly, believing now that Harry was really looking for a way out. "I'll tell you what I'll do," he said opulently. "I was stubborn about who was to blame for that suit. So I owe you something, I figure, and I'd like to make it up to you."

"How?"

"I'd like to make you a new suit. The best I've got in the store. Just pick out the cloth. How about it?" Then his heart sank as Harry's eyes hardened and Annie made a face at him. He began to tremble. "What's the matter?" he asked.

"I was sure you'd come and see me," Harry said coldly.

"All right, I came."

"About a suit. Look, what about me? Now you feel the pinch yourself, what about all that's happened to me? Listen, now you're here, what about all those things you've said—your public condemnation of me?" As Mike's eyes in turn hardened, Harry's voice rose. "I needed you to come. I needed Scotty to come out of jail. Just one human guy to show we all make mistakes even about our friends. This is what I get instead."

"I said I made a mistake," Mike said, standing up stiffly.

"God in heaven," Harry cried. "You don't come here to tell me you made a mistake, you come here like the smart little businessman you are."

"I'm a businessman. Should I be ashamed of it?" Mike asked, trying to hold on to himself. "You were a customer and I had a dispute with you about a piece of goods. I'm trying to make an adjustment."

"About the suit! My God, about the suit!" Harry shouted as he sat down on the end of the bed. His head was in his hands, his angry eyes full of bitter disappointment; he was so wrought up he looked nearly frantic. "Who wants your lousy suit?" he asked fiercely. "You poor blind slob. Get out of here."

"I tried to adjust this thing with you!" Mike yelled, hating the pale face and the angry and mocking eyes.

"With a suit, a stupid suit," Harry whispered; then he laughed a little wildly. "You ridiculous man. I want to laugh. I want to cry. Annie," he said turning to her, "lead this blind comic out of here. Tell him to take his suits with him."

"You heard him, Annie," Mike said, turning on her helplessly. "I came here and tried to adjust this thing. Now see that you tell people. Just see that you do."

"Are you that stupid, Mike?" Annie asked scornfully. "Do you think you can make amends with a suit? Haven't you an ounce of charity or humility in that fat head of yours? Can you only be wrong about the suit?"

"You may look like a million dollars, miss, but you're common, real common," Mike said, striding toward the door. Beside himself, he turned viciously. "Look at you," he jeered at Harry. "Here in this crummy place two jumps from the gutter with this woman. Why does she think you pick on her? Where's that Miss Morris you're so sweet on? Won't she touch you now with a ten-foot pole?" Then as he saw the pain come into Harry's eyes he shouted at him, "Look, if I ever see you in that suit again I'll wipe the street up with you!"

"Judge Kon has a big dirty mouth," Harry goaded. "Look, I'm going to the Bruno fight tonight. How about you?" he jeered. "Why don't you come out of hiding, heh Judge?"

"I *warn* you!" Mike shouted. He jerked the door open and went out.

Chapter 36

THE heavy downpour lasted only half an hour. It had been a very local thunderstorm. Outside the city it hadn't rained at all. Over the city inky blotches appeared in the scudding clouds, with stars faintly shining, then the moon came sliding into a widening patch of darkness. It was a good cool night for the crowd going to the Forum. It was the biggest fight crowd Eddie Adams had drawn in two years. Many who had been sitting at the ringside got up and were parading around during the intermission. Some stopped to speak to the men at the press table. The crowd in the cheaper seats stared raptly at the figures moving around the ring in the bright light. The fans liked recognizing local celebrities.

Sitting in a seat behind the boxes, Mike scanned the ringside rows of faces. He watched old Haggerty, late as usual, approach the press table where there was no room left for him. Raising his arm, Haggerty shouted for an usher and pointed angrily at the crowded table. The usher began to go slowly the length of the table, examining the press passes of the newspapermen. Finally he started arguing with a young fellow without a press pass who wouldn't yield his seat. They had to call a cop. Haggerty very huffily took the seat. Under the ringside lights all these movements had a hypnotic importance for those watching in the shadows of the cheaper seats.

Then Mike saw Harry strolling along the aisle toward the ring with Annie Laurie, and they were taking their time, talking easily to each other as they looked around, and Harry was wearing the light summer suit. He was getting into the ringside light just as he had done in the old days, laughing and inviting attention, with the air of being at ease. No one could have been more conspicuous. Leaning forward a little, fascinated, Mike watched Harry saunter toward the press table.

The Dutchman, in a purple robe, and his handlers were coming down the aisle and getting a good hand as Mike stood up, his eyes still on Harry, only now half furious, half stunned, grasping that Harry, being there, daring him, wasn't afraid of the fists, the pain, the knowledge that he, Mike Kon, a great old fighter, had deadly punches that could batter an untrained man senseless. Harry was actually there inviting the attack. The crazy man. Maybe suicidal. Or no—maybe not—maybe cunningly faking, feinting, getting him to leave himself wide open. For what? To make a monkey out of him? Anyway, maybe he should not leave himself uncovered, Mike thought warily. Still, it had to end tonight! Yet not with himself being led on, caught off balance. In Harry's room his mistake had been in blowing his top. No wild rush at him now. Get hold of him first. Have it out, let him see who was in charge, cold and hard, finding the right grim words so he could loom up himself for anyone watching, but not as a madman meeting a laughing maniac. A man. Handle him reasonably, firmly, as he would a juvenile delinquent. Now he would sit and watch the fight, take an interest, let it calm him, and meet Harry afterwards, coming out, and make him listen to reason.

Ray Conlin was leading Bruno down the aisle, the roar rolled and echoed long after Bruno had sat down in his corner. Trying hard to keep his thoughts off Harry so he could be himself, Mike watched Conlin as he stood idly in Bruno's corner with the home crowd yelling encouragement. Conlin stood there as if he had at last become a rich, opulent, indulgent conqueror. He had on a white sweater with big red letters JOHNNY BRUNO across the back. The arc light, glistening on his oily long black hair, made his face look smaller and even browner than it was. Bald old Herman, the other second, a quiet family man always anxious to get home to his children, also wore a white sweater with red lettering. He fussed with Johnny's bandages. In the other corner, the heavy shoulders of the Dutchman glistened with vaseline. Conlin, going over, complained to the referee and the handlers.

Those who had been loafing around the ring began to go back to their seats. Mike stole just one anxious glance at Harry, found him sitting down again, and went back to watching little Ray Conlin. He tried to concentrate on what was going on around him, and his heart seemed to be beating normally. Conlin's eyes were on the second row behind the Dutchman's corner where Rosso, the New York gangster, sat with a friend.

The house lights were dimmed, the big cone of light fell on the ring, and the announcer shouted, "The next bout for the middleweight championship of the world . . ." and Johnny Bruno did a little jig, his hands over his head, and the crowd rose and screamed and even the sports writers yelled encouragement. The Dutchman got a big hand, too.

At the bell Johnny moved out fast, popping the Dutchman with a light left on the nose.

Faster and much prettier to watch than the Dutchman, Mike thought, trying to get his mind off Harry Lane. Bruno had the legs, and the Dutchman with his bull shoulders, fighting from a crouch, his head bobbing, his long arms half hooked and held high, was ready to move in with the terrible short hooks. "Keep away from him, Johnny," they were screaming. "Away, away, away, away. That's it, away—away." The Dutchman missed and plodded on. Johnny, who kept popping him with his left, doing no damage but piling up points, nailed him with a right high on the side of the head and the Dutchman looked startled. Mike laughed with the rest of the crowd. Standing flatfooted the Dutchman let go with a halfhearted right swing, just to keep Johnny dancing away. It glanced off Johnny's nose. Blood gushed from the nose. Dancing back, Johnny shook his head and drops of blood sprayed over the canvas and on his own shoulders. When he grabbed and held on until the bell, the blood streamed down over the Dutchman's shoulder blades.

"It wasn't much of a punch," Mike muttered to the man in the seat beside him. "His cut man'll fix it." But he could see Johnny in his corner, spitting the blood bubbling from his nose into the pail, and he remembered the day Bruno's nose had been injured.

Coming out of his corner Johnny danced across the ring, but before he reached the Dutchman the blood drops fell on his gloves and his chest. He shook his head; he backed away, leaving a little trail of blood on the canvas. Grabbing him, the referee backed him into his corner and yelled for the Commission doctor, who climbed into the corner, pushing his bag ahead of him. They all watched the doctor feel the nose and apply a medication. He couldn't stop the bleeding. Finally he spoke. The referee, making a helpless gesture to the crowd, raised the Dutchman's hand. The crowd was still booing and jeering when the announcer, begging for attention, shouted, "Another bout to follow." Many of those in seats near the ring began to go home and Mike, trying to keep track of them, didn't know what to do, for he was afraid that when the lights were dimmed Harry might leave and get away from him. So he got up quickly and hurried out to the main exit.

In a little while the crowd began to come out; they kept coming as he shifted and watched and side-stepped, and then there were only a few stragglers left, and he knew he had missed Harry.

Going along the street a little way Mike went into a bar, had a Scotch and soda, then another one, and sat with his elbow on the bar, thinking of Mr. Singerman.

The third drink got him thinking of Scotty Bowman and he wondered why he couldn't sit down with Harry and talk about

Scotty? Then he thought, Oh my God, am I such a coward that I'm willing to put the best friend I ever had on the block just to appease that man and people like Singerman? No, my God, I'm entitled to some respect myself. A man doesn't go around asking for respect. He commands it.

Tossing a bill to the bartender he strode out, and on his way back to the corner to get a taxi he saw Ray Conlin coming out of the Forum all by himself, looking frightened.

"Mike," Conlin called, rushing to him, his little dark eyes bright and pleading. "You've got to help me. I'm in a real jam."

"You're a nuisance," Mike said. "Go away."

"I want you to speak to Haggerty before his column comes out," he said desperately. "It's about Johnny's nosebleed. Rosso won't see me. Rosso lost thousands. Little Augie came to the dressing room and told me to start running. They won't let me work with Johnny no more. Johnny's my boy. In this town it's just Johnny and my room in that hotel." The words came tumbling out of him, he was so scared.

Pushing him away in disgust Mike said, "I've got problems of my own. You were careless. Go away. You should have asked for a postponement."

"Please, I'm just a little guy, Mike," Conlin pleaded. "The fix was in for the Dutchman to go into the tank, and Johnny was to keep the title for six months so the Dutchman wouldn't have to fight Robinson. Johnny told them his nose bled two days ago. I'm through around here, Mike. I've got nobody behind me. I don't get paid now. I've got debts. I'll be thrown out of my room. I don't want to go back to New York. With Rosso against me I'll be found in the gutter. So I'm asking you."

"Asking me what?"

"Should I tell Haggerty about the fix?" he asked, his little dark face full of desperate anxiety.

"Suit yourself," Mike said. "Why don't you call him at his paper?"

"I called him. He's at Dorfman's. I can't go into Dorfman's. They won't let me."

"Well, I can."

"Speak to Haggerty."

"Out of my way."

"Too big for me, eh?" Conlin screamed as Mike got into a taxi. "Everybody says beat it." Conlin looked vicious. "Would I have had things on my mind if it hadn't been for you?" Then as Mike slammed the cab door he shouted, "You beaten-up old has-been. I wouldn't associate with you. That's one good thing I learned from Rosso. Never associate with men on the way down. That's you, Mike."

"Dorfman's," Mike said to the driver as he folded his arms across his chest. It was disgusting that he, Mike Kon, had ever accepted the notion that Dorfman's was Harry's sacred little fortress, and that he himself was an outcast. To hell with Dorfman.

But when the taxi was a block from Peel and St. Catherine they heard fire sirens, then a cop in the middle of the road stopped them. There was a fire on Peel, the cop told them. It was the night club, the Wishing Well. A fire truck was parked across the street. Firemen were dragging a hose toward a hydrant. Mike got out of the cab. A big crowd had gathered on the corner, but the streets was cordonned off and a cop tried to turn Mike back but he ducked around him. A thin stream of smoke was coming from the upstairs windows of the Wishing Well. Searchlights were playing on the face of the night club and big-booted firemen dragged hoses across the road, shouting. A policeman pushed Mike back toward the sidewalk. Blocked off as he was he could see no one he knew. The smoke, the flames, and the cops who drove him back every time he tried to go up the street stirred Mike's imagination. He felt blocked off, hemmed in and wild because he could see the light over Dorfman's. For a while he tried to stay quietly in the crowd and wait, but he had to jerk open his collar so he could breathe more evenly, and finally he went back to the corner, and east a block, then all the way up to Sherbrooke and back, and now Dorfman's was down the hill, with the crowd on the street smaller and not so many policemen, and he edged his way slowly from door to door till he was through, then suddenly he trotted toward Dorfman's.

Flushed, and with his collar opened and his tie pulled away from it, he approached the lounge and looked in. Harry Lane was there with Annie Laurie and Haggerty, and they were laughing; he could see that Haggerty still had his half-contemptuous good-humored indulgence of Harry. That's good, he thought.

"It's not next door to the Wishing Well," Annie was saying. "It is the Wishing Well."

"Get out," Harry said. "It's the restaurant next door."

"No, it's the Wishing Well."

"And they just had the place redecorated."

"So what?"

"Maybe they didn't pay the decorator and he's burning the joint down," Haggerty said.

"Imagine the Wishing Well burning," Annie said with a sigh. "I remember the first night I ever went there. I was nineteen. Ah, my beautiful youth. Now it's all going up in smoke. I feel so sad."

"You don't look it," Harry said and he laughed and was at ease and not bothered at all by Haggerty's condescending manner which showed a lack of respect for him.

Here he is in his little boozy heaven, Mike thought, and all his resentment of Harry showed in his hard eyes as he approached the bar.

"I can't serve you, Mike," the bartender said quickly. "Mr. Dorfman's orders."

"Want to make an issue of it, Charlie?" Mike said grimly.

"It's not me," the bartender said nervously as Mike dropped his cigarette in the ashtray. Without turning, Mike knew the others were watching him carefully.

"Well, Mr. Dorfman won't be in tonight," the bartender said

soothingly. "He was at the fights and he phoned. He has a touch of gastritis."

"I'm very lucky, eh, Charlie?" Mike said, mockingly. "Mr. Dorfman has gastritis!" and he swung around on the stool to face Harry, who was absolutely unimpressed by his presence. He had even put his hands in his pockets with a nonchalant air.

Through the open window came the cries of the firemen high on ladders down the street; a bell was clanging and then came a murmur from the crowd as flames shot from a window. Haggerty sat down, his elbow on the table, watching Mike reflectively, and Annie Laurie, very pale, picked up a glass. But for Mike, there was only Harry, who, smiling a little, took Annie's arm. "We were watching the fire, Annie," he said. "Come on," and he turned to the window.

"I want to speak to you, Mr. Lane," Mike said quietly, "and you're going to listen to me."

"How did you get in here, Mr. Kon?" Harry said.

"I go where I have to go." Mike took three steps toward Harry. "I'm settling this business with you once and for all with a warning you're going to respect."

"Come on, Annie," Harry said, with a shrug. "Let's go outside and watch the fire. No point in staying here and listening to this tiresome fellow. Come on." He took her arm. "So long, Haggerty," he said, and started to go.

Harry's easy indifference enraged Mike and he took a quick step after him. "I said you're going to listen to me!" he shouted. "I want to warn you once and for all." When Harry didn't turn to answer, Mike reached out and grabbed him by the back of his coat collar, jerking it down so Harry's arms were pinioned. Mike's crazy determination to make Harry listen showed in his eyes. Haggerty jumped up nervously.

"Go away, you fool," Annie Laurie cried and she tried to push Mike.

Harry hardly struggled and Mike thought he was going to listen to him. Then Harry pivoted suddenly; he jerked himself free; the light caught his pale face and his wonderfully bright blue eyes. Balancing flat on his feet, he punched Mike hard on the jaw. It was an astonishing punch, beautifully timed, for he was set right, and when he landed it Haggerty stood up, his mouth open in surprise and admiration as Mike went down heavily on his haunches.

"Come on, Annie," Harry said calmly. "Let's get out of here," and he didn't even hurry.

"Remember—just remember, Mike," Annie said fiercely. "That street out there is full of cops right now."

Sitting on his pants, Mike shook his head, then jerked it from side to side spasmodically. His eyes were glazed. He could see Haggerty, who was wiping a flake of tobacco from his lower lip. The astonishment in Haggerty's eyes seemed to degrade him and tell him that all along Haggerty, like everyone else, had been sure he had been trying to behave with restraint because he was a great old fighter who could beat up Harry any time he wanted to, and yet now he saw him sitting on his pants in the worst moment of his life.

Bounding up, Mike lurched a little and then rushed at the door, Haggerty and Charlie running after him. Harry was holding the door open for Annie, who had just stepped out. He turned, standing under the wrought-iron light over the door which made Annie Laurie's face look golden, and Mike shouted, "You—you!"

Mike went down into his crouch, his eyes, just slits now under the scarred brows, gleaming with a hatred and contempt for himself for all the indignities he had suffered as a friend of Scotty Bowman. His head bobbed a little to the left, and his right foot slid forward, then he suddenly shifted, and in the doorway Harry had no room to move away. He could have retreated quickly down the steps but defiant, not scared at all, his eager shining eyes tried to follow Mike's shift; in that space he was hemmed in and had no room to shift with him. Mike's right, as straight a punch as he had ever thrown, caught him on the point of the chin. Everything that Mike used to be was in the punch, and they heard a crack, and a kind of snap; and Harry, lurching, not tumbling but falling stiff like a post, toppled down the steps to the sidewalk.

He rolled past Annie Laurie who had both hands up, her purse hiding one side of her face as she screamed, and the wild lonely wail echoed down the street. She screamed again, "Harry," and stumbled down the steps and dropped on her knees beside him. The circle of light from the doorway reached only as far as her ankles and green pumps.

"My God," Haggerty said. He was wheezing as he ran out and knelt beside Harry. Even in the shadow Harry's face had a strange pallor, his neck was twisted awkwardly to one side, and there was a little blood on the sidewalk under his head. Coming down the steps, slow and hesitant, Mike watched Haggerty give a little slap to Harry's face, then another little one as he felt his pulse. He said nothing. Suddenly Annie Laurie sobbed, "Oh, no. Jesus, Mary and Joseph."

Mike swung round to her, startled. In a panic, he wanted to run, yet couldn't. One painful thought came to him: his fists, his fighter's fists, were deadly weapons to the police. This might be called murder, and he was in terrible trouble. No, he had witnesses, he thought, and he was with the law, no man more with the law. Yet his heart kept pounding. He felt wild with some kind of pain and mournful wonder, and his jaw sagged as if he had dimly grasped that he, who all along had been isolated in his lonely anger because justice had been seated in him, might now be grabbed and judged and condemned for a thing he was made to do by this crazy bleeding man lying here at his feet. He wanted to make a wild protest; he stammered, "He asked for this. You all know he did. What could I do? He just kept after me, begging for this." When no one answered him he turned away, his hands going up nervously to his face, wondering, My God, why am I here with this man?

"Get an ambulance," Haggerty shouted to Charlie. Mike watched the bartender run down the street toward the crowd, and then stop halfway down to talk to a policeman who had heard the shriek and had come running toward him. The policeman pointed across the road at another policeman. Charlie started to run across the road. The policeman came on alone toward them.

"That crack, that snap," Haggerty said to Annie as he stood up. "Never heard anything like it."

"His neck is broken. I'm sure it's broken," she whispered.

"He hit his head when he fell," Mike said nervously. "He fell down the steps."

"I think he's dead," Annie Laurie said. "My God, he's dead," and she put her hands over her face and wailed. Shaken by her sobbing, Mike looked at her as though he had never heard a woman on her knees wailing for someone close to her. "Don't die, Harry. Please, please," she begged him.

"I can't feel any pulse," Haggerty said.

"You don't know for sure," Mike said angrily. "He doesn't know," he repeated awkwardly to Annie.

"That's right," Haggerty said, but not believing it. "How do I know?"

Two puffs of smoke came from the night club windows, followed by a little flicker of flame; then Mike looked down at Harry and couldn't take his eyes off his pale twisted face until he heard the policeman's steps coming closer.

Grabbing Haggerty's arm, Mike said, "You saw what happened."

"I saw it, Mike."

"You saw him hit me. You're my witness."

"That's right. He certainly smashed you, Mike."

"You saw I only wanted to talk to him, eh? Anyone who hears the story will say I had a right to do it and that I should have done it long ago. When he hits me . . . have I a right to hit back?"

"Certainly you have. Take it easy. We saw what happened."

Turning to Annie, for she was the one he was afraid of now, Mike watched her morosely as she sat on the restaurant steps with the light on the back of her neck and on the calf of one leg.

Her skirt had got pulled up and her round knee showed, and a hole had been rubbed in the knee of the stocking when she had knelt beside Harry. The hole in the stocking seemed to fascinate Mike. She kept putting her fingers up to her lips to keep them from trembling, but her hand trembled too. Over and over again she did this, as if she were cold and shivering, and she seemed to be watching raptly something across the road, but there was nothing there. "Annie," Mike said, huskily. "You see, he knocked me down—you saw me on the floor."

"You poor driven fool, Mike," she said bitterly, and he didn't know what she meant.

Now the cop was there, kneeling beside Harry and listening while Haggerty explained what had happened.

The cop was French and young and had a black mustache. "Who's Mike Kon? You?" he said, looking up. "Me," Mike said. "You'll have to come to the station." "I don't mind at all," Mike said. Then they heard the ambulance, which had been parked up the side street, called there because of the fire, coming up the street, its red light flashing off and on. They put Harry in the ambulance. Annie insisted on going with him. Haggerty helped her in and the ambulance pulled away. There was only the little blotch of blood on the sidewalk.

"Get this down in your book right here," Mike said to the cop. "He hit me, then I went after him and hit him back. That's all. The guys saw it. He hit me once and I hit him once."

"That's right," Haggerty said.

But the cop, snapping his book closed, said, "We'll go to the station," and Mike and Haggerty walked down the street to the hotel where the cop called a police car.

In the station they stood in front of the sergeant's desk while the policeman made his report. Pondering, the gray-headed, gray-faced, gray-eyed sergeant shook his head.

"You saw all this, Mr. Haggerty?" the sergeant asked respectfully.

"I certainly did," Haggerty said. "A girl named Annie Laurie saw it too, and so did Charlie the bartender."

"We'll have to wait until I hear from the hospital. If the man dies there may be a murder charge here," the sergeant said.

"It was a fight, a couple of blows struck," Haggerty said. "Where's there any suspicion of murder?"

"What do you want me to do, give Kon a medal?"

"Even if Harry Lane dies you couldn't make any charge stick," Haggerty said sharply, and he turned to Mike, almost apologetically. "Don't worry, Mike."

Mike was astonished by his sympathy. Until tonight, Haggerty, like the others, had laughed at him and needled him. Yet now he was showing this surprising concern for him. Putting his shoulders back so he would stop trembling, Mike said, "At least I can get hold of my lawyer, can't I?"

"Sure, who's your lawyer?" the sergeant asked.

"Louis Applebaum," Mike said. "I want to get him right down here. I shouldn't have to stay here. I want him down here."

They let him phone his lawyer and it took a little time; Applebaum was on his way to bed. When he heard what had happened and that Mike had three witnesses, he said he would be down to the station in an hour.

"I'm going to stay here with you, Mike," said Haggerty, who was now worried and unhappy. With the excitement gone, he spoke out of a long reflective troubled silence. "You may need a friend."

The sergeant told them they could wait in a little room, a detective's room, to the right of his desk, and there they sat at the long table, sprawled out in the chairs, and were silent. Finally Mike took a cigar out of his pocket but when he tried to light it his hand trembled; he stared at the shaking hand and let the light go out, and as he put the burnt match carefully on the table he thought of his father and his shop, and he closed his eyes to hide his despair. A big detective came to the door, looked at them vacantly and went away. Then Haggerty, frowning and grappling with some aspect of the matter that bothered him, said angrily, "I liked Harry. Where could you have met a nicer guy? But you can't go against people like he did. You can't get away with it. You can't try to embarrass the whole world and expect to get away with it."

"Embarrass the whole world?" Mike asked, blinking his eyes at Haggerty. "That's a funny way to put it," and he was more deeply troubled; he didn't know why. "Do you mean . . . do you mean . . ." But Haggerty looked so uncomfortable Mike didn't want to finish the sentence. Haggerty might look more upset if he said to him, "You mean we all could have been wrong about the guy?" Haggerty might provide the answer. So Mike turned away, but his conscience was in a turmoil; the pangs it had been having the last two days now became a torment and he seemed to see himself isolated and filled with a lonely remorse.

"I saw little Conlin," he said suddenly, though he didn't know why he said it. "Outside the Forum, I saw him. Scared stiff."

"Who scared him?"

"Rosso and his boys."

"What's the pitch?"

"They heard about Bruno's nosebleed two days ago and blame Conlin. They've cut him off. They aren't even giving him his share of the purse and he owes everybody. He'll be thrown out of his hotel."

"He'll always find a hole."

"No, Haggerty. He has a life up here and he never had one in New York carrying water pails for Rosso. Can't you do something?"

"What can I do?"

"Give them hell in your column. He's a good trainer for Bruno. You know he is."

"It's a fact, Mike. Don't worry, I'll say so. It's a pleasure to take a crack at Rosso."

"Thanks, Haggerty."

He was back in the police station where he had been when he was a boy, Mike suddenly realized. The years since then had counted for nothing. The mysterious sureness of the fate that awaited him filled him with dread. All his anger was gone. Slumping in the chair and biting at his cigar he said, "If he dies—if they say I went after him to kill him—it's all wrong. I had a right to try and make him listen. That man wouldn't let me lead my life. Everybody knows he kept after me, hounding me from pillar to post. It's a terrible thing when a man won't let you lead your own life."

Another detective came to the door, chewing gum, and regarded them impassively. He took out a nail clipper and worked on his fingers until they satisfied him, then went away.

"Listen, Mike— Are you listening to me?"

"Sure, I'm listening," Mike said glumly.

"Well look, Mike, this thing will come up in a magistrate's court to see if you'll be committed for trial, and of course you can elect whether you'll be tried by a judge or jury. If it comes to that, take a jury. But listen, tell this Louis Applebaum as soon as he comes down here, right now, that for this preliminary hearing—get Roger Ouimet. Tell him to get Ouimet at once. Understand?"

"Yeah, yeah," Mike said slowly as he pondered. Then he jerked his head back more confidently. "That's a real idea. I don't care what it costs. It must be Ouimet."

Chapter 37

IN THE hospital they had set the two fractured vertebrae in Harry's neck and bandaged the wound at the back of his head. He had remained unconscious and Dr. Roberts, a middle-aged man with two little tufts of gray hair on the sides of a gleaming pink baldspot, was worried about the patient's condition. It appeared to the doctor that there was some pressure on the spinal cord for he could get no muscular or nervous response in Harry's limbs, although once, Harry had opened his eyes and tried to speak. The doctor was concerned with the possibility of paralysis.

They put a cast on Harry's neck and took him to a private room, which Annie Laurie had asked for. A plump young nurse sat beside him.

At nine the next morning, with the doctor and the nurse standing by the bed, Harry regained consciousness. Out of the corner of his eye he could see the doctor's head and he tried to make out where he was by staring at the cream-colored ceiling. Then he tried to shift his arms and move his legs and couldn't; there didn't seem to be any arms and legs. Frightened, he whispered, "Where am I? What's the matter with me?"

"Take it easy," Dr. Roberts said gently, bending over him. "You've got two cracked vertebrae in your neck." He smiled.

"I remember. I know how it happened," Harry whispered, and he, too, tried to smile. "I guess a man can't break his neck every day and get away with it."

"If you had really broken your neck you'd have severed the spinal cord and died at once. No two ways about it," the doctor said. "Perhaps there's a little pressure there now," and he sounded worried. "Just give us a little time." When he saw the panic come in Harry's eyes he said reassuringly, "Now don't go making up your mind about anything. This may be just a general nervous shock." He had a little stutter and was a very honest man, and found it hard to lie easily.

"The question is," Harry whispered, trying desperately to joke, "whether it's better to be dead from the neck up or the neck down," and the doctor smiled, knowing Harry was protecting himself with his sense of irony.

Then two of the doctor's colleagues, much younger men, came in, both crisp and confident yet deferential. Harry couldn't see them until they bent over him. They both had grave kindly eyes. The one with the black hair clipped tight had done some remarkable work in Boston and New York hospitals, Dr. Roberts explained, and he was interested to have their opinion. They took turns moving Harry's hands and feet. "The reaction could easily fit into the pattern I suggested," the black-haired one said, but it seemed to Harry that they both privately agreed with a hidden opinion of Dr. Roberts' and he felt desolate.

A little later, the plump nurse, when she was taking his temperature, told him that a Miss Morris had come to see him. Miss Morris had asked the doctor if she could speak to the nurse, and so they had talked, the nurse said. Miss Morris was very anxious to see him and would be back later. The nurse waited, but he didn't answer, or look at her. His eyes were closed as if he were trying to hide the sudden ache in his heart. Mollie and not the nurse might have been there beside him. Mollie's faint fragrance, her skin, the feel of her hand, he might have had all that. Everything that was young and ardent and tight and anguished and protesting seemed to brush against him. He

284

wanted to open his eyes and see her coming through the door.
. . . The night on the street when he had been with Annie
Laurie and they had both seen Mollie standing at the lighted
cake shop window. They had known she had seen them by the
way she had turned so abruptly. Now he could still see her,
hurrying away, only one thing in her mind, to duck around a
corner and get out of sight, to be beyond what he had done
with his life, not let it touch her at all. Ahead now was the
police court. If he lived or died, paralyzed or not, it had to be
in the police court now, an intolerable destructive disgrace
for her. Another sordid scandal making him an outcast forever
in her book, no matter how kind she tried to be. They could
never again have what they had had in this city, and she would
no longer pretend to herself that they could.

"Do something for me, will you, Nurse?"

"Certainly."

"Have the doctor tell Miss Morris I can't see her."

"You don't want to see her?"

"Tell her I can't see her. She'll understand."

"All right. What about the other one? The blonde?"

"Any time she wants to. It doesn't matter."

"Good-looking women seem to have a weakness for you," the
nurse said cheerfully.

At noontime Annie Laurie came, wearing a sleeveless gray
dress with a low neckline. "Well, you're going to make it," she
said, bending over him. "Indestructible old Harry. The Unde-
feated."

Her light air buoyed him up. "No, they can't kill me off, can
they?" he said. "Here I am, all ready to go another round. My
contract calls for a return match." But she was stroking his
hair gently and he looked up and their eyes met; her mouth
had an odd twist; it was like the mouth of a very young girl,
or a mother touching someone who was part of her own flesh
and blood, and he thought, She knows I'll be paralyzed. It made
him stare at the curve of her breast and throat in the low neckline so close to him, her hair brushing against his cheek; the

dress seemed to drop away from her, he could almost see her body, beautiful and close and brushing against him, and as he stared at her he was sure he would never be able to touch a woman again, and she knew it and that was why the gentle pity was in her eyes. His own eyes filled with tears.

"You'll be all right, Harry," she said. "Harry, Harry, I know in my bones you'll be all right. I'm telling you. You'll make lots of love yet—"

"Just as well you never counted on living with me," he said.

"I'd live with you if we had planned it."

"What am I to you, Annie?"

"Someone I feel very close to, Harry. It's almost better than love, isn't it?"

"It's a lot kinder."

"I'm just filling in but I like it."

Putting her head in the door, the nurse said a Detective Blanchard wanted to have a few minutes with Mr. Lane. The detective, a small, quiet man, came in very apologetically. He asked Annie to stay because she had been a witness to what had happened in Dorfman's. Taking out his notebook and speaking very quietly, as if he were taking a statement at a deathbed, he said, "Mike Kon assaulted you. Well, he's lucky it isn't murder. We'll look after him. Let's see if I've got the facts straight."

Staring up at the detective's sober thin face, Harry knew he needed to tell only the truth, nothing but the truth. His eyes became feverishly bright. Later, when he felt too muddled and weak and the detective's face began to blur, he tried to buoy himself up with a sense of ironic satisfaction in the truth. There it was. Everything going fine. Mike leading them right back to court. He could hardly keep his eyes open. With a faint twisted smile he tried to show he was alert, but he began to answer vaguely. Closing his book the detective asked Annie if he could have a few words, and they went out. Harry slept. When he woke again, the absence of familiar sounds told him he was alone and it was night.

His eyes shifted to the push button near the bed table,

though he knew he couldn't reach the button. If he felt himself going he would have to cry out. His heart began to beat heavily. He couldn't stop listening to the beating. He felt the panic of fear. It began with a pressure on some nerve back over his left eye, making his head grow dull and heavy, then it twisted down into his stomach while his pulse raced. When the little nervous spasm was over he felt ashamed and depressed. His whole life seemed to be a failure, yet he did not want to die. If he was to die, he should have died on the street after the fight. It could have been the end then and maybe it would have been right. But not now. No matter how he had failed, life still seemed beautiful. Once he had been sure he was the most amiable fellow in the world, liked by everybody. Even now it was hard to believe that anyone had anything against him, or that anyone in the whole world wanted him to die.

Waiting for the tremor of panic to resume with the weight over his left eye, he tried to mock his fear, to pretend that it was some repulsive creature who had wormed his way inside. Calling him "The Little Old Guy," Harry waited for the return of pain and of the conscience it brought with it. He waited, thought, Here he comes now, and fled from him by concentrating on Mollie's long white neck and her hair, her breasts, her beautiful body, the way she stretched sometimes, and everything about her that had been so warmly beautiful and alive under the mask of her conventionality. "Mollie, Mollie," he whispered. "Be with me. Come to me now. Help me, Mollie."

Later, he thought of his mother's hands and of the voice of his father in the house. This horrible phantom, this nearness of death, was only a nightmare. Still, he tried to pray. For a long time he hadn't said any prayers. Then, one by one, he remembered the prayers his mother had taught him. He tried but they seemed to get lost in the emptiness of his own heart. It reminded him of his father, who used to smile and jest as he explained, with vast tolerance, the reason why he put off praying. "There's time, always time," he would say jovially. "It's never too late. 'Betwixt the stirrup and the ground he

287

mercy sought and mercy found.' " His father's voice and the words, while he repeated them, seemed to hypnotize him for a while. But the fear came again anyway, worming through him. The loathsome "little old guy" again. His thoughts now feverishly bright, Harry again tried to mock him away. But the little old guy kept at it. "What's the good of it now, Harry? The parade of your innocence—it ends right here on your bed, eh?"

"Like hell it does," Harry mumbled desperately in reply.

But knowing he was weak and scared, the wily little old guy kept up the dirty wiggling at his conscience. He was smart. He knew nothing mattered to Harry now except that he shouldn't be frightened. The little old guy wouldn't be pushed away; he kept flashing pictures across his mind; a picture of Harry parading around with his amused disdainful air, making fools of Scotty and Kon, as though nothing else mattered. "Shameful. Shameful," the old guy whispered as if trying to make him see he had been committing an indecent act. "It's like you were a woman shouting, 'I'm a virgin, step up and see for yourself,' inviting attack. Same kind of a whoring, eh Harry?"

While he was trying to cry out weakly that he was dying and should be left alone, Harry perceived something; why, the little old guy was just another goddamned lawyer. Much smarter than Ouimet, too. A whisperer, using the dark and the fear, and witnesses who were now merely voices.

The old tobacco-smelling priest first: *"Now what about your fierce and contemptuous innocence?"* The little old guy slyly withdrawing, letting him say mockingly to the old priest, *"What is this? A new sin? The virtue of innocence becoming the vice of innocence?"* The little old guy lawyer had made a mistake. The old priest's appetite for argument was whetted; *"Innocence is so frail. Can it ever be acknowledged to oneself without becoming a vanity, a pride?"* What about that? Interesting, eh?

The little old guy seemed to get sore at the priest; he let him fade away, and back came the old silent pictures, digging at his desolation and fear. Scotty, coming into Mother Martin's for the first time, joining him for a drink. Scotty spoke. Talking pictures too now. My God, Scotty was really speaking. *"You charmed me out of my life, Harry. Think of it. If you weren't like you are, would I have become what I am? I'll be seeing you soon, Harry."*

"No, you don't. No," Harry moaned fiercely, as if he were drowning in the night and the fear. "Take your lawyer and beat it. I'll say my piece in court. They'll wheel me in but, by God, I'll say it. I'll say it!"

The sudden fight and the anger in him gave him back his life; it broke the spell of the night and the fear. At last he was left alone. He was himself again, lying there calmly wondering at all the phantoms that were in him. He fell asleep. Sunlight was in the room when he woke up. He lay there staring at the ceiling. Life was a view of the ceiling. This one had a mottled bar of sunlight from the window. If he lived on, his life might be a view of a series of ceilings.

Instinctively, he put his hand to the bandage on his head. Then aware of what he had done he began to tremble. He stared at his hand. It could move across his eyes. It had moved across his eyes. His heart began to thump with joy, and he yelled "Nurse," reaching for the button. When she came he waved to her, his eyes filling with tears.

"Really, really," she cried and started to laugh. "I'll get Doctor Roberts."

The doctor came in, little smiles rippling all over his face. "Well, well, well," he said, "those young men were quite right. The pressure on the spinal cord is lifting after the shock," and he pulled off the bedcover. "Try moving your legs," he said. The legs barely moved but the toes wiggled. "That's all right. Now we can be confident," the doctor said. Clucking to himself, he sighed.

The nurse returned to say that Miss Morris had phoned and also a Miss Rosamund Lacey had come to see him and would come again. The doctor stayed to chat a moment. He was a fine man, very gentle and unpretentious, who was sorry he had been too old for the war; he would like to have been a flier, he said. Then Annie Laurie came in and the doctor shook hands with her. The nurse had told her the good news. "You've got a good friend in this girl, Harry," the doctor said as he left.

Annie was hatless, her mouth red and her eyes happy. "Come here," Harry said and she bent over him, brushing her cheek back and forth against his lips. "I never rated a friend like you," he said. "All warmth and all woman, yet saying there's no love. I don't even think you want it." He put his hand on her head, then, unbelieving, he touched her shoulder; he felt her ear, he dug his fingers into her arm, holding her down against him. "I thought I'd never touch a woman again," he said.

"I seem to be in this world to be touched," she said, laughing. "Go right ahead, old boy." Her skin felt wonderfully soft and he fingered her hair. "You're going to make it, Harry," she said happily. "You're really going to make it. Didn't I tell you you were indestructible?" Her laughter in the room lightened his heart. Then he heard the sound of her hand brushing on silk in a rubbing motion. "I can't turn my head, you know, Annie," he said. "What are you doing?"

"Rubbing my knees."

"What's the matter with them?"

"They're stiff. I'm not used to being on my knees."

"What were you doing? Scrubbing your floor?"

"Not me. I was doing a little praying last night. I guess I'm out of practice. I went into St. Patrick's and I kept at it so long I could hardly stand up. It's hard on the little round knees. You know, when I walked out anybody who saw me probably thought I was bowlegged."

"You know something, Annie? A prayer from you might have a lot of influence in heaven."

"Not me," she said, smiling. "I told you once before I wasn't much good to you as an advocate. I just throw myself on the mercy of the court."

After a moment he said awkwardly, "Mollie tried to see me."

"You mean you wouldn't see her?"

"That's right."

"Why?"

"It's just sympathy. Nothing could have changed for her."

"Look, Harry. That girl has been in the back of your mind all the time." With a pretty toss of her head she smiled knowingly.

"What are they doing about Mike Kon?" he asked.

"His case comes up in a week."

"What's he charged with?"

"Assault with intent to maim, or something like that, I think."

"So the Witness goes to jail. You've got to admit it's quite a triumph for me, eh?"

"An unusual way of putting it, Harry."

"Well, Scotty was supposed to do time, wasn't he?"

"And so he should have."

"And now his loyal friend gets a turn. Oh, I fix them, eh Annie?"

"This time let the law take its course, Harry."

"No—this time it's *my* day in court." And Harry was suddenly silent, suddenly lost in his own thoughts, his eyes fixed and brightly staring beyond the window.

Chapter 38

IT WAS a fine late October morning when Mike Kon's case came up for hearing in the Magistrate's Court. This lower court had none of the distinction or solemnity of the courtroom where Judge Montpetit had presided at the trial of Scotty Bowman. Albert T. Hoare, the beery little magistrate with the rimless glasses, presented no solemn figure, nor was he accustomed to having well-known people jostling each other to get into his courtroom. Nevertheless the newspapers had printed big stories with pictures about the two former witnesses from the Bowman trial and their resulting feud, and treated the new charge against Mike Kon as a continuation of the Bowman case.

A half hour before the courtroom door opened, the corridor was crowded with acquaintances of Mike Kon and Harry Lane, who had to brush against wives of men being charged with drunkenness, friends of prostitutes, brothers of thieves and mothers of shoplifters in order to get in. When the door was opened the whole crowd jostled each other angrily, hurrying to the benches. Alfred Dorfman couldn't get a seat. The policeman at the door would have led him out, but Alfred, beckoning to a shabby little bald man in the corner seat at the back, took a two-dollar bill out of his wallet. The little man, friend of a thief whose case was coming up, let Alfred slip him the two dollars as he vacated the seat. In the same row, four seats away, Ted Ogilvie was squeezed between two fat women who had never heard of Harry Lane; they were friends of a shoplifter whose case was up that morning. Ogilvie, rising, asked them if they would move along so he could get a seat beside Alfred. They did. "It's what I'd call a mixed crowd, Alfred," Ogilvie said as he squeezed in beside him. "Have you seen Harry yet?"

"Not yet. I want to talk to him. They say he's got a brace on his neck."

"That'll really cook Mike's goose," Ogilvie said.

At the lawyers' table Henderson, the prosecutor, was having his own thoughts. He stood up, smiling, when he saw Ouimet coming in, bringing with him obvious legal distinction to a magistrate's court. Ouimet, too, smiled amiably and turned to Mike Kon, who followed him. Mike wore a double-breasted gray suit. He rarely wore one, but he thought it would help him to look more conservative, solid and respectable. Without a glance at the spectators, Mike folded his arms and waited with an air of untroubled calmness and dignity. The morning sunlight from the big window, falling on the table, suddenly reached the side of his face; he blinked and frowned and shifted in his chair. He felt none of the remorse he had felt the night of his attack on Harry. Since that night too many people on the street had spoken to him offering their sympathy. Others had telephoned him. He tried to believe that at last he had the approval of the majority of decent people. He could have believed indeed that he had the respect of everybody, except for one thing; he couldn't bear to tell his father he was being dragged into the common police court. It was too disgraceful. More than anything else Mike wanted to be respectable. And yet, oddly, each telephone call he got offering him hope for his acquittal seemed also to tell him no respectable man would be in his position.

Ouimet had told Mike not to worry, yet as soon as he folded his arms and glanced at the rows of spectators the familiar faces began to bother him. Ogilvie was there. So was the bank inspector, Slocombe. Dorfman was there too, and next to him a gray-haired shoe merchant. There were in fact all the same faces, whole rows of the selfsame faces he had seen when he had been in the witness box at Scotty Bowman's trial. How strange it was, he thought. No time at all seemed to have passed and there they all were together again. All but Scotty. Suddenly Mike was filled with a superstitious dread of what was about to happen to him. A dull red flush appeared on his face. His forehead was damp. Henderson was looking at him reflectively. Gripping his hands so hard the knuckles whitened, Mike opened his mouth as if to make a bewildered protest. It was all wrong, he thought. Just a few months ago with many of these same people watching, he had stood in the witness box telling the truth—now he was the prisoner. And all because he had told the truth about one man, and had refused to be ruined by another. Soon that other man would come in and the law would be on that side, on the side of that irresponsible man.

Harry Lane had him over a barrel. Harry Lane had finally got him where he wanted him by cunningly provoking him. He had led him on and trapped him triumphantly. All the spite and malice of the man had brought him this triumph, this present mockery of justice. Is it justice that I'm here? Mike thought. Isn't it all wrong that I'm here? Can't everybody see that Harry Lane should be here in my place? Justice! Justice! Is there no justice for me or for Scotty? Mike was glaring blankly at the spectators and Ouimet, watching him, frowned, and patted him on the shoulder reassuringly. Lowering his head, Mike tried to buoy himself up by thinking that Ouimet was waiting eagerly to cross-examine Harry Lane. That would be the grand moment. Ouimet would show him for the spiteful revengeful man he was. Ouimet would tear Harry Lane's story to pieces once and for all.

As the beery little magistrate with the rimless glasses and the dandruff on his shoulders sat down he showed no interest in Mike or Ouimet. He would get to them in turn. In the meantime, a man charged with drunkenness and resisting an officer was heard and sentenced. Just the usual mill run of shabby cases. A middle-aged prostitute, looking tired and dejected, was fined twenty dollars and costs. Henderson joked with her good-naturedly. So far the little magistrate had hardly raised his voice, had hardly looked up. Then, right after the prostitute, Mike's name was called. It was a humiliation to Mike to be following the old prostitute, so he raised his head and smiled and with a lordly calmness stepped into the prisoner's box and heard the charge of assault with attempt to maim read against him. Asked how he wished to plead, Mike said firmly, "Not guilty."

When Henderson rose, after glancing around the courtroom carefully, he outlined the case and explained in his slow earnest troubled style that the court was not dealing with a common brawl, but rather a premeditated action on the part of the accused which resulted in serious bodily harm. His first witness was Haggerty.

"You say animosity developed between these two men?" Henderson asked. "Did you see any evidence of this prior to the assault?"

"They had it out one other night," Haggerty answered. "I was there. There had been some trouble between them over a suit Kon had made for Lane before the Bowman trial. A piece of material didn't stand up under a cleaning fluid. Kon claimed Lane wouldn't let him fix the suit and was trying to make trouble for him over Scotty Bowman, and would try to damage his business reputation. Lane claimed Kon wouldn't treat him as he would another customer because of Bowman. So there was quite a scene."

"Were there any blows struck?"

"Well, no."

"Just a lot of bad feeling?"

"With Kon insisting Lane wanted to ruin him as he ruined Scotty Bowman. As a matter of fact, Harry Lane kept on wearing that suit, he never took it off, and everybody knew why. So

Bowman and Kon were always up for conversation with Lane around."

"Let me get this straight," the magistrate said irritably. "This tailor wasn't objecting to a man wearing a suit he had made for him, was he?"

"Well, it was a tropical suit and the cool weather came on."

"This is a new one," the magistrate said. "Well, go on."

"So Bowman seems to have been in the back of Kon's mind and Lane's, too," Henderson said. "Well, they seemed to have made their positions clear?"

"They certainly did," Haggerty said.

"That's all. Thank you."

"Just a minute," Ouimet said. "Now, Mr. Haggerty, let me put it to you in this way— Isn't it well known around town that Lane was conducting a feud with Kon, a spite feud, because Kon, giving evidence at the Bowman trial, had put Lane in a bad light?"

"Well, I don't know as I'd go that far," Haggerty said, looking troubled.

"Lane was out to damage Kon's business reputation. Out of spite. Didn't you see and hear a good deal that would indicate this?"

"Well, in fairness to Lane . . ."

"Yes?"

"He was in the doghouse. People looked down on him because of Bowman and they would kid him about Kon, and in fairness to him I'd have to say he would simply give his story of what had happened."

"He made them come to him. My, my, very clever."

"You might put it that way."

"And the story was spreading all over town that Mike Kon was a cheap unreliable tailor. This Lane seems to have been a bad man to get mixed up with. Now when the blows were struck, or just before they were struck, what did Kon say?"

"He said he wanted Lane to listen to him."

"Lane wouldn't listen, eh?"

"That's right."

"And Kon simply put his hand on his shoulder and asked him again to listen?"

"Not quite. He grabbed him by the neck and and held him and said, 'You're going to listen.'"

"And he got a punch on the jaw?"

"That's right."

"Thank you, Mr. Haggerty." Ouimet sat down.

Charlie the bartender told a story that agreed factually with Haggerty's; then Henderson said, "Annie Laurie MacNiece. Where is she?"

"Annie Laurie MacNiece," the policeman at the door called along the corridor.

People who knew her turned, startled; they had forgotten she had a surname. She came in wearing a black dress with a little white collar and a small white hat, and her eyes in her pale face looked enormous. Mike watched her morosely. He resented her elegantly sedate appearance and was sure she would tell lies. When Henderson questioned her about the fight in Dorfman's she answered as Haggerty had done and Mike relaxed. She didn't sound at all hostile.

"You seem to have seen a lot of Lane. Was he out to spite Kon?"

"Oh, no," she said, looking surprised.

"No?"

"No. You see, Mike Kon had been going around saying Harry had ruined Scotty Bowman, and now was trying to ruin him because he had been a witness and had been Scotty's friend. He frankly accused Harry of killing Scotty. Mike was being brave enough to say what everybody thought."

"And Lane felt wronged?" the magistrate asked.

"Oh, he was wronged all right," she said shrugging. "I knew both Harry and Bowman. Harry was incapable of misleading Scotty." Ouimet moved to interrupt, but Annie went right on. "He was a sitting duck for Scotty. All Harry did was try and save Bowman from the full force of the law. That was like him. He likes doing things for people. Maybe if you do a little thing like that the full force falls on you. But Harry is a gentleman."

"Your Honor, your Honor," Ouimet now protested angrily. "This is outrageous. This is not evidence at all."

"It may be outrageous and also irrelevant," the magistrate said testily, thrusting out his red nose at Ouimet. "But I'm trying to understand something about the background of this case. I'm also trying to decide something about your client. If you want to object you can do all the objecting you want to in a higher court."

"You say Lane believed he was wronged, not just by Kon, but by everybody?" Henderson asked Annie.

"Of course he was being wronged," she said. "Mike was being wronged, too."

"Really. You mean to say you saw Kon was being wronged, too?" Henderson asked as Ouimet watched carefully.

"Yes, sir," she said with a pretty but ironic smile. "Everybody knows now Mike Kon must have been wronged, because he punched Harry on the jaw and broke his neck. Isn't that right?" With a shrug, she added, "The trouble was Harry never had a chance to punch Scotty Bowman on the jaw so nobody believes he was ever wronged. People are like that."

"Really, this is intolerable," Ouimet protested.

Again he half rose, disgusted, but the magistrate, smiling, said, "It may be simple enough to be profound. Still, I don't think we should have any further reference to the Bowman case from the witness."

"But how can you talk about Harry Lane and Mike Kon without talking about Scotty Bowman?" Annie asked mildly.

"One thing more," Henderson said, smiling. "You're doing a lot of talking, but you can't vouch for any of these things, can you now?"

"Oh yes I can."

"How so?"

"Harry Lane told me the whole story."

"Oh. And of course you believed him."

"Yes, I believed him."

"I see," Henderson said, still smiling. "Now when Kon tried to settle with Lane—"

"I think Mr. Kon was goaded into it," she said quietly.

"Goaded into it? You mean by Harry Lane?"

"Oh, no. Goaded into it by everybody."

"Everybody?" Henderson asked, astonished as an indignant murmur came from the spectators.

"Yes, everybody," she repeated firmly. "What's so strange about it? You know how people felt about Bowman dying and Harry, as they thought, going free, and Mike being Scotty's friend and witness." Turning apologetically to the magistrate, she said, "Sorry. I know you didn't want me to mention that again."

"Well, you managed to," he said.

Taking a little time, Ouimet walked up and down in front of the magistrate, as if still wondering whether Annie Laurie had helped or hurt Mike's case. Then he turned to her almost genially. "By the way," he said. "How do you earn your living?"

"Well, one way and another. I'm a model," she said stiffly.

"A model. Model and actress. That usually covers it, doesn't it? Well, how do you live? Tell us, please."

"I live well enough."

"On money you get from men?" When she didn't answer he said coolly, "And I suppose in return you have to give them a certain amount of sympathetic understanding and belief, if they pay for it."

"I suppose you wouldn't call me respectable, Mr. Ouimet. It's a matter of words, isn't it? However, there's a point you're missing. A man doesn't have to lie to me to impress me. The world is full of liars, as you know. Harry didn't help himself having me on his side—not with people like you—Mr. Ouimet. Figure that out, and also this one, too— Whatever Harry

Lane is, it ought to be clear by now that he isn't a coward. Somebody was, somebody turned the whole thing on him, and I don't mean Mike Kon."

"All right, all right," Ouimet said angrily. "I defended Bowman once and it's not going to be done again. That's all."

Mike watched her uneasily as she walked toward the door and stood there, a little over to one side, frowning, and then Henderson said, "Call Miss Morris."

Mollie came toward the stand wearing a loose black coat, a long string of pearls swinging against the coat collar. Though she had extraordinary composure, her face had a grim eagerness in it as if nothing could have kept her away. Stepping into the box, she rested her black leather purse on the rail, swore to tell the whole truth, and looked around. She hoped she might see Harry before he was called, she wanted him to see her there on the stand, in the common police court. When he had refused to see her at the hospital she had cried all night, and the pain had lasted. She kept remembering how she had pleaded with him that this thing should not happen, and was sure it would be in his mind too. Each day of waiting seemed to bring him a little closer to her.

All her waiting was at her studio, for there they had had their love, and things as they used to be had still belonged to him there, and he would come, she thought, because all his bitterness and hatred had been over the loss of those things. And it would grow plain to him now that she had only tried to keep them for him, to keep him as she knew and loved him. It would be like coming home to someone who had never lost sight of what he really was. At night she hadn't gone out at all. If the telephone should ring she wanted to be there. A step on the stair made a lump come in her throat, and sometimes she began to write to him and then would think, No, he'll know I'm waiting for him here in my place and it can be as it used to be. Each day she had telephoned the hospital asking about his condition. Yesterday, when she heard he was being discharged, she left her door open when she went out in the afternoon. That night her lights were on till morning, and she hardly slept.

A newspaper photographer, who had been standing near the door, moved over quickly and snapped a picture of her. Flinching, she knocked her bag off the rail. Her right jaw trembled a little. The magistrate, who had also been startled, said angrily, "Get that photographer out of my court." The photographer ducked out the door before a policeman could speak to him.

"Now, Miss Morris," Henderson began respectfully, with his best reassuring smile. He had great admiration for her father and showed it as he asked her to tell about her encounter with Mike Kon. In her clear firm voice she told of Mike waiting for her outside her apartment, and how he had asked her to warn Harry to stop making trouble for him. She told of Mike's threats and how he had finally said he would take measures himself to stop Harry wearing the suit.

"Just what did he say? His own words."

"His own words? He said that if Harry kept on with it he would beat him into a pulp."

"That's all. Thank you very much," Henderson said.

All grace and courtesy, Ouimet moved closer to Mollie. "Miss Morris," he began gently. "When did you decide that this conversation with Kon was so important you had to relate it to the police?"

"After I learned what he had done to Mr. Lane."

"You thought it was your duty to go to the police?"

"I certainly did," she said firmly.

"By the way—you were engaged to Lane?"

"Yes."

"All right. Let's get at what went on between you and Mr. Kon. How did he start off?"

"I tried to get away from him. He insisted on going over the whole thing."

"Opening his heart to you? Telling you he was being mocked and bedeviled, his business slandered by this man?"

"Yes, it was astonishing. No awareness at all that he had ruined Mr. Lane. I had no sympathy for him."

"What did he want you to do? Here he was pleading with you, telling you that the last thing on earth he wanted was a brawl with Harry Lane, eh? What did you say when he begged you to talk to Lane and try to make him listen to reason?"

"What did I say? Why, I told him to be a man and talk to Harry Lane himself."

"I see," Ouimet said, smiling. "If someone had to beard the lion it wasn't going to be you, eh?"

"I told Mr. Kon he was a most presumptuous man."

"In thinking he could drive you to Lane?"

"With this story? Certainly. I told him how outrageously blind he was."

"Blind?" Ouimet repeated. Then he dug at her in his bland sly innocent tone. "You mean he ought to have known, as everybody else did, that with Lane carrying on the way he was you wouldn't even be seen with Lane? This poor tailor ought to have known that Lane's behavior so disgusted you, you had washed your hands of him?"

"If you mean I wasn't seeing him—"

"I mean you got angry and abusive because Kon dared to suggest that you might deign to talk to this man who had made himself a social outcast."

"No," she said, stricken, and stared at Ouimet with hatred. "You don't understand. How could you?"

"You say you were actually frightened for Harry Lane?"

"That's true."

"So frightened that you could bear to hurry to Lane to warn him? Did you?"

"No," she whispered.

"Speak up."

"No," she said, all the color draining from her face again.

"Of course not. In your mind it wasn't worth mentioning to anyone, was it, Miss Morris?" As she started to protest he shrugged and smiled. "That's all, Miss Morris," and he turned away, brushing her off without even condescending to take her very seriously. Her hand clutched the rail so tightly her knuckles stood out. She seemed to understand that Ouimet had used her against Harry, a witness against his conduct in any event, and she turned to the magistrate as if she was going to plead with him. In the agonizing silence of the courtroom, with everyone staring at her, a dull flush crept up her cheeks, but her eyes hardened.

"The witness may step down," the magistrate said.

Her mouth trembling, she kept her head up going toward the door, and when she was halfway there she stopped, for Annie Laurie, her face full of sympathy, rose in her seat as if she wanted to speak to her. Only then did Mollie really look humiliated. She went round to the back, hiding herself in a seat in the back row.

"Call Harry Lane," Henderson said.

"Harry Lane," the officer called, and then another officer at the door opened it and called along the corridor, "Harry Lane."

Let him come, Mike thought. All he asked was that Harry Lane shouldn't come in looking crippled and have an advantage.

"Harry Lane," came the loud voice again from the corridor. They all waited. Finally the officer at the door said, "He doesn't answer."

"Where's this man Lane?" the magistrate asked Henderson. "Why haven't you got him here?"

"I can't understand it," said Henderson, and he put both hands in his hip pockets and swung toward the door. "I spoke to him yesterday. He seemed most anxious to come. All keyed up, in fact. After all, the man had just about been half killed. I would have said nothing was as important to him as getting here. I should say," he added, reflecting a little and growing troubled, "I called his place an hour ago. Some things I wanted to get straight. He was gone for the day, they said. I didn't gather . . . I thought he was on his way here."

Listening raptly, Mike realized that Lane wasn't going to appear, and he didn't understand it, and was bewildered. He turned to Ouimet.

"If Lane doesn't choose to appear," Ouimet said with a broad smile and a shrug, "doesn't that just about tell the story?"

"The charge was laid by the police," Henderson said irritably. "I can subpoena Lane. I'm asking for an adjournment."

"I'm asking for a dismissal," Ouimet said flatly. "The plain fact seems to be Lane doesn't want this charge pressed. What else can you say? Anyway, on the evidence already heard how can the charge as laid be supported? Where's the case?"

"There is evidence here," Henderson said irritably, "of a calculated and planned intent to commit a crime—a violent assault. I should say that there is evidence that Kon announced in advance his intention to do harm to Lane."

"Lane doesn't seem to think so," Ouimet said dryly.

"Well, I can ask for an adjournment and subpoena Lane."

"Am I to take it," the little magistrate asked, scratching at his left shoulder, "that Lane won't deign to appear unless he's forced to?"

"I merely said that he showed no embarrassment when I talked to him," Henderson said uncomfortably. "I didn't know he wouldn't appear." And he turned again toward the door, as if hoping that Harry might still walk in offering some apology, an accident on the way perhaps, or some trouble from his injury that might have delayed him.

The three reporters at the table, half believing that Henderson had some knowledge that Harry was not far away, also turned. Then their heads came together and they whispered, two young men and old Entwhistle of the *Sun,* and as they whispered, they stared at Mike too knowingly, sharing some cynical knowledge that he was a party to the deal; he had got to Lane, mollified him, fixed him, given in to him. Mike's face reddened. He was infuriated. Taking out his handkerchief he wiped his mouth. They all seemed to believe that his fate was in Harry's hands. It was intolerable. He lost his head and blurted out angrily, "Could I say something, sir?"

"No," Ouimet said sharply as he moved over to him. "At this hearing you don't have to say anything. We're reserving our defense."

The magistrate, hunching himself forward on his chair, threw a quick glance at Ouimet, whose confident smile seemed to provoke him. His mottled worldly little face was full of arrogance as he made a clucking noise with his tongue and shook his head at Henderson. "This is a serious charge and I'm trying to decide if there's a case for committing this man for trial." In an obvious determination to dominate his own court, he took over. "Are you sure you want an adjournment, Mr. Henderson? Supposing you and he, the 'murderously assaulted' man, are here and he shows he wants no part of the proceedings, which would be the truth if you had to subpoena him, are we going to be more enlightened than we are right now? Won't the facts still stand as they are? He took a punch at Kon and Kon took a punch at him and he got the worst of it. Am I to commit Kon for trial on that evidence?"

"If that were all the evidence," Henderson said, "the charge, of course, would have to be reduced."

"I'm afraid so," the magistrate said. "What have we got here? Evidence that Kon took Lane by the arm and said, 'You're going to listen to me.' The point is he wanted him to listen. He didn't try to brain him first. He wanted him to listen, is that conceded?"

"No, I don't concede it."

"You don't? Well, what am I missing?"

"What happened in the restaurant," Henderson said, walking up and down with his hands behind his back. "What happened in the restaurant surely has to be taken in conjunction with Kon's threats made well in advance to the witness, Miss Morris," and he turned and looked for Mollie. "Kon was in the restaurant looking for Lane and looking for trouble. He was going to settle with Lane. A man of his word. So much so in fact that he broke Lane's neck. He's lucky Lane isn't dead. Surely if you accept Miss Morris' evidence there's a case here."

"Well, I'm troubled a little by the evidence of Miss Morris," the magistrate said slowly as he rubbed his cheek.

"If I could be of any assistance in assessing that evidence," Ouimet said politely.

"I always appreciate the assistance of learned counsel," the magistrate said, fixing Ouimet with his sharp shrewd eyes, "but I prefer to do this myself." And it was plain to everyone in the courtroom he was saying with his eyes, "You don't often come into this courtroom so now I'll show how I assess a piece of evidence." As he cleared his throat, the expression on his face changed and he sounded grave and conscientious. "Of course Miss Morris showed a strong prejudice against Kon. It was only natural that she would, and obviously it would color her thinking. I've got all that in mind. But I have to ask myself if there was any real evidence from her of Kon's determination to seek out Lane and maim him. What in the world was the matter with Kon coming to her to ask her to use her influence to end the quarrel with Lane? It may have been offensive to her—she certainly made it plain she was hardly on Lane's side—but I have to ask myself if she wasn't really giving evidence that Kon was going out of his way to show that he wanted no trouble with Lane. Her evidence is certainly inconclusive. Indeed it is. You can look at it either way. And why doesn't Lane want to appear against this man?" Pondering he looked out the window, pursing his lips, then he said to Henderson, "Surely this charge should have been reduced."

"Well, possibly it ought to be reduced," Henderson said, shrugging and throwing up his hands.

"If it's to be common assault," Ouimet said, smiling at the magistrate, "we'll find ourselves being tried summarily by you." Then he turned sympathetically to Henderson. "I'm afraid, though, my learned friend will be without a complainant. If there's no case for a committal for trial on the charge as laid, surely it is apparent that Lane will be just as reluctant a party to any common assault charge. He knows the story. The man simply does not want to appear in court. Let's face it."

"What do you say, Mr. Henderson?" the magistrate asked.

"What can I say? How can I press for a committal for trial under the circumstances? As for a lesser charge, without Lane's co-operation—well—" He swung his arm and walked over to the table.

"There's just one thing I'd like to say," Ouimet said. "A lot has been said here about the Bowman case and Lane's belief that he had been wronged and, as proof of it, that Kon, to show his contempt, wouldn't even fix a suit he had made for him." Then his tone became sharp and vindictive. "Lane seems to have made it a point to try to disturb the conscience of anybody who had anything to do with that case. This is the way to drive men crazy. All Kon wanted to say to Lane was 'Get out of my conscience, don't try to twist it by damaging my business.' These men like Lane, who feel wronged, take it on themselves to go around tormenting people who merely did their duty, as I did my duty in that case, as Mike Kon did his duty . . ." And then, as he glanced at Mike, he faltered, for Mike seemed to be begging him with his eyes to stop talking.

"I've made up my mind," the little magistrate said. "It seems to me that the accused, under extreme provocation, was trying to defend himself. Once the accused had been struck by Lane it was not unreasonable that he should strike back. It was unfortunate that the restaurant steps were there. The fact that Lane isn't here today is important. Maybe he feels he was to blame. Case dismissed."

There was a burst of applause which the magistrate didn't try to restrain. The policeman, standing beside the dock, said roughly to Mike, "All right. On your way."

But Mike stood there, taking a deep breath which he let out slowly. "Thank you," he said to the magistrate.

"Don't thank me," the magistrate said. "In my opinion you're a lucky man that Lane wouldn't condescend to come here and testify."

"Condescend?" Mike asked, very pale. "Oh, it's just like him. Just like him." And he remembered the night in Dorfman's when Harry had tossed the coat at him, then had picked it up and walked out, rising above him disdainfully. His face was burning, and the pain of his humiliation showed in his eyes; then he began to struggle desperately to find some dignity in his position as he stood in front of the magistrate.

"Could I say something, sir?" he said huskily to the magistrate, and he longed to put himself above this situation.

"Certainly."

"The Bowman business has been mentioned again and again here . . ." he stammered.

"Come on," Ouimet said to him impatiently. "The case is dismissed. On your way. You don't have to say anything more."

"No, there's one thing I've got to say," Mike said doggedly as he turned to the magistrate. "I've got to say it here and now." Taking a deep breath he hesitated, half bewildered and half driven, and looked at Ouimet for help, then at the door as though weighing whether he could hurry out. Lifting his head, he said with dignity, "Scotty Bowman was my good friend as everybody knows. That's why I'm in this court today. I did accuse Harry Lane of ruining Scotty Bowman. I did it openly and made no bones about it. But this is what I'd like to say here in this court. I had no right to make that accusation and try to stick by it. I lost my head; you see, everybody was against Harry Lane and so was I, but I was carried away by my sympathy for my friend Scotty Bowman. Maybe I had no way of judging the real facts. Maybe I had no right to judge Harry Lane. After all, how do I know what went on between him and Scotty Bowman? Maybe I was blinded by my friendship for Scotty. That's all. Thank you."

"I said, come on, now, shut up for God's sake," Ouimet whispered to him, looking distressed. Not a spectator had moved. They were all watching Mike.

"Well, it's up to your own conscience. You know best," the magistrate said thoughtfully. "I must say you sound more like a man to me now. Next case, please."

In the corridor friends crowded around Mike, shaking his hand and congratulating him on his acquittal, but most of them had an embarrassed air. Some just stood a few feet away watching him, and those who shook hands with him didn't know what to say because he looked distressed.

As the courtroom emptied, the little crowd around Mike grew larger. These spectators seemed to believe he owed them some kind of an explanation, so they gaped at him and waited. Even Ted Ogilvie, standing there with Annie Laurie, hesitated to speak to Mike.

"It's an odd thing," Annie said thoughtfully to Ogilvie as she eyed Mike. "Harry was going around seeking an advocate, wasn't he? Well, he's certainly found one now."

"You mean Kon?"

"Mike Kon. No less, darling."

"Well, he doesn't look too happy about it. Look at him."

Mike held the attention of the little crowd because he didn't look like a man who had been acquitted. Standing with both hands in his pockets, discouraging any handshaking, he seemed to be lonely and confused. Old Haggerty, pushing his way in, grabbed him by the arm. "You got off, Mike, and I'm damn glad," he said. "But what the hell were you trying to do?"

"You ask such a question, Haggerty?"

"I sure do," Haggerty said, worried himself. "You didn't have to say all those things."

"Don't tell me what I had to say. You're not a very understanding man, Haggerty," Mike said angrily.

"What the hell is this, Mike? Why does everyone want to sound so big?"

"What's the matter with you?" Mike said. There were tears in his eyes. "Don't you think it was hard for me to say those things? I loved Scotty Bowman."

"I guess you did," Haggerty said awkwardly. Somewhat embarrassed he patted Mike on the shoulder, then moved over to Ogilvie and Annie Laurie. "Did you hear old loving Mike? What's he going to say when he sees that apologetic speech of his in all the newspapers? What about that?"

"Maybe he won't mind," Annie said. "Maybe in his own way Mike is an honest man."

"Sure, we're all honest," Ogilvie said grinning. "Just the same, I'm wondering if old Mike isn't going to become a crashing bore."

"A bore. How so?"

"One of these people who have to explain and explain," he said cynically. "Just to prove he's honest, won't Mike have to explain how he could have been wrong and misjudged Harry? Won't he though?"

He had paused, staring along the corridor, and Annie Laurie said, "What's the matter, Ted?"

"There's Mollie Morris."

"You know something, Ted?" Annie said, turning and watching Mollie, who had come toward them, then stopped, turning away. "I feel a little sorry for her."

"Wouldn't she love that. Excuse me, I'll speak to her," and he went to her. "I was wondering where you went, Mollie," he said.

"I went to do some phoning," she said. Her eyes were too bright. She was angry and worried and baffled and humiliated. "Imagine that man leaving me stuck here alone," she said jerkily. "Is he absolutely unpredictable now? I called his roominghouse. They don't know where he is. All they know is that he said he wouldn't be back all day. Where in the world is he?"

Chapter 39

HARRY was sitting by himself in a booth in a shabby little restaurant on St. Lawrence in the East End, far away from his own neighborhood. It was eight o'clock in the evening and he was the only customer left in the restaurant. The French-Canadian proprietor, a little man with a thin black mustache who had brought Harry three cups of coffee, stood by his cash register watching him dubiously. He couldn't figure Harry out. He had seen him come in half an hour ago, a well-dressed man in a dark blue suit, a white shirt and a blue tie. He had noticed him because he had what looked like a small brace or a heavy bandage on his neck. The proprietor couldn't figure him out, because he had come in with the evening newspaper which he had spread out on the table, ordered a cup of coffee, put a coin in the jukebox and had then sat down staring at the front page of the newspaper. But he didn't turn the page. He would lean forward, his elbows on the table, read for a minute, then lean back troubled and look dreamily at the ceiling. Whenever the jukebox stopped playing he would get up and put in another coin and play the same record again.

A truck driver and his girl came in. The girl was like a tiny doll and the truck driver beamed with pride of her. Looking over at them vaguely, Harry picked up his newspaper again.

On the front page was a picture of Mollie, her head tossed back with an air of startled disdain as if dirty hands were clutching at her dress. Every word she had said in court was in the story of the proceedings. The picture was so utterly unfair to her, Harry couldn't bear even to glance at it again. It was Mike Kon's speech about him that he was looking at now, looking at it with the same wondering surprise and relief he had felt the first time he had read it. Leaning back in the booth he pondered, fumbling for a cigarette, then a flush came on his face, as if he felt that Mike's statement somehow mocked him a little. Why had Mike Kon felt compelled to make such a statement? he wondered. It hadn't been a part of the proceeding, it hadn't anything to do with the courtroom justice, it had come after the case against Mike had been dropped and he had been free. A gratuitous thing. An impulsive gesture beyond prediction, like a man making a separate peace with himself. And to think how close I was to showing up in that court, Harry thought.

Late last night when he had gone to bed he had been looking forward to his day in court. At last he would be asked to explain his behavior, they would even insist he tell his story, he assured himself with grim satisfaction, and they would hang on every word. Some days ago he had heard that Mike Kon had retained Ouimet. What a pleasure it had been to think of Ouimet questioning him! The whole scene which had been in the back of his mind for weeks came magically alive for him as he lay there in bed. Ouimet and his stupid questions! He had played with Ouimet, made him brighter than he was, built him up, gave him even more cunning, gave him devilish insight.

Maybe he had been falling asleep, maybe the court scene had been in his mind too long. Half asleep, half dreaming, he conjured up ingenious variations of the questions, giving Ouimet free rein, then suddenly the imagined scene seemed to shift and telescope into the nightmare scene of the hospital hours when the phantoms had dug at his heart. Ouimet said, "All right, let's assume Bowman took advantage of you, and you were entirely innocent. What an evil thing this innocence became in your hands. Weren't you using it? Didn't it occur to you that you were using it as a murderous weapon to destroy the man who was Bowman's friend?"

"No," Harry said aloud, suddenly wide-awake and sitting up in bed. His agitation bewildered him. He didn't know why he was tormenting himself, but he went on doing it. Staring at the crack of light coming from the space between the ill-fitting window shade and the frame, he wondered if it was true that he had belonged among that host of terrible men of old who walked in wounded righteousness demanding the vengeance of the Lord on those who had wounded them.

A little bar of moonlight was on the foot of the bed. When he stretched out his hands the bar of light touched them. He did an odd thing. He looked at his hands. Then he wondered if innocence was like a two-edged sword without a handle, and if you gripped it and used it, it cut you so painfully you had to lash out blindly, seeking vengeance on someone for the bleed-ing.

Why was he tormenting himself in this way? Why *now* raise barriers against going to court against Mike Kon? Growing angry he told himself he was entitled to have a court know something of the truth about him and Scotty, and if the only way to bring the truth out was to let the law take its course against an arro-gant violent man, there was nothing wrong with it, it was the general pattern of justice.

Yet he was so worried that he got up and began to walk up and down in his bare feet. What baffled him was that he felt close to betraying himself. It was no crime, he thought, to seek recognition of the fact that he had been misjudged by everyone, especially now that they could hear about it.

As he padded up and down, his doubt growing, he wondered if he was shying away from the justice of the court because he knew he had got a little real justice and truth in those hospital hours when he had seen himself and Scotty in another focus. Was there some falseness now in his position, something he was unaware of, he asked himself. Was that why he was so worried?

There seemed to be some terrible contradiction in his position. The greatest of sins was unawareness, he had heard it said somewhere. A naïve man! Was he offering himself to the court again as the naïve man who was the old Harry Lane? Unawareness, by this sin fell the proudly innocent, he thought sardonically. Fell into what? My God, it need not be into corruption—why not into some awareness that could give width and depth to a man's whole life? And he must have gained some of it for himself now or his mind would not be in such a turmoil, understanding that there was this contradiction in his position. What was it? Could it be that he was trying to have his cake and eat it? he asked himself. Did he imagine he could appear in court and try to serve two masters; the one longing for a new world of new relationships with people, and the other one—having lost the remnants of his life day by day—now clinging desperately to this last remnant, a comeback triumph in court in the jailing of Mike Kon?

Standing in the dark, motionless and rapt, he had been filled with a sudden grim exultation as if he saw that this was the hour of his real and ultimate need of Mike Kon: Mike was there so it could be shown whether he could leave Mike and Scotty alone: so he could show whether he was ready to walk away from them.

There in the restaurant as the jukebox music stopped he looked up vaguely, fumbled in his pocket for more coins, found only a fifty-cent piece, got up and went to the proprietor who was standing at the cash register, and asked for some change.

"Mister, you play that same record again?" asked the proprietor dolefully as he gave him the coins.

"Sure. Why?"

"I have other patrons, see?" and he nodded at the girl and the truckdriver. "Look, mister, there's some great new records there. Rock and roll. New ones."

"Some other time."

"I don't know what that one does for you," the proprietor

said, grinning and showing some bad teeth, "but just for now, haven't you had it?"

"Maybe you're right," Harry said, smiling faintly. "Maybe a change is as good as a rest."

He dropped a coin in the jukebox, and as he went back to his booth he wondered if the piece he had been playing had had a nostalgic charm for him, reminding him of some place where he had been with Mollie. Again he glanced at that bad picture of her that told him how she had suffered and it hurt him and he wanted to comfort her. Suddenly she seemed to be all around him, touching with her gentle concern, her anger, her laughter, offering him again the sweetest, the truest and best parts of his old life. He seemed to see her at her place, her shoes kicked off, walking across the carpet in her stockinged feet, her toes turned out so naturally in the way that had always made him smile. Leaning back in the booth he closed his eyes and thought of what it would be like if he went over to her apartment now and offered his explanations. He thought of her tears and the reproaches and the generous forgiveness; as if he had come home. Poor Mollie, he thought. "Let's look at the lions and the tigers," she had said. It seemed a long time ago.

Then he realized he was looking back on her, that even when he had been waiting in his room for her, even in the hospital when he had sought the warm whiteness of her body in his dreams, he had been saying weakly to himself, "If only it had been different, if only she could have been here." Since he had left the hospital he had kept away from her, as if he knew that ever since he had left her place after their quarrel he had been clinging to her with his backward glance.

But supposing she was waiting to tell him now that his life was her life, and wherever he went she would go? he thought. Suddenly there flashed into his mind a story that had been in his family, a story his father had told him years ago about some Irish grandparents on the female side. The Irishman and his wife had come out to the ship in the Irish harbor. Queenstown, the port was called then. They had come out to the ship on the tender with twenty other emigrants to the new world. Then they had stood at the ship's rail looking back at the land they had loved and they had been full of tears, and some of the men had been singing and some of the women wailing. Harry's great-grandfather and his wife had got separated but he hadn't worried about her until the ship had sailed. Then he couldn't find her. Later one of the crew had told him he had seen a woman passenger making her way back to the small boat and being taken aboard. Her husband knew she couldn't bear to leave the land she loved and had gone back. It would happen with Mollie, Harry thought. It would always be happening.

"How about giving me some notepaper and envelope and a stamp," Harry called out to the proprietor.

"You drink coffee and want I should give you a letter-writing service?"

"Bring me a coffee. I'll pay you for the notepaper."

"Maybe we haven't any," the proprietor grumbled. "It's not a department store. Well, maybe my wife has some," he said grudgingly. "I'll see." In a little while he returned with three double sheets of pink notepaper, an envelope and a stamp. "My wife's," he said. "Thirty cents. A service charge, see."

"Thirty cents it is," Harry said and he paid him and took the notepaper and started to write to Mollie. The words wouldn't come easily. Each word seemed to tear at some good memory he had kept of the old days.

He owed her an apology, he wrote, for he knew how painful it must have been for her to appear in court. He was sure she had forced herself to do it out of a sense of justice and out of concern for him. When he hadn't shown up, he wrote, she must have felt taken in and cheated; everything that had happened between them must have seemed like a falsification. Not at all. He had seen that his appearance in court was a way of going back to something, or getting back something.

If he couldn't go back to what they had, neither could she. He wrote slowly, pondering over it, almost too moved to put

down the words. Maybe no one could ever go back with someone to what they had had. It seemed to him they both now
knew a little of the truth about themselves; they knew what
they ought to be and must try to be. The time of their love had
been when they had been going the one way . . . and because
of the way they were now, no matter how close they wanted to
be, they would only be brushing against each other, while held
together, maybe forever and forever in their hearts knowing
they wanted to go different ways.

From the time she had struck at him on the street, he wrote,
she must have known intuitively that the man he had become
didn't belong in her life any more. He had asked too much of
her. It had been like asking her to give a real part of herself,
to leave her father and her mother and her brother, the very
mold she was cast in, the very shape of her heart, to make up
what must have seemed to her to be a cheap vaudeville team
that made fun of her life. He couldn't expect her to change, he
didn't expect the world or anyone else to change, but he hoped
to change his own life so that everything would be in a different
focus.

Then he wrote quickly: his only regret was that she had got
drawn into the affair again in an ugly fashion that would seem
disgraceful to her parents; she would feel, he knew, that she
had cheapened herself to no purpose. He was sorry if her in-
volvement with him had left any scar on her. He was sure it
wouldn't for, from the beginning, she had acted according to
her light, and she was such a lovely woman she would surely
have a good life.

Sealing the letter he addressed the envelope, got up, walked
out and dropped it in the corner mailbox. He took a deep
breath and looked around.

It was the hour when the neighborhood came alive for the
night. People wandered along the boulevard seeking pleasure
or excitement or just new sights, or new merchandise in the
store windows. No one paid any attention to him. He was a
stranger to them. Loafing along in the crowd he found himself

looking with interest at the passing faces. A plain plump woman with her thin husband bumped against him. Three young men, hatless, their thick shiny black hair carefully combed, stared at him coldly. A taxi stopped at the curb and three men and three girls scrambled out and rushed at a doorway to a dance hall and went running and pushing each other up a long flight of stairs. He could hear the clatter of their footsteps and their laughter on the stairs. It was a fine clear evening. As he passed a dingy little candy store where the prostitutes were allowed to sit undisturbed, one of the girls smiled at him, then saw someone she knew on the street and got up eagerly. An old Jew with a beard and grave eyes passed by, then a tired old man, then a boyish-looking seminarian, plump-cheeked and clean, his eyes cast down, then a pretty girl with her stern watchful mother. An opulent fat man, a rich drug peddler who held court every night at a table by the dance floor in the biggest beer hall in the neighborhood, got out of a new car with three obsequious young fellows. The opulent-looking man had an evil face, Harry thought.

It was a tough neighborhood of ordinary people. Kids with long smooth hair and leather jackets, workmen, a lawyer taking a stroll, a serene-faced old man, girls in sweaters and short straight hair, and middle-aged men with pale hard faces and shifty eyes—they all brushed against him on the way to their cafés.

But on this wide crowded boulevard at that hour were all the faces of the world; some were evil, some pious, some greedy, some just didn't care, and some no doubt avowed their sins, suffering whatever torments. Yet they looked as if they could handle their lives and be comfortable together. There would be some though, he was sure, who would really be alone, knowing the terror of their innocence.